If Jumpstart Your Future had been around a couple of decades ago, it surely would have saved me several significant missteps and money. Chock full of tips and easy to use tools, this is a must read playbook for any young person wanting to get on the road to success, both personally and professionally. Read this now, you'll be glad you did!

Melissa Albers, Owner,
The Authentic Leader

Ben is a very successful business leader, father, husband and friend. He is quick with a smile, encouraging word and thoughtful insight to issues. This book provides a look inside what has made him successful in business and life. A great book to launch your adult life!

Bret Weiss, President & CEO,
WSB

As a pre-condition to the privilege of writing this endorsement, I promised Ben I wouldn't share his book until it was published. But it's everything I can do to not send it to my three kids *right now*. They are young adults, living far from home, making ways in a world that increasingly pressures them to have answers to tomorrow's questions yesterday. Ben's words at once are simple, hopeful, and supportive, so timeless and vital. I only wish I'd been the one to impart the wisdom!

Tom Whaley, Executive Vice President/Owner, Saint Paul Saints Baseball Club

Do you think you are ready? If so, what's your next move? In this book, Mr. Lampron takes you on a spiritual journey with personal testimonies and advice to move you towards a brighter and more secure future. Most of our life is spent learning and trying to achieve standards without actually having a clear understanding of basics. We live to survive, when we should be living to live. Lampron wants you to consider the basics. "Do not accept mediocrity, and you'll be noticed" he says...to me that's living! To young and old adults who are working to live, this book is your guide to doing so!

Omar McMillan, Educator and Head Varsity Basketball Coach at Richfield (MN) High School

JUMPSTART YOUR FUTURE

JUMPSTART YOUR FUTURE

LESSONS LEARNED IN CAREER BUILDING, PERSONAL FINANCE, AND RELATIONSHIPS

Ben Lampron

JONES MEDIA
PUBLISHING

Printed in the United States of America

ISBN: 978-1-948382-17-5 paperback
JMP2021.3

To my wife, Gretchen, who walks
side by side with me through life.
I'm thrilled and blessed to hold your hand.

CONTENTS

AUTHOR'S PREFACE

My parents tell me that I've been curious and active since the days I was crawling around my crib. From when I was old enough to remember, I've wanted to experience as much as I can in life. Whether it was playing any sport or game I could get involved with, signing up for any additional class that was available, or taking the chance to travel whenever I could, I've always wanted to do *things*.

Living life actively has afforded me the chance to learn about the world, people, science, love, and myself. They say you learn something new every day, and from my experience, they are right. Life is a series of pages and chapters that are written continuously. After many years of good times, struggles, and scars, you have a story to tell.

While I've spent over twenty-five years in a variety of roles supporting technical business, my dream job has always been to be a teacher. Having grown up watching my amazing mother in action as a teacher, I cannot imagine a career that has a more direct impact on people. I often say that someday I will become a high school math teacher and basketball coach. While I've filled that emotional bucket through coaching sports and mentoring people at work, I've had a more burning desire to share my life lessons in other ways.

Given this desire to teach, I started to collect thoughts around my life learnings so I could share them with others in an organized way. Originally, I was going to fit them onto an eight-to-ten page presentation to give to small groups. Ultimately, it turned into this book. I wrote it to share what I've learned with those just entering the real world. People often say, "If I knew then what I know now, I'd be much better off!" The purpose of this book is to help solve that problem—to share now what I've learned with people who are getting started, just as I did when I graduated from the University of Maine in 1995.

INTRODUCTION

You're new to the workforce and this thing called adulthood. Welcome to this fabulous new stage in life! Now what? Are you feeling nervous, worried, or wondering what to do next with your life, your career, and your money? Fear not, as you're not alone. I lived through it myself. I've witnessed those feelings of doubt in not only newly employed people but also those that have been around for a while. Here are a few examples:

Recently, I've been mentoring a new engineer in our company. He's about three years out of college, married, and a proud father of two young kids. By all normal standards, he's off on a successful career while raising a family with his wife. During one of our weekly meetings, we were talking about our families, and I asked him if he had started a 529 plan for his kids. He responded, "What is a 529 plan?" The 529 plan, as you'll read about later, is a wonderful gift to us from the US government where you can invest for your kids in a way that allows that investment to grow *tax free* all the way up to and through college. The plan is a fantastic advantage to any parent and future student, especially if started early.

I've been very involved in coaching throughout my children's lives. I've met kids from across the socioeconomic spectrum and from diverse backgrounds. When I ask kids what they want to do when they grow up, they usually usual answer, "I have no idea." That's fine and normal, because it's a rare person who knows exactly what they want to do at age seventeen. However, when I dig deeper and ask questions like "Do you understand how debt works?" or "Has anyone told you about investments, compound interest, or how to search for a job?" the answer often also is, "I have no idea."

A good friend of mine is forty years old. He has a decent job and a nice house, family, and lifestyle. He called me the other day and we discussed the stock market. At the time of my writing of this book, the Dow Jones Industrial Average is near it's all time high. He asked me "Do you think now is a good time to start investing?" I replied, "Yes, it's always a good time to start investing," but I followed up with, "Wait, you have never invested before?" He does have some small amount in company 401(k) (thank goodness), but that's it.

There are countless times when I meet with new employees who are looking for some professional mentoring. Often the first line of questioning is about how to get promoted or get a raise. When I ask what they have done to earn it, to promote themselves, or to make themselves more valuable to the company, they struggle to answer. They haven't learned some of the basic strategies of career management.

These talented people, with a variety of educational backgrounds and upbringings, were missing key ideas that could help them develop building blocks for their lives. I concluded that there are so many things that we're left to learn on our own as we grow up and head out into the real world. Let's face it—how do we all learn that we have to file taxes each year? Is it in some adult handbook I didn't receive around graduation? I'm fairly sure my parents taught me all about Uncle Sam and how he wants his share every April 15th, but I don't specifically remember it.

Most of us learn over time about the things I'm going to write in this book—through trial and error, from sleepovers at our grandparents, or from attending the School of Hard Knocks. The benefit of this book is that you can read about basic and instrumental life lessons early in your career. You can leverage the power of that knowledge to get off to a great start in your adult life. I want to share my knowledge and experiences with the college graduate, the high school kid, or the young parent.

In the book, you will find references to sample spreadsheets and charts that are available for you to view and download on my website www. benlampron.com. I welcome you to use them as you see fit as you start your journcy!

Not much of this book is proprietary. You can certainly read about these lessons in other books and in online articles. It certainly isn't meant to be a hardcore life methodology. I don't pretend to be a certified financial planner, marriage counselor, or career coach. I encourage you to address specific concerns with trained professionals. However, in this book I will share some concepts that I've learned and that I hope are helpful to you as you get started on your new path. Let's dive right in!

STARTING STRONG

I grew up in the humble community of Lewiston, Maine, where I attended an average elementary school, worked a paper route, and spent most of my free time on the playground playing baseball or basketball with my brother Matt. We certainly weren't wealthy when I was growing up, but I was truly advantaged. I have two loving and dedicated parents who love each other and love their two sons deeply, and I can't imagine what else could be more important to growing children. When I think back on my childhood, I consider myself very blessed and I don't take that for granted.

My parents and grandparents taught me from a very young age the importance of hard work. Always show up, always be ready to do the work, be the best you can be, be polite, and strive for the top. There were many times during my childhood when I didn't want to go to school, practice, or church. When the weather was bad outside, I certainly didn't want to go do my paper route. However, in our household, those were not options. When you sign up for something or have a commitment, you show up, you answer the bell.

During the first week of sixth grade at Martel Elementary School, I had the first big grown-up realization of my life. I was in Mrs. Richard's class and we had a pop quiz at the end of the first week. Luckily, I had read my homework assignments that week, and I got a perfect score on the examination.

I had done well throughout elementary school; it was never too difficult for me. But what happened next in Mrs. Richard's class was powerful. She had us do an exercise where we were to fill out, in advance, what we thought our grades would be for the year. I remember I wrote down something like this:

Math	A
English	B
Science	B+
Social Studies	A-
French	B
Technology	A

Each student was to bring their scorecards to Mrs. Richard's desk individually and she would review them with us. When I showed her my card, she was completely surprised. She said "Ben, why would you score yourself so low? From what I've seen, I expect you to have straight As!" I remember the conversation like it was yesterday.

Since the start of the semester, I had been engaged in her classroom, raised my hand often, *and* I had aced her first pop quiz. Bing! A super bright lightbulb went off in my head! I had gotten off to a great start and had already set her expectations for my performance. I was already ahead of my peers and destined to succeed the rest of the year. In fact, I believe that not only did I have momentum on my side but I had also earned Mrs. Richard's ever-important benefit of the doubt. Trust me, you'll need that a time or two in life.

My twelve-year-old brain had to prove this theory. That winter when basketball season started, I was determined to make my mark early. In previous seasons, I was the shy kid, and while I could play pretty well, I never really got the ball or made any meaningful plays during games. I showed up to the first practice and really got after it. I sprinted, I dove for the ball, I shot the ball when I was open. I made my mark as early as possible. By the end of the first practice, I was already deemed a starter and a key player on the team in the coach's mind. I distinctly remember this practice and thinking to myself that I was on to something.

That following summer I went to basketball camp in Casco, Maine, at a place called Hoop Camp. If you're a kid, and you love basketball, I can't think of a more perfect and idyllic place. Settled in the woods on the shores of Pleasant

Lake, you'll find basketball paradise. In previous years, I had always loved Hoop Camp but had never made the elusive all-star team. Armed with my newly acquired theory of the power of starting strong, I decided to show up on Sunday and immediately attack it. I got to the court early. I shot hoops and practiced dribbling while the other kids were messing around. The first morning I was up before the breakfast bell and working on my free throws. I worked harder than everyone else for that first twenty-four hours. And you know what, it was noticed. I got put into drills when the coaches were demonstrating; I got extra coaching by the counselors in between sessions; and I got the ball when it mattered in the games. I made the all-star team that summer, and I'm convinced that it was because I started so strongly. I was so very happy; I hugged my parents when they picked me up. The lesson of **starting strong** was burned into my brain forever.

There are many examples of where starting strong pays dividends for the person or group who does so. Think of your favorite music album.

Chances are the very first song is the best one on the release. Most often, the band comes right out and hits you with the best you'll hear in the first thirty seconds. The rest of the record is fantastic, but the first song gets you hooked and sets the stage for the rest of it.

I grew up around the sport of boxing and really enjoyed it. My father, Tony Lampron, trained a fighter from Lewiston named Joey Gamache to a pair of professional boxing world titles. Having the opportunity to grow up in that environment was an amazing learning experience. When I got to college, I decided I wanted to try my hand at the sport.

While I was preparing for my first fight, I read an interesting statistic: In a three-round amateur fight, the winner of the first round wins the fight 80 percent of the time. Now statistically this makes sense. First, the winner of the first round would have to lose the next two rounds to lose the fight. Second, the winner of the first round is most often the better fighter. However, I think you can break this 80 percent advantage down even further. How does the fighter win that first round? I'll tell you how: be first, start strong, impress the judges quickly. In a three-minute round you have to get after it fast, be the aggressor, and score points early. If there's ever an event or competition where starting strong is paramount, amateur boxing might be the best example.

So how does all of this apply to you? You'll have so many beginnings in your life where you can leverage this lesson repeatedly. As you use it, you'll become more and more convinced of its power, and you'll harness it. Here are some examples of where starting strong really matters.

While Dating. They say that first impressions mean everything and that couldn't be truer than in the dating world. I thoroughly believe that if you can't bring your A game to the dating world, it will be a struggle for you. Not just with your potential partner, but with their parents, families, and friends. Do the little things, and treat your date as the center of the world. Side tip: don't ever stop doing those things!

On a Sports Team. Like in the story told above, getting off to an aggressive and hungry start is paramount in a competitive situation. When everyone is looking for minutes or reps, it's crucial that you claim the territory early. If you're a new coach, it's vital to get off to a quick start with your team to set the tone and expectations for a successful season. Wait too long as a player or a coach, then the opportunity for greatness will pass by.

On a New Job. More on this later, but you need to start each new job as if it's the most important time in your career. If you overdeliver early, you'll set a new bar for yourself that will not only impress the bosses and set you up quickly for success but also give you something to continue to improve on.

The person that starts strong in any of these areas of life is destined to outperform others. You'll be in a better position than your peers right from the beginning of any endeavor, and that's a massive advantage. You'll earn the benefit of the doubt and everyone else will be playing catch up.

Drop Your Anchors

As you move through stages of growth in all areas of life, try to think about claiming that new territory with each improvement. I like the mental image of **anchors**. As you start strong and set a new expectation or achieve a new level of performance, think of dropping an anchor down on that spot. Think to yourself—I've made it here and despite the natural setbacks that might happen, I've this anchor in the ground, I'm tethered to it, and I can easily recover to that level, regardless of the circumstances. Consider this chart:

It describes my life in almost all aspects. Life isn't a straight line. It has its ups and downs. However, if you start strong and use your anchors along the way, the long-term trajectory of your life will continuously move upward. You'll find that your financial life, your career, and your personal relationships might all look like this. You work hard and make great progress only to have a minor setback. But you have your anchors. Leverage them to pull yourself back to the levels you've already achieved.

Fitness is an area that will certainly resonate with most people my age. You train hard, improve for a time, and then plateau. Life gets in the way, you lose focus on your routine, and backtrack. However, you'll find that snapping back to your high level comes quickly with effort. Sometimes the retreat allows you to use the momentum of the recovery to break through to a new level more easily!

Life ends up being one big loop: start strong, drop your anchor, regroup, and start strong again. If you follow this process and not let the downs get to you, you can recover from almost anything knowing that the long term prospects are in your control and can be extremely positive.

On Integrity

It needs to be written early in the book that the most important thing you have is your integrity. I learned this lesson very early in life. When I was about five years old, I was at the grocery store with my father. Back then the store had a bulk candy section where you could pick one candy and put a nickel in the metal slot. It was all on the honor system. My father gave me a nickel and I took *two* candies.

As we were walking down the aisle a few minutes later, he noticed I had two and asked me why I had them. I knew I was in trouble. He took me by the arm and literally dragged me to the manager of the store. I had to admit what I had done. I was terrified. But believe me, that confrontation has been frozen in my mind for years.

Be honest. Treat people well. Put in a fair day's work. Don't shortchange people or yourself.

I'm not sure anything else really matters if you can't look yourself in the mirror at night and know that you gave everyone around you, plus yourself, a fair shake. You can start strong all you want, but it doesn't mean much in the grand scheme of things if you take advantage of people, take shortcuts, or cheat yourself.

There's a clean and fresh start in almost everyone's life. That moment when you graduate and you enter the full-time workforce for the first time. All the times in your life when you have started strong have been important, but getting off to one in adulthood and your professional life is mission critical.

Think about how you're feeling at this exciting moment in your life. Everything is in front of you but you don't have all the answers. Don't worry about it. None of us did or ever does. However, if you employ simple tactics and start strong at any new beginning or restart, you'll greatly increase your chances of a life full of success.

MANAGING YOUR
EARLY CAREER

You have done a ton of work to get to this point in your life, and I'm hoping you have had a lot of fun along the way. When you think about all the days you went to school, did your homework, played sports, and worked a side job all while being part of your family, it's truly quite impressive. Congratulations! But in the game of life, what you've really completed is the equivalent of baseball's spring training. You learned, practiced, and exercised your intellect to prepare for the real world.

Ah, the "real world," where the future possibilities are endless: you have earned the freedom of adulthood, and the time comes to become a full-time taxpayer. What comes next is scary and not always straightforward. It's up to you to find where you fit best, then to grab the bull by the horns when you get that opportunity.

I had a conversation with an employee recently named Colin. By any measure, Colin is an extremely hard worker. He always gets to our plant on time and puts in an honest day's work. It took him a while to get where he is now, as his path wasn't easy or clear. He told me his story, which I found very powerful.

Colin had worked for several companies in a variety of entry-level manufacturing roles. He had manufactured products, had driven fork trucks, and even did a fair bit of janitorial work. However, he never really advanced with his companies and got stuck. Companies didn't invest in him, so he got discouraged and found himself struggling to stay fully engaged.

At some point, Colin ended up at our company. He started strong, showed up early every morning, and wasn't afraid to do whatever was asked of him. This was noticed, and he started getting attention, training, and additional opportunity. When we spoke recently, he couldn't have been more excited. He told me how much he loved working for our company and couldn't wait to grow within it. He is invested in us and we are invested in him. Like a personal relationship, you have to find the connection that works for you and the company. Find it and you can short-circuit the route that Colin had to take.

On Finding an Employer

A couple of years after college graduation, I believe there was a fifty-fifty split between people from my class who were fortunate to find a great company to work for long-term and those that were quickly looking for a change. This seems like an inevitable occurrence, as everyone is so eager to grab the first job offered.

If you have been successful in school and have marketable skills, this is usually not necessary. I encourage you to spend the time to find a company that fits you and your personality and will give you the chance for growth. Don't settle unless you absolutely have to. It's more important to find the right job than having a job lined up early in your senior year!

As you apply for jobs and go through the interview process, you must find a company whose culture is in alignment with your own. Further, you should join a company that values you. During the interview process, it's up to you to ask the proper questions to determine the fit. Interviews are meant to be two-way streets, so you need to invest the time and energy to determine if the company you're joining is really something you can support fully. If you don't align, you'll end up going through the motions to collect a paycheck and your career will quickly stall. Align completely and there will be no end to your energy, creativity, and excitement to go to work every day. That's where you want to find yourself!

It might seem obvious, but honesty is paramount during the interview process. I've interviewed so many candidates that have a resume that doesn't look quite right. Simple questions or Google searches can root out the misleading information and the recruiter immediately rejects the candidate. Resist the temptation to embellish your resume or history. Chances are you have enough wonderful things to share with them that are 100 percent true. Clean up your social media presence. Companies can and will scour the sites to find out who you are or pretend to be. Be sure to delete anything that you wouldn't want your employer to see.

To help find a company where you'll maximize your chances of growth and learning, make a list of the things that are important to you and be laser-focused on finding them.

Find a company that's growing. A growing company will have much more opportunity for promotions for you in the future. If a company is flat and stagnant, chances are you'll be stuck in your role for quite some time.

Find a company with a great and ethical leadership team. This one is harder to figure out early in your career; however, the online resources these days are plentiful in this regard. Find out if the values of leadership match your own. Perhaps you can find leaders with similar interests and backgrounds. That won't hurt when you begin internal networking.

Be sure to interview with the person who will be your boss. Find the boss that you connect with and will look forward to coming to work for every day. It's the single most important relationship you'll have in your early professional life.

Choosing the right company and position out of the gate is a huge advantage. Take your time. Be thorough in your research and gain all the insight you can about the companies. Take the job knowing fully that you're all-in!

On Your Commitment

Now that you landed your dream job, it's extremely important that you start strong! Some of these concepts might seem obvious, but consistently doing the simple things will put you ahead of most of the other new employees. The company has taken a chance on you; your commitment to it must be clear and obvious to everyone. I consider these next few points to be the basic table stakes of immediate success.

Put in the time right away. Show up early. Stay late. You might hear or read in other places that "working smart" is better than "working hard." Don't believe that nonsense. Early in your career you have to put the work in and earn your reputation.

Whatever you do, be the best at what you do. If you're hired to sort the mail, be determined to be the country's best mail sorter. If you're hired to make 100 widgets an hour, strive to make 110. Every job is important in every company. If it wasn't, the company wouldn't have it. Do not accept mediocrity, and you'll be noticed. You won't be sorting mail for very long.

Work until the job is done. If you want to get ahead, you cannot watch the clock and head out the door at exactly 5 p.m. If you're close to completing a job, or part of a job, put in the extra time and finish it.

Don't job hop. I spent the first twenty-three years of my career at one company. I've followed that up with the last three years at my current employer. That seems to be almost unheard of these days as I see so many resumes with five jobs in eight years. It might seem attractive to leave to make a bit more money. However, real growth comes through working through the ups and downs in a company and learning how to navigate long-term challenges. I suggest five years minimum with your first company to gain meaningful experience.

Family should be your first priority, but work needs to be second. Family comes first in most people's lives as it does mine. If this isn't the belief of your company, you're likely in the wrong place. However, early in your career, your family is really all that should come before work. As you look to make your mark, you'll have to make some sacrifices in other areas of your life. While all your friends are out for happy hours all nights of the week, you need to be different. It's not for everyone, but if you want to get ahead early, you have to ramp up your commitment to the company and make it your number two. Further, from time to time, you might have to ask your friends or family for forgiveness and forgo a personal event in order to satisfy a key work issue.

Remember that we're all replaceable. While you think you might be uniquely qualified for a certain job or project, the company will survive if you happen to leave. In many ways, you must continuously prove yourself and re-earn the job. Come to work every day with the attitude that you're going to remind the company why they hired you in the first place. Be consistent with that effort and you'll be in great shape.

Workplace Differentiators

One late Friday afternoon in my sales career, I was traveling with a mentor who I really respected. It was about three o'clock and we had a good two-hour drive home ahead of us. We had had a successful week-long road trip, and I was excited to get home. If all broke right, I would be home to enjoy a full Friday evening with my family. Then Niels said "Ben, let's stop at that paper mill right there." I was confused. It was late Friday afternoon. Niels then said "Ben, always make the incremental sales call!" That lesson has stuck with me for my whole career. Who makes sales calls at three o'clock on Friday? Hardly anybody, but we got the appointment and made some progress with a new customer. Whether you're in sales or any other role, stretch the day or the week when hardly anybody else does.

Most of us show up at the office with a general idea of what needs to be accomplished that day. Some people like me are list makers: we literally write down a task list for the day. Whatever your method for organizing the day is, I suggest that you do the hardest thing first every day. What one task is the most difficult, stressful, or annoying? Sit down and get it done. Better yet, get to work a little early and hammer it out. If you get the toughest things done first, the rest of the day is a breeze!

No matter the company or job, take the time to talk to everyone. Many new hires with jobs they consider to be important, don't bother to spend time with people deemed to be below them or those that aren't associated with them. This is a huge mistake. If you want to be successful, it really helps to have the support of everyone. You never know when you'll need someone to have your back when you least expect it. Plus, you'll learn things you didn't expect to find out by hanging out with the operators, the admins, or the finance team!

Whether you're just starting out or in a managerial role, be a champion of inclusion in the workplace and in your life. You will encounter people from a variety of socioeconomic and cultural backgrounds, so it's essential that you embrace the differences. Working and associating with different types of people not only will broaden your perspective but will make your company and your teams stronger.

Once you have settled into your role, don't be afraid to take decisive action. If you have found a great company, they will encourage you to make decisions, try new things, and be brave. Surely, you'll make mistakes, but if you're making the best decision with the data you have at the time, that will be respected and typically not negatively judged. When the boss asks for volunteers on special projects, raise your hand! You don't have to overdo it here, but be the person who takes on the special challenges. If you have no idea what you're doing, don't worry, you'll figure it out when you get there! Stand out and do the extra things when asked.

Treat your company, and the company's

money, like it's yours. If you have a budget, treat the checkbook as if it was your own. When caring for employees or customers, behave as if you're protecting your family's reputation. By caring for your company in this way, you'll stand out from others who treat their job as if it's just a job.

Whether you want to or not, always show up for company events. During your career, you'll be invited to things like Christmas parties, summer picnics, and team building exercises. Especially early in your career, you have to go. If you don't participate, people will notice. "Optional" in these circumstances is really "mandatory" in my book.

Finally, no matter the situation at work, you want to be known as a stopper. A stopper is someone that management can count on that will either get the job done or take the necessary steps to work with a team that can. Stoppers don't delegate issues or pass them on to someone else. The buck stops with them. If you're someone that executives can count on, more challenges will come your way, which will build your credibility! Don't sidestep problems, be a stopper!

Thinking Forward

From the first day you're on the job, you have the right to immediately begin thinking about your future. What do I have to do to be successful? How do I get ahead? What is the next step in my career? Where do I want to be in twenty years? You have to ask yourself these questions because nobody else is going to do it for you.

As I worked through the first few years of my career, I didn't follow this advice. I believed that the company was looking out for me and that I was certainly part of their overall succession planning. I had great performance reviews yearly, and my boss would give me continuous strong feedback.

In my first year, I won the Region Employee of the Year award. (I was going somewhere!) But at some point it dawned on me though that those words, while sincere and meaningful by the managers giving them, didn't say what I thought they were saying. Feedback and promises are generally meant to satisfy you as the employee and to encourage you to keep up the good work—

they are not guarantees about your future.

Understand immediately that you, and only you, control your future from day one. You have to earn promotions by delivering great work in your current role while advocating for yourself in the meantime. You have to let your superiors know of your desire to move up in the company and be prepared to take uncomfortable assignments to get there.

Beware of statements like: "You have a ton of runway at this company." While that may be true, it's an appeaser. It sounds great when you hear it, but doesn't really mean anything concrete. You have to imagine your career path, figure out what needs to be done to move along it, and then execute a game plan. If after some reasonable amount of time you're not getting what you need or expect from the company (I believe three to five years at an absolute minimum), then it might be time to move on.

Always remember to continuously learn. Learning doesn't end the day you pick up your diploma. Read, attend conferences, associate with smart people at the company, and take in information like a sponge. You have to work on your craft every day to be the best you can be and to prepare for the next role. It's particularly helpful to go out of your way to learn about functions that are different than yours to get a holistic view of the business. If you're in accounting, learn about manufacturing. If you're in sales, learn about the science and technology behind the business. Crosstrain your brain and you'll be very valuable to those in charge.

Finally, keep track of your accomplishments over time. During many company's annual review process, where it gives ratings for performance, you'll be asked to "self-score." It's powerful to have a specific list of the values you added to the company during that year. Your boss won't remember everything, so you should do it for them. An annual review is a two-way process. List your accomplishments and make sure you get the credit you deserve.

Finding Your Paul

I was very fortunate early in my career to work for a leader at Honeywell named Paul Orzeske. He has always been the kind of person for whom you enjoyed working. He cared about your growth not only as an employee but also as a person, spouse, and parent. He was always engaged with my career, and I respected him greatly. To say I would run through a brick wall for him is no real exaggeration.

When I went through a divorce at a relatively young age, I was devastated. I could hardly concentrate on work; days were cloudy. My performance began to struggle, and I was heading for a real depression. One afternoon, Paul, who lived in Chicago, gave me a phone call and invited me to the "Windy City" for a weekend. Paul took me to dinner and we went to a Cubs game, and he generally had his arm around me for the entire weekend. Paul didn't need to do that, and he didn't have to be concerned with my personal life. But he was: that's who Paul is.

Thinking back, I'm convinced I wouldn't be where I am today without Paul. He was a great manager, mentor, and inspirer. When I was at my lowest, he was there to pick me up. He probably has no idea the impact he had on me and others. Now, when I'm in a tough spot at work, I think, How would Paul handle this? Early on in your career, find your Paul. Find the person who will look out for you when times are tough. You'll grow from it now but will also learn many leadership qualities to make use of as a leader in your own right down the road.

3

BUILDING A
FINANCIAL BASE

The first Friday after you have started your
new full-time job is a huge day. You receive your
first paycheck electronically deposited into your
bank account. Wow! You have really made it.
You have a job, you have some money, and now
you have to decide what to do with it. Emotions
can run the gambit when you earn meaningful
money for the first time. You might feel extremely
rich and have the temptation to run out, buy a
new car, and spend a pile of cash. Alternatively,
you might be looking at your college debt, your
apartment rent rate, and your daily expenses and
wondering how you'll make ends meet. Either

way, it's very important to take stock of what you have and begin working on your financial base.

Like any building, the base on which you build the rest dictates the strength of the structure. Later, we will cover investment strategies, but before we get there, let us discuss some concepts that will help you build some financial stability into your life.

Set a Simple Budget

When you first start paying bills for the first time it can be a bit overwhelming. Don't worry, you'll get comfortable with the routine of your monthly income and expenses. You should take some time to create a simple budget to deal with it constructively. Contrary to what you might read elsewhere, this doesn't need to be complicated at all but something to serve as a general outline for your money. Take a sheet of paper or a Microsoft Excel spreadsheet, put your take-home monthly income on the top and then list all of your periodic bills and other monthly expenditures. I've included an example of the type of spreadsheet we use below. You can also find it on my website www.benlampron.com for your review and use.

Monthly		$
Income	Paycheck	$3,500
Expenses	Mortgage/Rent	$1,230
	Groceries	$400
	Car	$375
	Personal Care	$250
	Savings	$225
	Entertainment	$200
	Cell Phone/Wi-Fi	$140
	Gas	$100
	Clothing	$100
	Insurance	$100
	Travel	$100
	Utilitites	$85
	Total Expenses	$3,305
	Remaining Balance	$195

If your spreadsheet shows you're going to spend more than you earn, this big red flag should point you to make some immediate life changes. However, if not, you can get comfortable with a spending plan and then use the rest of the monies productively elsewhere. Don't spend like all your friends do. Don't "keep up with the Joneses"— budget within your means.

As you take on more responsibility over time (house, spouse, children, charitable donations), your budget will get more complicated. At the end of the day though, it really is just a math problem. Money in minus money out equals leftover to be spent, saved, or invested the way you choose. Having the discipline to stay within your budget week after week will be a great first building block to financial security.

Build an Emergency Fund First

Having remained true to your budget, it's time to consider what best to do with the precious leftover dollars you have earned. I strongly encourage you to start with the creation of an emergency fund. Life will throw you some curveballs, and since you can't see them coming, it's no better time than the present than to prepare a financial plan to handle them. This fund should be in a savings account that pays some sort of interest and is easy to access. You should determine how much money should be in the fund, then work aggressively and immediately to fund it.

The emergency fund amount will go up over time and should remain in line with your current lifestyle and level of responsibility. A common rule of thumb is to have six months of expenses put away in case of emergency. Typically, in an early career, this might sound like a difficult amount to save. I believe that you should start with a more manageable number. Even $1,000 in the bank would help you deal with the unexpected car repair or medical bill. Once you're there, look for three months of the basics to be covered: rent, car, utilities, and food.

Open an account and take whatever you can each paycheck to put in your emergency fund. These days, you'll find the best interest rates at online banks. They work well and monies can be moved easily back and forth from your main bank's checking account. Once you have reached the three-month level, you can begin a balanced savings approach that includes investments and the six-month emergency fund goal.

The emergency fund doesn't need to be built overnight, but I encourage discipline. Decide how much you can afford to save out of each paycheck and have it automatically transferred. The "automatic transfer" discipline is one of the key habits of a successful financial life. When the money isn't in your wallet from the beginning, and you don't have to manually do the transactions yourself, you'll not even miss the money!

When you have reached your goal, and the emergency fund is whole, you'll feel a wonderful sense of relief. You'll not be overwhelmed with an emergency, and you have some back up in the event you happen to lose your job. There's great long-term and sustaining comfort in knowing you can handle these types of problems should they arise. Further, getting ahead of the game and having an emergency fund will help you avoid going into meaningful debt.

Speaking of debt . . .

Debt Is Your Enemy

You have to think of debt as a disease that can continue growing and spreading within your financial world. Especially early on in your career, resist the temptation to buy things that cause an ongoing balance on credit cards. If you get behind, the interest will compound making it harder and harder to catch up. I repeat: **DO NOT CARRY CREDIT CARD BALANCES**. Some examples of tempting spending that should be avoided as you build up your base include the following:

Buying new cars. Cars depreciate the moment you drive them off a lot. Look for a solid used car that has low mileage and still in warranty.

Eating out every day for lunch. Do yourself a favor and bring your own meal to work. It will not only save you tons of cash but it will be healthier in the long run as well. Ten dollars a day for lunch for 200 working days in a year is $2,000. As you'll see in the next chapter, that money invested really adds up over time.

Stopping for coffee every morning.
Somehow coffee companies have convinced Americans that $4.99 for a cup of coffee is worth it. If you avoid this every workday, that's another $1,000 in your pocket annually. Make your morning beverage at home, or drink the coffee the company provides.

The way-too-often happy hour. Of course heading out after work for a couple of drinks with friends is fun occasionally. But it's expensive. $8 for a beer or $15 for a cocktail is borderline robbery. Stock up at your local liquor store and have cocktail hour at each other's homes. (and take taxis. Goes without saying that a DWI puts a damper on all your other progress).

I think you get the point. You should enjoy yourself for sure, but spend within your means. Try to avoid debt like the plague. Credit card use is fine for convenience, but be sure to pay off the bill every month!

The only debt that makes real sense is a mortgage on a new home. This debt is "secured" debt—meaning, the loan is covered by the value of the house. You sell the house and you can pay off the debt. Further, most home loans are tax deductible with very low interest rates these days. Leveraging a good mortgage is actually a wise financial move over the years.

Eliminating any unsecured debt that you have built up is the very first step in any financial plan. If you have college debt, credit card debt, or even a car loan, you should be working very hard to eliminate these. There are advanced strategies where you can leverage very low interest rate debt (say 2 percent or below) and use those monies elsewhere. In general, however, I would work to pay down debt as soon as possible to get to a clean sheet from which to build.

Some Good Habits

Depending on your personal situation, make sure you have the proper amount of insurance coverage. If you're single and renting, you should purchase automobile and renter's insurance. When you buy a home, you'll need homeowner's insurance. When the time is right, especially when you have started a family, consider life insurance. Learn about insurance and make sure you have developed a good strategy.

Every time I'm considering a purchase, my parent's voice rings in my ears: "Never pay full price for anything!" Be consistent here whether you're buying a car, a new suit, or a tennis racket. Almost anything you buy will go on sale at some point or you can negotiate the price. If the price won't budge, either wait, buy something else, or simply move on. Thinking further, buy used items whenever you can—especially when trying new things. If you wake up one morning and decide you want to try skiing, get some used gear at a ski shop to see if you like the sport before going all-in.

Stay on top of recurring bills like your cell phone, cable bill, and streaming and radio subscriptions. These bills will creep up over time without notice, so you have to remain vigilant. If your bill goes up, call the company and find out why. Look for alternatives to your current provider and you'll almost always find a better deal or your current provide will drop their price. It takes discipline but these little reductions add up over time.

When shopping online, always think to look around for online coupons or codes. It's rare to find a website that doesn't have a promotion/coupon code box at the checkout screen. If you take the time, you can usually find codes that slightly reduce your price or offer free shipping.

Learn to have fun with loyalty programs early on. I discovered this way too late in the game and left tons of value on the table. Most business and credit cards have free programs that give you some sort of value when you use them. Don't spend just to get the points, but take advantage when you can. We have a lot of fun with this, especially when eating at a restaurant. In some cases you can win in four ways: (1) get points for using your credit card, (2) get a discount using online sources like Groupon, (3) get points from the restaurant loyalty program, and (4) earn airline miles by being signed up for their dining programs. We get irrationally excited when we can make all of those things happen in one restaurant visit!

Be sure to sign up for rewards accounts as soon as you fly anywhere or stay at any national hotel chain. The programs are well-run, and soon enough you'll have enough points to fully fund a great vacation. Most program's points don't expire, so sign up as soon as you can so that you harvest all available points.

You Are What You Track

A common question you might hear or even ask yourself is, What is your financial situation? An answer might be, "I've got sixty bucks in my wallet, a small 401(k) plan, and some savings in the bank." Everyone is somewhere along the financial journey, and the dollars that you have and where you keep them will change over time.

However, the answer to the financial situation question is much more complicated than the basic one. To understand your current financial health, you need to be able to answer the following three big questions:

- What is my cash flow situation?
- What does my total spending look like?
- What is my overall net worth?

Tracking these three metrics like a hawk is the key to long-term financial well-being. When I say track them, I'm talking about down to the penny. Line by line recording of expenditures, income, and wealth accumulation on a monthly, if not weekly, basis is necessary. Without tracking and measurement, you'll lose track of dollars and fall into bad spending and savings habits. Here are some tools you can use to get off on the right foot.

For Cash Flow

For many years, I made use of old-school checkbook ledgers that they give you freely at the bank. I meticulously tracked every dollar in and out of my checking account with a pencil. In my filing cabinet, I had stacks of these ledgers just waiting to be reviewed at any time. While this taught me the discipline to track my money, it certainly is not the most efficient way to do things. Mind you, pencil and paper tracking is better than nothing, but today's software offerings make it so much better.

When I married Gretchen and we sat down to pay our first bills as a couple, I remember her literally laughing at me when I took out the checkbook and ledger. She said, "Ben, haven't you ever heard of Quicken?" Quicken is a software program that allows you to enter in all of your incomes and expenses, and it does your future math for you. I was aware that programs like these existed but had resisted this new-age fancy way of doing things. Moreover, I didn't trust the safety of my data being on a software platform.

After about a year, she finally convinced me to give it a go. Wow, what a game changer it was for me!

Quicken, and its alternatives, do several things in terms of income and expenditure tracking. However, the most powerful aspect of Quicken is the ability to see well into the future, so that you can see things like: "Well, in June I'm going to hit zero in my account" or "Come December I will have an extra $1,000 in my account." Having this information early is so helpful. You can take action now to prevent the account shortage or plan a better way to use or invest the extra.

Back in my paper ledger days, I could figure this out manually, but with Quicken, you can see it automatically, quickly, and at any point in the future. Make some changes on the fly, increase savings amounts, or load in periodic charges like utilities and Christmas gifts. You can gain such a feeling of comfort having all of your expenses loaded into Quicken and knowing whether you have the income to deal with all of it.

For Spending

Knowing where every dollar you spend goes is extremely important. While it might seem like overkill, Gretchen and I have a monthly Saturday morning date where we review the previous month's expenses. We collect inputs from our credit cards and online bill pay mechanisms. Since we use hardly any cash at all, we can easily see where every dollar has gone electronically.

Once we have all the inputs, we enter them into a very simple Microsoft Excel spreadsheet that we built together. That sheet breaks down all purchases by categories (house, car, groceries, entertainment, our dog, travel, etc.) and totals them up for any given time period. Each month we look at the totals in each category, compare them to our budget, and review the pie chart graphs that we've built into the tool. In minutes, we come up with conclusions like: "Well, we really spent too much at restaurants this month" or "Great work! We saved more than we planned!" An example of this type of sheet is posted on my website for your review and use.

Tools like Quicken will do this process for you as well; however, I think you get a ton out of doing this semi-manual process regularly. By doing so, you'll become keenly aware of your spending habits and can come up with obvious ways to improve them. We now have several years of expenditures by month, which gives us great insight into our financial life. It would be very difficult to make any real change to your financial well-being without having this valuable data.

For Net Worth

I spent most of my childhood playing sports. When I wasn't playing sports, I was playing chess, cribbage, or video games. In short, I'm a competitive person and I like to keep score. It didn't take me long to figure out that money has its own scoreboard—the financial world calls it *net worth.* Your net worth is simply the total dollar value of everything you own converted to cash minus any uncovered debts you have. Assets include savings accounts, investment accounts, the equity in your home, and any other valuable items you own. Uncovered debts include credit cards, car payments, college debt, and the like.

At any given time, I know our net worth down to the dollar and believe this discipline keeps us on track. If you have a goal and a scorecard, what are you going to do with the extra $500 you get for a bonus? Spend it on a toy or invest it?

I track our net worth on a very simple spreadsheet that I could recreate in five minutes. I've used a sheet similar to the one below for my entire adult life. Be sure to go to my website to check out an example. You can certainly use tools like Quicken, which can be linked to all your accounts, to track net worth. However, I believe the practice of manually building and updating the spreadsheet keeps you in tune with your portfolio's performance. This simple habit will train you to notice patterns that should trigger activity as you gain more wealth in your career.

Net Worth Calculator	
401K	$7,000
IRA	$1,500
Company Stock	$1,350
Mutual Funds	$2,700
Home Equity	$9,700
Savings	$2,500
Car	$3,000
Debt	-$4,600
Net Worth	**$23,150**

The key to all these tools is to recognize that they really are part of a healthy and effective financial lifestyle. Make a game of it, keep score, and track your progress. After some time, you'll become comfortable working a balanced budget, tracking your income, spending, and recognizing how to manage to have some dollars left over each month. When you have developed a solid financial base, created an emergency account, and learned how to manage savings, you can begin to look forward.

While I certainly encourage you to spend some of that well-earned money on toys and fun, you should consider harnessing the power of simple, long-term investing to build real wealth. In the next chapter, we will talk about investing in a way that's simple and productive and that will prepare you for a wonderful retirement. Retirement seems like a long ways away, but it's closer than it seems!

Low-Maintenance
Investing

"Ben, I am on a mission to make my first million dollars by the age of forty!" This is what my first boss said to me during a lunch meeting in my first year with the company. I thought this was quite a personal statement to make as we didn't know each other very well, but it had an amazing impact on me. I would guess he was about thirty-three at the time, and the thought of having $1,000,000 in the bank at that young age seemed like an outrageous goal. I was impressed, I was mesmerized, and I wanted to learn more. How could someone outside of the professional athlete, actor, or investment banker ranks acquire so much wealth by age forty?

At that point, I had learned just a couple of basics of investing. My father had introduced me to the concept of the 401(k) program and he told me to invest as much as I could in it. A couple professors in school had shared some thoughts on the topic, so I knew it was something I should explore. That was pretty much all I had to go with, but thanks to my father, those professors, and my first boss, I was inspired enough to learn more and to dive in.

I became interested in investing in my twenties. I've read many books that covered investing and money management; I feed off the energy presented in them. Some of my favorite beginner books include *Learn to Earn* by Peter Lynch, *The Millionaire Mind* by Thomas Stanley, and *The Intelligent Investor* by Benjamin Graham. While each book has their own spin on things, all the information helped me frame savings and investing as if it were a sport. If I work hard, do the right things, and stay persistent, I will put points on the board and win. I encourage you to read as much as you can on investing, but here are some of the highlights that helped develop my financial strategy.

Pay Yourself First

The first key discipline in successful, long-term investing is to pay yourself first—always. By this, I mean to treat your investment strategy like a bill. Since you "owe yourself," it becomes a required periodic bill that needs to be paid. Preferably, you want to have this done automatically with each paycheck. Investing regularly, and automatically, will take the burden off you to execute the savings each week. As I mentioned before, you'll not recognize the money is missing and will grow to live with the remaining monies in your account.

Add "Savings" or "Investing" as a category in your budget. It can be any small amount to start. Just get in the habit of doing it, and it will become second nature to you. If things are tight, you have options that can help create some incremental investable monies.

First, find some things in your budgets you can reduce or cut out. Visits to the movie theater, buying books instead of using the library, smoking, drinking, and gym memberships are possibilities for adjustment. I'm not saying to eliminate these altogether (everyone has to live), but if you can reduce them and put a few dollars away, you'll be better off.

Second, you can funnel any additional money that comes your way into investing. Every time you get a raise, forward those monies into savings. Every time you get a bonus at work or a gift from a family member, earmark that for investing. You have to scratch and claw your free dollars and put them to work for you. Able to work some extra shifts and earn some overtime? You guessed it: invest it.

Third, consider a side hustle. Can you pick up an extra job on the weekends or at night that can provide you with the extra money needed to invest? Find something that also gives you some satisfaction. If you're an athlete, maybe referee some kid's sporting events. Love clothes? Pick up some shifts at a department store. The part-time job will give you motivation to know that those dollars specifically are going to your investment account and will pave the way for your financial future!

Investment Concepts

When you're ready to start investing, it's important to understand a few key investment concepts. Anytime you acquire a dollar, recognize that a dollar today will become X dollars in the future when invested. This is a very powerful thought especially when you consider buying something. If you want to buy a new $50 sweatshirt that you really don't need, it theoretically costs what that $50 will become down the road after invested!

The *Rule of 72* is a simple way to calculate future growth of those dollars. In short, the number of years it takes your money to double is 72 divided by the rate of return you're earning on your money.

Years to Double Money = 72/rate of return

If you have your money in the stock market, and assume an 8 percent rate of return, your money will double in nine years as 72/8 = 9. If you have your money in a savings account earning 0.5 percent, your money will take 144 years to double! The good news is that your money will double again in the same time. For example, if you invested the $50 you were going to spend on that sweatshirt at age twenty-two, and assumed an 8 percent rate of return, it would become $100 at age thirty-one, $200 at age forty, $400 at age forty-nine, and $800 at age fifty-eight. The sweatshirt seems a little more expensive when you consider you're spending $800 of future money!

Now imagine if you invested $5,000 at age thirty, and assumed that same 8 percent rate. That would become $10,000 at age thirty-nine, $20,000 at age forty-eight, $40,000 at age fifty-seven, and $80,000 at age sixty-six. Yes, this is correct! You invest $5,000 at age thirty and it grows to $80,000 at retirement.

Unfortunately, The Rule of 72 works the same for debt. Many high-interest credit cards can charge 18 percent or more for your balance. This means that your credit card debt will double every four years (72 divided by 18). Further evidence that debt is your enemy. In just eight years, an innocent credit card balance of $5,000 becomes $20,000 after two doubles. Make sure you leverage this rule in the *positive* direction.

One key factor in that long-term growth is *dollar cost averaging*. Over time, you'll invest in companies or funds at different prices. As the market moves up and down, you'll pay more or less for the shares each time you buy. Dollar cost averaging gives the investor the benefit of not having to time the market. Sometimes you get the shares "on sale" which drops the average purchase price of the shares you own.

By investing in regular increments, you don't have to worry about what the price of the shares are on a given day. Continuous and disciplined investing over time is your most powerful tool to reduce the anxiety of market fluctuation and to take advantage of market dips.

A second key factor in long-term investing is the earning of *dividends*. Usually quarterly, most companies pay out dividends to their shareholders as a way of distributing profit to them. You can find out online what a specific company or mutual fund pays out each quarter. Be sure to set your accounts to "reinvest dividends," that way those earnings will automatically reinvest into more shares.

Finally, understand the concept of *compound interest*. As your investments grow through appreciation and dividend reinvestment, you'll then be earning interest on that ever-growing base number. If you earn 8 percent on $100, you'll earn $8 and have $108. After another period, you'll have earned $8.64 on the $108. As time goes by, the interest compounds and continues to grow. Another way that time is your best friend in investing!

Fun with Math

Here are some practical examples of how investing over time can add up big. Using the concepts above and an online investment calculator, you can play with numbers using all sorts of examples. All examples in this book assume that you'll earn an average 8 percent growth rate. This has been the average return while continuously invested in the S&P 500 since the 1950s. In addition, all calculated values have been rounded up or down.

"Mmmm. Coffee." Let's say you stop for a $5 latte every business day from age twenty-two to sixty-two. That money continuously invested will end up being $322,000 at the end of those forty years. Of that, $48,000 will be your original purchases and the remaining $274,000 is the growth on the investment! This makes the free beverages at work sound a little more drinkable. Side benefit of drinking work coffee: you avoid wasting time in those long lines at the drive-thru.

"Make it a Rueben with fries." If you love to go out to eat at noon, it really will cost you. Let's assume you spend about $12 a day for lunch. If you chose to invest it

instead, that money becomes $773,000 at retirement. $115,200 is the sum of all your lunch money and $657,800 is the growth on it. Remarkable! Bring your leftovers to work. They taste great, are generally healthier, and save you a ton of investable cash.

"Ahh, that new car smell." You likely need a car to get around unless you're fortunate enough to live in a city with great public transportation. Let's imagine instead of buying a new car every so often you either drive used cars or drive one car for a really long time. Because of this choice, you save an average of $300 a month on your car payment. That $300 invested each month becomes $966,500 at retirement! Almost a millionaire simply by driving cheap cars and investing that car payment. It's math like this that encourage me to drive my trusty Volkswagen named Bill until it dies!

"Time to hustle!" There are a few years, before you have a family especially, where you might have some extra time to earn. This is when you can find a side job to create a little extra cash to invest. Perhaps you pick up a job at the local department store earning $12 an hour. Imagine if you put in sixteen hours a week at that second job. For simplicity purposes, that would lead to take home pay in the $140 a week range. That money earned weekly invested from age twenty until age thirty? About $75,000. Not a bad little nest egg for when marriage and kids start to come around.

"How do I become a millionaire?" I'm glad you asked! Assuming you have forty years until retirement, you could become a millionaire by investing $72 a week and earning an average of 8 percent over those years. The real key is to start NOW. Your best friend is time. If you wait until you only have thirty years left to work, that same $72 a week will turn into only

$439,000! If you wait until you only have 20, the $72 a week turns into $177,000!

OK, I don't have $72 a week, what do I do now? If possible, it's important to start some sort of investing now. Here is a ramped path to $1 million over a career that could correlate more closely to what you'll be able to afford throughout your career.

Years 1–5: invest $25 a week. You'll end the time period with $7,900.

Years 5–10: invest $50 a week. You'll end the time period with $27,500.

Years 10–20: invest $75 a week. You'll end the time period with $117,500.

Years 20–30: invest $125 a week. You'll end the time period with $351,500.

Years 30–40: invest $309 a week. You'll retire with $1,000,000!

Starting strong really matters. In the first example, you get to the $1 million mark by investing $72 a week consistently throughout your career. If you wait until year ten to get to that point, it really puts pressure on you to increase those savings in a big way to catch up. Find a path that's achievable for yourself!

The Rest-Easy Investment Strategy

Having learned enough about the stock market to be excited, it's time to set up a long-term strategy for yourself. I believe the best strategy is a simple one. People say "less is more" and that's appropriate in this case. The less you do and have to manage the better off you'll be long-term.

Have the discipline to set it and forget it. Have your monies automatically withdrawn from your checking account, deposited into your investment accounts, and don't look back. By using a cash flow tool like Quicken to understand your cash position, you can increase your contributions over time when you see you can afford them. I believe this relentless and continuous strategy is the simplest way to grow your wealth in a way that allows time and money to work together.

There are countless ways to invest your money. I want to share with you some of the more practical ways to do so. The Rest Easy Investment Strategy is a seven-step methodology that I've fine-tuned and used over the last twenty-five years.

Step One: Contribute to your company 401(k) plan. The 401(k) plan is a tax-advantaged investment account offered by most employers. You can typically choose either a traditional 401(k) plan or a Roth 401(k) plan. In a traditional plan, you invest into it *pre-tax* and it grows that way until you take the money out at retirement. You'll pay taxes on the original investment and it's appreciation as you withdraw it. In a Roth 401(k) plan, you fund it with "post-tax" money. However, the investments and all gains are available tax-free at retirement. For most new employees, funding the Roth 401(k) makes more sense.

You should contribute to either plan at least up to the percentage of your "company match." If your company match is 3 percent, you must contribute this to capture the free money your company is offering you. There are few places in life where you can get a 50 percent or even a 100 percent return on your investment! Take full advantage of the company match.

Invest in your 401(k) as much as you can, up to the federal limit (currently $19,500 per year). Once in the 401(k) plan at a young age, I recommend that you fully invest those dollars in a low-cost index fund. Index funds, which include a basket of stocks covering a large portion of the stock market, have very low fees and give you great diversity. Mutual funds that track the S&P 500 give you broad exposure to 500 of the largest publicly traded American companies with very low management costs. Reinvest the quarterly dividends and have dollar cost averaging and time do the work for you. As you get older, you'll throttle back to a more conservative portfolio over time. 401(k)s can usually be accessed without penalty at age fifty-five if you're retired.

Step Two: Invest in your company's employee stock purchase program if the shares are offered at a discount. These plans are phenomenal and allow you to put money aside every paycheck up to a limit (10 percent of your income for example) to invest in the company stock. After a period of time saving (six months, for example), the company will convert those saved dollars into shares of the company at a discount. Some programs offer a predetermined discount (say 10 percent) off the closing stock price on the day of the conversion. However, some are even more generous, offering a discount off the low price of the entire investment period. Take the discount!

Step Three: Invest in a Roth IRA (individual retirement account). This engine, similar to the 401(k), allows you to invest your after-tax money and let it grow tax-free until retirement. The current annual limit per person is $6,000. If you maxed out your 401(k), or want to diversify your accounts, this is the next best place to invest your money. You can open up a Roth IRA account with a number of brokerages. Roth IRAs can be accessed without penalty at age fifty-nine and a half.

Step Four: Invest in a nonretirement, low-cost index mutual fund. Once you're comfortable with your retirement savings schedule, it's time to consider investments that will help you build wealth before retirement. One thing to remember with this investment is that any sale will trigger you to pay taxes on the capital gains realized in that current year. As you age, the size of this account will ultimately determine when you can retire. If you build this to a meaningful amount, it can become the "bridge" to retirement and the access to your 401(k) plan.

Step Five: Invest in 529 plans for your children. The 529 plan is another tax-advantaged investment vehicle that allows you to invest in your children's college education. The growth of the investment over time withdraws tax-free. It's not a stretch to imagine that the tax-free portion of your account can pay for half of your kid's college education! Start early as college isn't cheap!

Step Six: As you get older, medical bills will become more prevalent. Consider funding a Health Savings Account (HSA) each year. These monies are pre-tax, can be used in the future for most medical bills, and can grow just like any other mutual fund account. Further, any withdrawal used for medical expenses is also tax-free. It's a double win!

Step Seven: If you have a strong desire to do so, consider a small speculation account. I don't do this myself as I don't have the time or desire to dabble in individual stocks. However, if this interests you, I'd encourage a very small amount, say 5 percent of your money, to go into a brokerage account to buy individual shares of companies.

That's the seven-step Rest Easy Investment Strategy. If you're consistent and disciplined, increase your contributions over time, and resist the temptation to sell, I'm convinced you can achieve financial security. Maybe even much sooner than you realize is possible.

How Aggressive Should
My Portfolio Be?

When you set up your investment accounts, you'll face many choices around what funds to invest in and how aggressive you want to be with your money. Investing does come with inherent risks, such as market fluctuations that you have to stomach. When getting started, you can afford to wait out those bumps in the road. Remember, the market has been climbing over time at an average clip of 8 percent.

Keeping things simple, I only manage the ratio between low-cost index funds and cash-like investments. This is particularly an important decision to make in your long-term retirement accounts, as you'll want to become safer as you get closer to retirement.

One commonly discussed rule of thumb is to take your age and subtract it from one hundred. You would invest this percentage aggressively. Therefore, early in your career, you would have roughly 80 percent of your dollars invested aggressively while at age 60 you would have only

40 percent so.

While this concept is a good place to start, I generally believe you should be slightly more aggressive than this early on. When you have decades until retirement, you can afford the risk that comes with aggressive investing. Go all-in early. Keep perhaps 5–10 percent on the sidelines so that you have some dry powder to invest in case of a significant market downturn. At age forty, I think moving to an 80/20 split makes sense. At age fifty, it might be time to throttle back to something like 65/35. When you get to age sixty and closer to retirement, it will likely be time for some more conservative moves.

Things to Avoid

Investing takes a ton of patience and discipline. You'll see your value go up and down sometimes severely. You have to be confident in your long-term investment strategies and count on the historical averages to lift you up over time. I've made many mistakes in my investment choices, but they all boil down to these six main errors:

1. **Avoid chasing the market.** By that, I mean don't try to time the market and buy and sell based on rumors or momentum. Ride the waves. Stay patient and continuously buy. If you try to time the market, you're more likely to make a mistake or miss a big upswing in the market. Frankly, when the market drops, it's better to buy then to sell! You get shares at a discount!

2. **Never sell.** In my over twenty-five years of investing I've sold only once. For good reason, I needed dollars to make a down payment on a house. Basically, I switched one investment for another. You might need to sell at some point for an emergency, but make it a real one. In general terms, don't ever sell. It triggers a tax bill and gets you out of the market. Being out of the market leads to missing some of the biggest up days, and you can't get those back. On March 16, 2020, the S&P 500 had dipped all the way to 2,304 thanks primarily to the COVID-19

pandemic. If you had sold out of panic that day, you would have missed the nearly 50 percent gain that happened between that day and Thanksgiving. Be brave, be patient, don't sell.

3. **Use only a small portion of your money on individual stocks.** As mentioned previously, it's OK to dabble. However, it's really easy to have your portfolio torpedoed by one mistake. In addition, managing individual stocks can take up a huge chunk of your time. Stick with mutual funds and index investing for the easiest emotional path.

4. **Ignore the latest tips you might hear at the office or read online.** The investment pros are always way ahead of you. You wouldn't challenge an NBA player to a game of one-on-one. Don't challenge the investment pros at their game either. Join them in funds.

5. **An investment advisor is generally unnecessary, especially early in your career.** Advisors charge a significant and continuous fee to allocate your dollars. You'll outperform most of them simply by investing consistently in broad market index funds. Perhaps an advisor would make sense later when your portfolio is more complicated, but most likely not when you're just getting started.

6. **Resist deviations from your plan.** Set up automatic investing and savings. Be ruthless with your money decisions. Set it and forget it!

5

ENJOYING YOUR
MONEY

Having built your financial foundation by developing healthy habits, creating an emergency account, and beginning a funded long-term investment strategy, it's time to consider the importance of enjoying your money. There's an old saying that "you can't take it all with you when you die," and we have to remember it.

There have been times in my life, even today according to Gretchen, that I fail to enjoy money. I remain steadfastly committed to the principles I've shared in this book and rarely deviate from them. Given an extra dollar, I would prefer to save it or invest it rather than spend it. If you happened to visit our house, you would find that we have very few "toys." No boats, no extra cars, hardly anything of material value. However, it's important to enjoy the fruits of our labor, and I wanted to share a few ways that I think will bring value to your life.

Find Your Happy Place

Life can be chaotic, stressful, and one big never-ending list of things to do. You have to have a *happy place.* Somewhere that's uniquely yours, somewhere where you can disconnect from it all and have inner peace and where you can recharge the soul. If you're going to enjoy your money, make it count! My place is sitting in the stands of any professional baseball stadium.

As of this writing, and by my count, there are 261 professional baseball stadiums in the USA and Canada. This includes all thirty Major League Baseball teams, teams affiliated with the Major League Baseball clubs at a variety of levels, and teams from several independent professional leagues. In addition to the 261 stadiums, there are an unknown number of stadiums that have closed down during my adult life. To date, I've visited 153 pro ballparks and have wonderful memories from them.

While traveling to these stadiums is a great hobby and a part of many of our family vacations, sitting in a crowd midsummer is my absolute favorite place to be. Regardless of what is going on in my life, I can completely disconnect while at the game. The hum of the crowd, the crack of the bat, the flow of the game mesmerizes me, and I become engulfed in the environment. You can learn about the team and area history from the friendly ushers, enjoy food and beverages from local restaurants and breweries, and strike up conversations with other fans. I've seen several minor league teams market a baseball game as "The 9-inning vacation." That really resonates with me. I check my problems off at the ticket window and escape into summertime bliss.

Some of my favorite minor league stadiums include McCormick Field in Asheville, North Carolina; Hadlock Field in Portland, Maine; CHS Field in Saint Paul, Minnesota; and

Lindquist Field in Ogden, Utah. At the Major League level, I believe there's a clear group of the most amazing stadiums: Fenway Park in Boston, Massachusetts; PNC Park in Pittsburgh, Pennsylvania; and Oracle Park in San Francisco, California, are the best for their own reasons. I could write pages about the wonders of all these parks and many more. My goal is to attend a game at every stadium on my list, and I can't wait to see what I've been missing.

An additional bonus of this happy-place hobby are the stories I can share and the connections I can make in other aspects of my life. There have been many times in my business life where I'll meet someone and ask where they're from. If someone says, "Nice to meet you Ben, I'm from El Paso, Texas." I get to say, "Home of the Chihuahuas!" Almost everyone finds this amazing: "How in the world do you know about the Chihuahuas?" I talk about the baseball team, the local bar, restaurant, or landmark down the street. It's an immediate and valuable point of connection that pays amazing dividends.

Find your baseball. Find the place where no matter what's going on, you can escape. It's like a pressure release valve for your psyche. I can't think of a better way to invest my hard-earned money.

Travel and Discover

People love to buy things. Things to me are dust collectors that ultimately fall apart and are thrown away. You know what never goes away? Experiences, memories, and understanding — those things stay with you forever. Spend your money on these and you'll not only enjoy them in the moment but also learn amazing things and build memories that you can look back on and share for the rest of your lives. Cut back on expenses you'll never remember to be able to spend on experiences you'll never forget. Go to new places and develop perspectives that will help you in your personal and professional lives.

Traveling doesn't have to be expensive, and early in your career you won't have a ton of extra cash for elaborate journeys. Travel close and explore local towns, state parks, and landmarks.

Make lists and check them off (every golf course in the state, all breweries within a four-hour drive, every museum in the city).

When you're ready to venture out further, there's so much to explore right here on our continent. Some of my favorite places are Hawaii, Oregon, and my home state of Maine. I like lists because they help me figure out where to go next. To date, I've visited forty-nine of fifty states (I will get to elusive Alaska as soon as I can). I've two Canadian provinces left to visit, but really love Quebec. I've visited every city that's home to a sports team in one of the four major leagues. I would also like to go to the highest point in every state, but having summited only seventeen, that goal seems like a reach!

Ultimately, you'll want to travel out of the country. There's so much to see nearby in Canada and Mexico. I've really enjoyed my visits to Australia, Ireland, Iceland, and Italy, to name a few. Every time I travel to a different country, I feel like I come back full of energy, with new perspectives and a hunger to learn more. Take the time and money to spend on travel, do the things you like to do while away, and soak it all up. Money well spent!

Spend More on the Few Key Things

We try to be frugal with our money. However, there are some things in life where spending extra makes sense. Our choices won't necessarily match up with yours, but it's OK to voluntarily surrender to some items that add extra happiness and value to you. Some of those things for us include the following:

Your Home. In most cases, your home will be your greatest investment. A good rule of thumb is to purchase a home and carry a mortgage that's about 25 percent of your income. Go too much over that and you might be "house poor" and not have the dollars to invest. Don't be bowled over by aggressive mortgage brokers. Buy less house then they say you can afford.

Food. There's no question that good, fresh, healthy food is expensive. Spend most of your money on the outer ring of the grocery store. That's where the fresh vegetables, meats, and dairy are. Learn to cook with wholesome ingredients. Invest in yourself by making delicious and nutritious meals at home. Also, use those leftovers for work lunches!

Clothing. It's important to look great at work and out on the town. Rather than buy inexpensive clothes often, take the time to invest in quality clothes that will last you many years. I hardly ever shop for clothes, but when I do, I'm not afraid to spend money on quality (although usually still on sale!).

Simple Hobbies. I'm a huge music fan, and I love supporting my local record stores. I enjoy relaxing by my record player; I play my albums repeatedly. Again, it's more of an experience than just a toy.

Exercise Equipment. Staying motivated to exercise is hard enough on its own. Treat yourself to good footwear, clothing, and equipment that will make the job easier and more comfortable.

Toilet Paper. I lost this battle when I married Gretchen, and you know what, she was right. Spend the few extra bucks for the additional softness on your bum. It's worth it!

Volunteering and Charity

You'll be presented with many requests of your "time and treasure" throughout your life. I encourage you to not only donate what you can to causes that matter to you but also find ways to give your time to organizations that can use your skill set. Believe me when I say that more often than not, you'll get much more out of the experience than what you put into it.

I discovered early on that I had a real passion for coaching. I coached most of my kid's teams as they grew up and thoroughly enjoyed it. Not only did I get to experience it all with my kids, I helped many others and built genuine relationships with other parents, coaches, and officials that I wouldn't have had otherwise. Coaching led to other opportunities, like becoming president of a booster's club, finding a men's prayer group, and meeting potential new clients for work. The time and money that I invested into sports has paid me back in more ways than I can quantify.

Find organizations that support the causes you care about and share with them regularly. One-time gifts are always appreciated, but most nonprofit groups run on a shoestring budget and can really use recurring donations, no matter the size. If you could set up even a $5 monthly contribution to a charity, you will get at least three benefits: (1) you're doing a world of good, (2) the charity can count on that recurring donation for planning purposes, and (3) you get to use the donation as a deduction from your income taxes. Talk about a win-win!

A local high school basketball coach that I respect tells the story of how his mother always found a way to be involved with his team when he was growing up. She worked the night shift so working at games was difficult. That didn't stop his mom. She found a way to run fundraising campaigns, to make meals, or to provide snacks. She didn't let her schedule be a hindrance to volunteering. That story by the coach sticks with me.

Whether it's giving your money or your time, it's important to share some of your blessings with those less fortunate. Find your passion and share your gifts!

Preserve Your Memories

When you're retired and sitting on a beach somewhere with your spouse, you'll want to have a mountain of memories. Start immediately spending time and money creating and preserving them. Multiple times in my life, people have encouraged me to write journals and to take photos to capture all the important moments in life. I've done some things correctly but not nearly enough.

Fortunately, our smart phones come with cameras, so capturing memories can easily be organized by date and location. Take it a step further. Invest in a quality camera that you can use for the most important times and events. You don't need it every day but the difference is noticeable.

Journal. I'm not going to suggest how or how much to do it, but just start doing it now. Keep track of your life because it goes by so fast and you forget so much. Frankly, I've no idea what I was doing in the summer of 2012 and can't distinguish it from 2009 or 2017. That's a missed opportunity for me to remember something small and special that might have happened that year. I remember the basics of my kid's earlier childhood but not hardly enough specifics. Don't make the same mistake as me. Write more things down. Time goes by too fast.

TAKING CARE OF YOURSELF

As different as we all are as individuals, we're all in the same boat as humans: We're born with one life, one body, one mind to develop and take care of. It's extremely easy to take this for granted when we're young, full of energy, and seemingly invincible. Through high school, college, and my early career, I worked at an extremely fast pace. My life was full of achievement, and to most observers, I was on the fast track.

Through my twenties, I was so consumed by performance that I forgot to take care of myself the way we all need. I felt sluggish, overworked, and mentally drained. I'm not sure if I was heading towards a medically diagnosed nervous breakdown, but I certainly struggled with anxiety and sadness. I had to figure out how to balance my life, enjoy my successes, and deal with my struggles in a healthier way. This balance comes from simultaneously working on your *mind*, *body*, and *spirit*.

I think of this as three legs of a stool. I've discovered that if any one of these three gets out of balance, I can feel my center start to wobble. The good news is that by working to address any one of these, the others feel the benefits as well. The following are concepts that I've learned to remain centered, while also striving for continuous improvement in myself.

Mental Health

Our minds are extremely powerful. They are capable of solving problems, creating amazing things, and imagining all that's possible. However, there's a darker side. If we let it, our mind can drift to worry, fear, and stress. This is in all of us to some degree. Working hard to improve your ability to manage your mental health should be a lifelong effort.

I once had a manager named Dennis. One of the more important influences in my early career, Dennis was a no-nonsense, straight-to-the-point leader. He was a hockey player from the old days when leading the league in penalty minutes was a badge of honor. He was a hard driver but would do anything for his troops. One habit I used to have was always imagining the worst during a sales campaign. I would obsess about the big wins. So much so, it would hurt in my stomach. Dennis said to me one time, "Ben, do not create data where it doesn't exist." That line has stuck with me for decades, and I use it as a settling technique regularly. It helps me focus on the facts, discard the fiction in my head, and move forward.

An affliction that I still battle is what I call the "Sunday Night Blues." Weekends go by fast. You enjoy your Friday evening, sleep in a little on Saturday, then have a productive and fun day, get up for Church on Sunday, and then have a nice afternoon with your family. Then, like a right hand on the chin from a heavyweight fighter, come the blues. They settle in hard and fast. For me, this meant miserable evenings and not much sleep. I encourage you to recognize these early for what they are. I've found the best way to handle this is to take some time on Sunday afternoon to yourself. Get all your worries on paper. If they are actionable, write a list for your workweek or personal life. Get it written down, come to terms with it, and go enjoy the rest of your weekend. If you can master this, you get an extra evening back every week!

Parents or teachers surely told you to not sweat the small stuff. It's easy to become stressed about life's inconveniences. One tool to help you deal with them is the "6-month rule." If whatever issue you're dealing with now will not matter in six months, don't lose sleep over it. Things blow over, they change, and you can handle almost everything thrown at you. If it's major enough to have a definable impact on your life six months out, then meaningful stress is understandable. If not, write it down on your to-do list and go hang out with your loved ones for the night.

To help me with these challenges, I've developed relationships with two therapists. While acute and significant experiences were the genesis of those contacts, I've learned to appreciate having both of them long-term. There's certainly a stigma around mental health, but I'm a firm believer that everyone can use this sort of advice. Having an impartial and trusted advocate to work through issues, get things off your chest, and discuss paths forward is invaluable. Fortunately, most insurance carriers cover some mental health coverage. You should leverage this whenever possible. Thinking of your mental health in the same manner as your physical health is nothing of which to be ashamed.

When things seem to be spiraling out of control, it's vital that you take the time to slow down and regroup. You know how parents give their kids time-outs when they misbehave? Think of this as the adult time-out. This skill needs practice, as it's not natural. When you feel unwanted stress seeping into your life, take healthy action. Things that work for me include taking our dog for a walk, going for a workout, reading a new book, and calling my parents to say hello. If there are things bothering you and you're unable to address them in the moment, avoid wallowing in your stress. It will eat at you and cause real long-term damage to your emotions. Learn to recognize your unhealthy stress and take care of your mind.

Physical Fitness

Your body is your most important tool, and it might seem like nothing can stop it when you're young. Once you start your career, you'll find it challenging to keep it in shape. As children, we have time to be active. We were encouraged by our parents and schools to take part in extracurricular activities that worked our bodies. Even simple things like running around the neighborhood with your friends was good for you. Jobs, dating, happy hours, and ultimately, kids of your own all slow down the unplanned ways to stay in shape.

Having been a competitive athlctc all my life, I found myself unattached to any sort of organized sport once I graduated from college. To be honest, my twenties were not great in terms of physical fitness. Other things took priority, but thankfully, I got back on track before things got too far out of hand!

Finding your way to physical fitness is very personal. There are many gyms, online programs, and strategies people use to manage their health. The choices are endless. You can use any of those tools to keep your body sharp, but I stick to these core concepts to stay on track:

Eat well. It seems like common sense, but you have to be disciplined and feed your body well. If you're living off fast food and packaged processed foods, you'll not be able to perform your best at work or in the gym. Eat real fresh food as often as possible and give your body the nutrition it needs. Choose your beverages wisely. Avoid sodas, energy drinks, and other sugar-filled drinks that fill you with empty calories. I've narrowed my drinking to coffee in the morning and water for the rest of the day. Avoid the constant temptation of junk food offered at the office. It's relentless at times. At home, leverage online tools, like www.plantoeat.com, to help you plan and organize a healthy eating lifestyle!

Get your sleep. For a long time, I lived on six hours of sleep at night. Burning the candle on both ends on a regular basis isn't healthy. It will age you quickly. Find a routine that gives you eight solid hours of sleep. Even better, go to bed and wake up at the same time every day. Your body will thrive on this habit, and you'll be able to start the day strong and go to sleep quickly at night.

Mix things up in the gym. When I plateau with my fitness, it's because I've gotten into a routine that has bored my mind and body. Diagnose this quickly and make an adjustment. Change gyms, get outside instead of inside, play a new sport, find a new workout partner, and so on. I need a meaningful overhaul to my routine roughly every three months. This keeps things fresh and keeps me motivated.

Create a lifestyle. Having your body physically fit doesn't come from a magic pill or a product hawked on an infomercial. It comes from long-term commitment to a lifestyle. It has to be part of who you are and how you live. The choices you make every day directly affect your overall health. Simple things like taking the stairs instead of the elevator, doing exercises while watching the news, or doing your own yard work all pay dividends. Everyone's path will look different. I encourage you to find your path early to feel strong throughout your entire life.

Spirituality

As I've grown, I've realized the importance of understanding and caring for my spirituality. I'm a church-going Roman Catholic but I'm not referring to only religion here. There's a part of our being that needs to be nurtured. I believe it's my soul, but others use different words. Our spiritual center makes us who we are. It's as important as your mind and your body, and you have to develop it.

I've found that being consistently engaged in my church is extremely powerful. I've experienced the power of God at Mass and revel in his greatness. When I'm at Mass, I'm able to tune everything else out and focus on God and my spiritual well-being. That weekly quiet touchpoint with the Lord allows me to heal my soul and rejuvenate my spirit for the week ahead.

I find great peace and learning in reading the Bible. Whether it's church, prayer, meditation, or spending time with loved ones talking about the spirituality that works for you, you'll benefit greatly from watering your soul. When I'm struggling with aspects of my life, I look to this part of my being. Am I taking care of it? Have I been asking God for his help? Often times, this part is easy to forget, as it's less visible in our everyday lives. Make sure you come back to it often and it will become routine and ever nourishing.

Always Be Learning

Make it a habit to always improve through learning. Whether it's gaining knowledge about your profession, your hobbies, or your family life, feed your brain the good stuff. Here are some ways I keep learning even though there seems to be no extra time in the day:

Reading. Rarely do I have time to sit down for an afternoon and read; however, I find that short stints of reading really help me learn quickly. Whether it's thirty minutes before bedtime, on a flight, or while waiting for an appointment, I take time when I can to read about a topic of interest. Some of my favorite ones are finance, leadership, and history. If you can pick up one or two key points from a book, then the time is worth it. Use your public library. The fact that we have unlimited knowledge available for free is one of our country's greatest assets.

Podcasts. I have a thirty-minute commute to work each day. That's one hour of free time that I use to learn. Podcasts are largely free for the downloading and are chock full of information. Simply search for a topic that interests you on your podcast app and download free information. It really is incredible. I subscribe to podcasts that cover economics, leadership, and my favorite sports teams. I get to learn free one hour every day. It's priceless.

Community Workshops. Most cities, towns, and local universities will sponsor and host workshops that are either free to the public or offered at a small cost. You have to do some digging to find them either in a community bulletin or local online event calendars. Experts on everything from gardening to starting your own business are happy to share what they have learned with you. Take advantage of these great opportunities to learn and to meet others with similar interests.

As you exercise your brain, be sure to monitor the diversity of topics and ideas you're exploring. Download podcasts from people with alternative views, watch news from the stations that don't regurgitate your political beliefs, and read books on topics that you know nothing about. Doing these things will stretch your brain and teach it to be open to new valuable concepts.

New hobbies are a key to keep the learning going. Something that keeps me going is playing guitar. I learned how to play at about age thirty, and it's a real passion for me. When stressed, I pick up the acoustic, strum a few chords, and I can literally feel the anxiety leave my body. Learning new songs or chords challenges my mind in a different way than my other day-today activities.

Finally, learning doesn't have to be a solo adventure. Joining clubs, prayer groups, and project teams will drive creativity. Having your mind, body, and soul all in harmony will make you a great team player. Being all you can be will make you a wanted teammate in all sorts of relationships.

7

DEVELOPING
MEANINGFUL
RELATIONSHIPS

When I graduated from the University of
Maine in 1995, I made a spontaneous decision
to move to Hanover, New Hampshire, with
my great friend Andy. My new job allowed me
to travel all over the northeast; I could live
anywhere within the territory, and Andy needed
a roommate as he entered Dartmouth Medical
School. This one decision has led to one of life's
most amazing gifts. While in Hanover, I became
a part of a group of nine amazing men that have
found a most incredible way to stay connected.

Each spring, the nine of us come together in a different city to conduct a fantasy baseball draft. That's right: we take three to four days away from our families and jobs to make up fake baseball teams. While the game itself is highly competitive, and all of us want to win the coveted trophy, the last twenty-six years have allowed us to develop a true close friendship. A friendship that challenges us as adults, gives each other comfort in times of need, and serves as a sounding board when tough decisions arise.

We connect to each other on Signal. We have a never-ending string of messages that cover a variety of topics, but most are politics or sports related. Since we find ourselves on a variety of spots on the political spectrum, sometimes things get heated and virtual yelling happens. Nevertheless, in the end, we all love each other and find ways to respect each other's opinions.

Why am I bringing up this group of men? First, they mean the world to me, and I look very much forward to our weekend together each year. Second, this shows the importance of relationships in our lives. When you find this connection, no matter the size, you must embrace it and develop it. In times of trouble, or celebration, you'll need a network to lean on. At the end of the day, life is about the relationships we build, how we care for them, and what experiences we share.

Marriage

I'm certainly not a marriage counselor, and there are many books available on the subject. However, since it's one of the most important relationships in some of our lives, I wanted to share just a few things I've learned along the way. As you're considering marriage or a long-term committed partnership, I think there are four areas where you and your partner should strongly align before you buy the rings. It's easy to overlook them, but these areas could become issues down the road if not addressed at the beginning:

Aligned on religion. It's easiest to marry someone who shares your religious affiliation and lifestyle. If you go to church and they do not, this can be problematic. However, if you're of different denominations but can agree on how things will work (religion of the children, how to celebrate holidays, where do you go for services), that's a good start. Make sure you have a plan that you both endorse.

Aligned on politics. As our world becomes more and more politically polarized, I would not suggest marrying someone on the opposing end of the spectrum. They say opposites attract, but in this case, I would beg to differ. Marriage is long and you don't want to have to deal with major relationship issues based on who is president.

Aligned on finances. Life is so much easier if you have the same financial habits and goals as your partner. Teaming up makes things much more productive than fighting each other on money. If one is a saver and one is a spender, I predict many long nights of arguing. Get on the same page before marriage using the simple tools lined out in the previous chapters!

Align on similar interests. When you're young, everything seems blissful. You can't wait to see each other, be in each other's arms, and pass the time holding hands. News flash: this honeymoon period wears off. Be sure that you marry someone who likes to share activities with you. If you have a basket of similar interests, you'll have a lot more fun as best friends!

Once married, always remember to put your partner ahead of yourself. You chose to be with this person and it's up to you to take care of them. My wife, Gretchen, is my most important relationship. I love her with all of my heart and do my best to put her needs ahead of mine. I can't imagine being without her. When I screw up, I try to apologize and make it up to her as best as I can. Marriage is intended to be lifelong. Invest in it more than anything else in the world remembering these things:

Time is the most important gift you can give your spouse. Be with them, be present, and listen. I've been guilty of not focusing on my wife as my head gets really noisy sometimes. Find times, set dates, and follow through on your promises. Create space where the relationship can really grow.

A connected relationship is extremely critical to marriage. Be sure to be intimate with your spouse, to have close connection, and have meaningful fun. If you don't have this together, I strongly suggest you hire a counselor to find out why and how you can get there.

Don't cheat. Infidelity, in my opinion, is just unacceptable. If you find yourself wanting to cheat, stop and consider why that is. Do you need to work on your marriage? Should you consider leaving the marriage? You should explore

many options before breaking this most
sacred bond. Side note: any sort of
communication behind your spouse's
back, or done online, is most certainly
cheating. Emotional cheating is as
harmful as physical.

Never go to sleep angry. My wife and
I have vowed this to each other, and while
we don't always follow it, we understand
it's importance. Say you're sorry. Don't
let things linger. Hug. Cry. Whatever it
takes. Be a big person, admit you were
wrong, and love each other.

I think if you put your partner first, find
common ground on issues, and always look to
have fun together, everything else will work itself
it out swimmingly.

Children

Your children will be one of your life's
greatest joys. When you're an expecting parent,
you'll read volumes about the adventure ahead,
so I'm going to share just a few thoughts:

Yes, it does go by fast. I heard this from my parents and you'll hear it too. Eighteen years seems like a long time, but it isn't. They're in a crib and then the next thing you know, they have a diploma. Love them, spend time with them, breathe it all in. Soon, they will be gone.

The kids will find their own way. You might have plans and dreams for them, but our kids are individuals. The activities my three kids chose to do, they discovered on their own. I had no idea my oldest would dive into mountain biking and politics, my middle would fall in love with fixing cars, and my youngest would commit herself to dance. Let them find their own way.

Be there no matter what. You never know when your kids will need you. They might want a hug, some advice, or to just be in the same room. You have to have your antenna up because it might not be obvious. Listen to them when they speak to you and just be present. This was really hard for me. After I realized I missed what they said a few times, I made a conscious effort to get better at it. Your listening, attention, and presence is all they really want and need.

Family Traditions

Family traditions celebrated year after year bring so much value to your overall happiness. Some pass from generation to generation and are as common as sharing Thanksgiving dinner together or setting off fireworks on the Fourth of July. However, I've enjoyed the quirky, family-specific traditions so much more. They help weave a fabric of togetherness that only you and your family can understand or appreciate.

I don't remember the first time I saw *Emmet Otter's Jug-Band Christmas*, but I believe it was around age ten. It was shown every Christmas season on TV, and I looked forward to it every year. This wasn't a tradition with my family as a kid; however, it meant a lot to me. For those who haven't seen it, the movie is about forty-five minutes long and has puppet animal characters who celebrate the meaning of Christmas in their own way. They all sing wonderful songs, make sacrifices for each other, and remember loved ones from the past. Throw in the introduction by Kermit the Frog and I was hooked. I strongly recommend that you watch it this Christmas!

While in college, I remember talking about Emmet with my friend Todd; the connection brought my love of this film to the next level. We broke into song and talked about what the movie meant to us. Not your typical college party!

As my family grew and my children were born, watching Emmet became an annual family tradition. Typically watched on the day that we put up our Christmas tree, it has gone through many phases. When the kids were young, they absolutely adored Emmet and the movie. Through early teen years, it became annoying to them but they did it anyway. Now that they're a bit older, I can see that they now understand how much it means to me personally and to the family, and I think they secretly really enjoy it.

The sixty-minutes that includes putting the angel on top of the tree, sitting down with a beverage of our choice, and all cuddling in to watch Emmet is probably my favorite hour of the year. Be sure to start traditions like this early in your married years and as a parent. You'll be reminded of them throughout the years, as undoubtedly they will come up in a song, reference, or conversation. Just start some, the earlier the better. They mean so much, and you'll get to look back on years and years of connection and love.

Your Go-Tos

As you navigate adulthood, it's imperative that you have develop a trusted list of go-to people. You build the relationships that you can count on to help you get things done. The quicker you fill up your roster of resources the better. Why? Because it's important to know your limits and capabilities. I figured out early in life that I shouldn't operate a table saw or run electrical wires through my house. Some may be good at this, but I don't do it nearly enough to be safe or effective. Here are some people that I've on my team that have proven invaluable to my success, development, and life management:

Handyperson/Contractor. I've developed a great relationship over the years with Alan. If I've a list of things that need to be fixed or if I'm in an emergency, I can call Alan, who will come over and help. He has bailed me out on many occasions. This type of relationship takes a while to develop because the people who are good are busy doing more valuable things to them. Over time, a friendship develops and they will fit you in around their busy schedules.

Therapist. Developing a relationship with a mental health professional is a brave and important step in your life. It certainly has a stigma in some circles, but there's an old saying that "everyone can use a little couch time." Be sure to find a person who connects well with you—and don't settle. I've developed a relationship with a great therapist who's there when I need him. I don't go often or on any sort of regular schedule. However, when I need help or just someone to talk to, he's just a phone call away. I always come away from the sessions feeling recharged, refreshed, and relieved.

Attorney. There's no question that as you navigate life you'll encounter treacherous waters when legal assistance will be important. Issues will come up in your personal life, with your neighbors, at work, or with your finances. The key is to have someone who knows you and your background to go to for advice and help in the moment without having to find a resource online. In many circumstances, time is of the essence and you'll want immediate help.

Career Mentor. There will be times in your professional life where you feel stuck or when the pressure is overwhelming you. You have to have one or more formal or informal mentors that have your back. I don't believe these can be arranged or forced easily. They are normally earned. But once you realize who those people in your life are, ask them directly if they will mentor you. Are they available to help? More often than not you'll be pleased with the answer you get.

Primary Care Physician. There will be many reasons to see a doctor in your adult life and there are many avenues these days to see one. MinuteClinics, ERs, and even nurses at department stores are available. I believe it's extremely important to shop around for a general practitioner that you trust and with whom you feel comfortable. They will have history with you and be much more helpful in times of need. I recently lost mine as he relocated to a different city, and I feel a loss. Time to find a new relationship for me.

Spiritual Advisor. Not everyone is religious and that's OK. If you are, I encourage you to invest in a relationship with someone in the Church. I'm Catholic and I believe that the vast majority of priests would be of assistance to me. Having one that I know really well has given me great comfort, advice, and guidance. If not religious, find another relationship that you can work with to develop your spiritual core.

Tax Person. Many software programs allow individuals to do their own taxes each year. For many, that might be a completely acceptable choice. However, I believe that developing a long-standing relationship with a reliable and informed tax accountant is extremely valuable. As your financial life gets more complicated, the choices you make will have more of an impact on your bottom line. It's comforting, and well worth the money, to have a professional do your taxes for you. You'll know they are done correctly, you have maximized your return, and you have a resource you can call with questions throughout the year. I look forward to my meeting with my accountant every year and appreciate our relationship.

Insurance Broker. This one took me a little longer to figure out. There are many options for insurance in your life. House, auto, life, umbrella, disability, and so on. You can spend a lot of time trying to find the best deals and coverage options in all these areas or you can develop a relationship with a broker you trust. I call my broker once a year, and we review my needs. Once he understands any changes we have had in our life, he educates me on products and options that we might benefit from. Then he does all the research for me. He puts my business out on the market and checks for better pricing options and then develops a package that fits my needs best. Some years we roll with the same coverage and others we make big changes. I find that relationship saves me time and money.

Car Mechanic. I dislike dealing with cars. I don't like buying them and I don't like haggling with dealerships when something is wrong with them. Since I don't have a great deal of knowledge around cars, I never feel like I'm getting a good deal. If you can develop a relationship with a car mechanic, do it.

Barber/Hair Stylist. For several years, I've shaved my own head, so I no longer need this resource. However, my father and brother and I all enjoyed many years of going to the same barber. Ernie was our guy and he got to know everything about us. It was fun to go back to him over the years and getting caught up. Many people I know find the long-standing relationship with their hair person to be comforting. You also want to have someone you trust taking care of your locks.

Business Relationships

You'll have a variety of business relationships in your career with coworkers, superiors, outside contractors, and customers. Some of these will be more meaningful than others and many will develop into friendships. This professional network will be one of the more important in your life. From this group will come comfort when challenged, opportunity for career growth, and learning.

LinkedIn is a powerful tool to create and maintain your network; however, make sure that your business relationships are two-way. People are looking for connections that benefit both people. Be available and help when you can. Also, be vulnerable and learn how to share some personal feelings in a way that doesn't cross lines. Learning to trust others in business takes time, but it can be very fruitful.

Write letters. I'm talking about old-school hand-written letters. Everyone texts these days, and it feels like we've become less personal as a society. Imagine how you would feel if you

8

AVOIDING THE BIG MISTAKES

There are icebergs in life that you need to try to avoid. Sometimes they get in your way, especially when you least expect them to, and you hit them. I think the following four categories are important to understand and to avoid if possible. When I started my professional career, I felt I could stay away from these issues, but some of them have hit me hard. Think about them now, pay attention to the warning signs, and then course-correct before they have a significant negative impact on you.

Debt

I covered this earlier in the book but am addressing it here also because it's so important. Leading a financially stable life relieves you of one of life's biggest stressors. Debt, on the other hand, is like a weight that relentlessly drags you down. I'm extremely lucky to have parents who drilled this into my head as they raised me. I had to save for everything when I was a kid and have done all I can to avoid any sort of debt.

I've met many hardworking people who can't find a way out of the debt they have created for themselves. Sometimes, they had no choice but to accept this debt to help pay for an unavoidable challenge. When you're young and just starting, you have the power to do all you can to avoid it.

If you haven't gone to college, do your best to create a plan where you'll graduate with little or no debt. Consider community college if you're low on funds. Work while in school to minimize the college expense impact. If you're in a low demand program and graduate with loads of debt, it might take a lifetime to pay it back.

If you're just graduating and find yourself with college debt, put together a strong financial plan to pay this down as soon as you can. If the interest rate is low and the monthly payment isn't too cumbersome, then perhaps you can string it along for its entirety. However, as soon as it's paid off, you can redirect the money to investments and other meaningful expenditures.

Live below your means always. Never be spending more than you earn. It should be a crisp and clear directive for you. If you don't have money at the end of the month to spend on extra things, either pick up a side job to earn more money or be patient and save for the goodies.

Don't make the mistake of getting yourself into debt that you can't handle. You'll drown financially and it's very difficult to come back from that.

Divorce

I've read that roughly 50 percent of marriages end in divorce. I find that statistic to be very troubling. Divorce damages families and, in many cases, the kids of the divorces really suffer. I hope you consider my quick pointers on marriage that I shared earlier in the book. Choosing a partner that aligns with your values, dreams, and outlook on life give you a great chance for a wonderful marriage.

My first marriage ended in divorce. While we both had the greatest of intentions when we got married, it just wasn't a great fit. We're quite different as people, and we both made mistakes that ultimately led to the end. I spent several years learning from my mistakes and considering how I would be a better husband later in life. There's no doubt that the divorce was difficult for me and set me back in many ways for a period. However, this setback in life allowed me to become a better husband, father, and person.

Fortunately, it has all worked out wonderfully in the end. I met the love of my life, Gretchen. When I told her grandfather Mark that I loved her, he asked me, "What are you going to do about it?" So, I proposed to her! I try hard to not make the same mistakes with Gretchen. When I do, I acknowledge them immediately, own up to them, and she usually says, "Babe, that was nothing." Well, as long as we keep having "nothings" I know we're going to be just fine.

Fear

Growing up in a financially conservative home, I'm a risk-averse person. I avoid debt, I stayed with one company for twenty-three years, and I don't take many chances. When I look back though, some of the fear was irrational and damaging. Here are a couple of things I could have done differently.

I was offered an important promotion while at Honeywell that would have taken me to Brussels, Belgium. I would have been in charge of a business unit for all of Europe and Asia. I was about thirty-three years old, so this was a stretch role at that point of my career. I toured the building, looked for a place to live, and met my future coworkers. The learning experience both at work and in life promised to be amazing. However, I got skittish. I ended up turning down the job. While my family had some health issues that I wanted to stay in North America for, that wasn't the real reason I turned the job down. I got conservative. I didn't take the chance to move to Belgium and start a new adventure. Looking back, I let fear get in the way of a fantastic once-in-a-lifetime opportunity.

Financially, I've followed my prescribed financial plan as closely as possible. However, a fear-based habit continues to haunt me to this day. I've been far too conservative with my investments. In 2000, I was burned badly by a NASDAQ investment. I spent my first meaningful commission check on the index that turned out to be a massive bubble. My investment went down every day for seemingly weeks. I eventually sold at a loss.

Having that experience in the back of my head has made me far too conservative with my investments. I'm always waiting for the "next big crash" to put dollars in. It's a good thing I've automatic investments set up or I'd probably never take the plunge. When you're just starting out, you have tons of time to ride the ups and downs of the market. Don't be conservative. Unless there's a dangerous macroeconomic environment in the country, go all-in until you're at least forty. Then, you should have at least 65 percent of your investable dollars in the stock market until retirement is in the near future.

Regrets

The vast majority of conflicts or issues you encounter in your life can be handled immediately or in the short-term following them. In fact, that should be your priority! Don't let things fester and get worse. Address issues head-on whenever possible. If you don't, you'll have regrets.

When I was in college, I spent a couple years as a boxer. I trained during the week in the basement of my fraternity house and went home most weekends to train with my father. I had a ton of fun, won a bunch fights, and have a deviated septum to show for it today. I was committed to the sport and trained very hard. Hardly a day went by when I didn't do my roadwork with my best friend, Doug, or train in the gym with my father who also happened to be my trainer. That all makes this next story so continuously bothersome to me.

I was training for a big upcoming fight in our hometown gym. It was time for the nightly sparring session, and my father put me up against Carlos. Carlos was a younger and lighter fighter, but certainly an up-and-comer. The round started and we exchanged punches while circling the ring. Typically, sparring sessions are among teammates, so nobody normally throws massive blows.

After a couple of rounds, Carlos got a little aggressive. He was fast and I was struggling to parry his punches. He hit me with a strong right hand and then I suddenly quit. I dropped my hands, walked toward the ropes, and left the ring forever. My spirit felt broken. I told my father I was done.

My father later said it's healthy when a boxer knows when he's done because he could get hurt otherwise. While that's true, I regret how I ended things to this day. Why didn't I finish the round? Why didn't I finish the night? It's probably a good thing I didn't fight the actual fight I was training for. I likely would have been destroyed. However, giving up like that, in front of my father, has haunted me for years.

Earlier in the book, we talked about starting strong. It's equally as important to end strongly. Don't short-change yourself or others who have invested in you. I didn't end my boxing career the way I should have; both my father and I deserved better. That mistake has stayed with me and helped me avoid doing it ever again. Finish what you start. Run through the tape at the finish line. Have no regrets.

9

TALES FROM THE ROAD

I've been fortunate to be all over the world and to face all kinds of interesting circumstances. Every now and then, a tidbit of information that I learned pops back into my head when I really need it. Here are twenty-six of those lessons I've picked up along the way that are apropos of nothing. I hope you enjoy them and have a chance to leverage them at some point along your journeys.

1. **Don't get sent to prison!** My kids will certainly get a kick out of this handy little piece of information. What parent tells their kids this throughout their

childhood? I did! It might seem obvious, but avoiding the long arm of the law will keep you get ahead of a good chunk of the population.

2. **Don't smoke.** The warning is right there on the pack. In other countries, they do things like print giant skull and crossbones on the box to warn you to stay away. Smoking is awful for your health, and it gives you bad breath. Furthermore, have you seen how much cigarettes cost these days? See chapter 4 to see what you could do with all that money instead.

3. **Do not drink and drive.** Do NOT drink and drive. Ever. No excuses. You could kill yourself or someone else, and rideshares are cheap and available almost everywhere these days. Even when you think you're OK to drive after drinking, find someone else to do it for you.

4. **Just say no to drugs.** I learned this one from Nancy Reagan. No further explanation necessary.

5. **Do not speed, especially when you travel to Europe and rent a car.** I'm serious, don't do it. Most of the developed countries there have speed trap cameras. No one warns you about this and I've learned the hard way. Tickets show up several months after you come home. This happened to me in both Italy and France. You have no choice but to pay the euros.

6. **When traveling overseas, get your cash at an ATM machine in a city.** Avoid your local US based bank, the airport ATM, airport exchange stations, and hotel cash exchanges when possible. All of them charge higher rates; you'll get the best bang for your buck with a simple withdrawal at an ATM downtown.

7. **Don't bother having yard sales.** These events take weeks to prepare for,

take up an entire valuable weekend to run, and generally don't net you much money. A far easier way to rid yourself of the things you don't want is to donate them to charity and take the tax exemption. Of course, if something is really valuable, have it appraised and sell online. Otherwise, donate it.

8. **Learn some version of self-defense.** It's a sketchy world sometimes, so you would be well served to know how to defend yourself.

9. **Take your PTO (paid time off).** Many people are so dedicated to their company that they fail to take their vacation time. In some cases, people even lose it at year's end! Don't be this person. PTO is something that's *earned*. It's yours. Take it. Most experts would tell you that taking it makes you a more creative and efficient employee.

10. **Avoid heated political discussions with friends and family.** It seems

that in the past few years, politics in our country has made us more and more divided. Your family and friends aren't worth sacrificing for the cause of your favorite politician. I always encourage (and often find myself in) *healthy* debates with my family. However, if you feel that one or the other is about to cross the line, better to change the subject and move on.

11. **Avoid long-term gym memberships.** As was discussed previously, fitness is a critical part of your overall health; however, I'm skeptical of gym memberships for a couple of reasons. First, I'm a big believer that most things can be done at no cost either outdoors or in a well put together home gym. Second, it's very common for people to get bored at the gym they have signed up in after a few months. The dollars involved with going to the gym and switching gyms really add up. Take advantage of the outdoors and exercise naturally—at least

for a good part of the year. If you happen to find a gym you like, try to avoid the long-term commitments.

12. **Weekends are priceless.** There are about 3,000 weekends in your adult life on average. When you look at that number, it doesn't seem like many. One time I was at a conference and the speaker said to fill a big jar with 3,000 marbles and take one out every weekend. Although I never did it, the image remains. Treat every weekend specially. Hang on to Friday night as loooooong as you can. Once Saturday morning starts, the weekend is over in a flash.

13. **When in conversations, listen to listen.** Don't be preparing to answer the whole time someone else is talking. I'm very guilty of this. I try to recognize it and improve. It's so natural to wait for the other person to stop speaking so you can have your say. Resist this. Really listen to people.

14. **Lift with your legs!** It seems everyone has to learn this lesson the hard way, but it's true. Don't bend over and use your back to lift things, you'll hurt yourself at some point. Practice when you're young and use your legs.

15. **Don't believe it when your spouse or partner says, "I don't really need any presents for this holiday."** Your best bet is to ignore this. However, if you choose not to buy gifts, do not, under any circumstances, forget the special day. You still need to treat them special on birthdays, anniversaries, and the like in a non-gift way.

16. **Always try** to have something to look forward to. When you're in the day-to-day grind, it's great to have something out there to dream about. It could be a vacation, a long weekend with your partner or a special dinner at home. It's calming to have a star marking your calendar with fun coming up.

17. **Mind the location of your hotel room.** When making a hotel reservation, ask for a room that's far away from the elevator and icemaker. The constant humming and dinging will keep you up at night.

18. **When renting a place to live, invest in renter's insurance.** It's not well advertised, doesn't cost a lot of money, but will give you great piece of mind. If you have loss due to theft or fire, for example, your personal items are covered. You can also buy liability insurance to protect you if someone is injured at your rental.

19. **Don't forget to call or visit your parents and grandparents.** Life gets busier and busier as you get older. You'll find yourself seeing your relatives less and less. Stay in touch. Your elders won't be around forever, and you want to experience all you can with them before it's too late. Learn as much as you can from them now!

20. **Be a great tipper.** They say the standard tip at a restaurant is 15 percent. To me, that's what you give for basic service. If the server is excellent, tip 20 percent, or even 25 percent. Usually servers make very low base salaries. If you tip well at establishments you visit often, they will treat you even better over time.

21. **In that same vain, be exceptionally nice to flight attendants.** They fly long hours, work in cramped spaces, and are there for your safety. Be pleasant.

22. **When buying a home, do your best to avoid private mortgage insurance (PMI).** PMI is an extra charge that homeowners have to pay when they don't have a down payment that meets some threshold (say 20 percent of the home value). The rates are significant, and you'd be better served to save up the down payment before buying your home. If you do get PMI, be sure to eliminate it as soon as possible. As soon

as you think you might have the requisite equity, get your house reappraised and shed the PMI.

23. **When buying a home, don't buy the nicest house on the street or in the neighborhood.** The other houses will keep your house value down. Aim to be in the middle of the pack.

24. **Consider a safety deposit box at your local bank.** They are inexpensive and give you a secure place to store valuables, important documents, and keepsakes. You can access those things easily with bank protection.

25. **Don't buy the cheapest wrapping paper.** I'm terrible at wrapping presents. However, thanks again to Gretchen, I discovered that the slightly more expensive varieties of paper not only look better, they are also much easier to use.

26. **Use Sundays to cook.** It's a great value to cook something like a whole turkey on a Sunday afternoon. You not only have a delicious meal for that evening but you have several days' worth of leftovers for lunch. Cooking whole turkeys, pork roasts, hams, and the like provide excellent value per pound and are much healthier than processed deli meats.

One of the great pleasures of life is building your own library of learnings. Some are serious, some are practical, and some are just silly. You learn from bumps and bruises or from a conversation with a stranger. Keep your ears and eyes open, and you'll become an interesting and unique encyclopedia of information!

10

A CALL TO ACTION

Someone is sitting in the shade today because someone planted a tree a long time ago.

—Warren Buffett

Throughout my adult life, I've read several books and countless articles about the "Oracle of Omaha," chairman and CEO of Berkshire Hathaway, Warren Buffett. His quotes have filled books with wisdom about investing and life in general. Much of what I know about investing comes from Buffett's teachings. One of the reasons why I enjoy reading about him is his thought process goes well beyond investing. The quote above is really a statement about life. To reap benefits later in your career, in your financial life, our in your personal relationships, you must plant the seeds now.

Recall this chart from earlier in the book:

All of us are somewhere along that curve. No matter the stage of life you are in, or what part of life you are talking about, there will be ups and downs. Nobody figures it all out overnight and none of us lives in a straight line. The key is to continuously assess where you are and take action on what can be done next.

What's next? Take immediate action based on what you have learned in this book and lay the foundation for your future. You cannot accomplish everything at once, but taking meaningful steps in the following areas will get things going in the right direction. You'll begin to drop those so-important anchors. Do not dillydally. Hit the ground running hard in everything important that you do. You can do this!

Your Career

Consider where you are in your career today. It's time for an honest self-assessment. Have I started strong? Do I know what my goals are for the next twelve months? Have I thought about where I want to be in two to three years? Start with the end in mind and use the tools presented to make an actionable roadmap for the year ahead. Write it down. Share this plan with your boss or a trusted colleague. Once you have a solid plan, start living it.

Your Finances

Take some real time to think about where you are financially. Be honest with yourself. Start with a fresh spreadsheet and figure out your debt position, your net worth, your cash flow, and your budget. Use the tools shared to find out a true current state. Make a plan, even if it's a small one, and start executing it NOW. Get your spending in order, make a plan to eliminate debt and establish an emergency fund, and then start investing using the Rest Easy plan. Slow and steady wins this race. Each day that goes by without a plan is literally costing you money. If you're to do only one thing immediately, set up one automatic withdrawal program for your emergency fund or your investment portfolio. Get in the habit today. Remember, time is your friend.

Your Well-Being

Don't forget about yourself. Your mind and body are your two most important tools, so invest in them. If you haven't already, block out time right now in your calendar to exercise, learn, and develop your spirituality. I find that by blocking out the time each week I'm more likely to get it done. If you focus on keeping all aspects of your person healthy, you'll likely live longer and you'll be much more helpful to all of those in your life.

Always be working on relationships. At the end of the day, it's our connections with people that color our world. Whether personal or professional, appreciate everyone you meet and work to return to them the value they give to you.

Let's Get This Kicked Off!

There's nothing more important than taking action now! When you finish this book, create a checklist like the one below to get started. If you have already done the things listed, look for the next step in that area. It doesn't need to be complicated or overwhelming; it just needs to *exist*. The key is to make a deal with yourself to always take meaningful steps toward building your future.

- ☐ Visit www.benlampron.com to view and download financial tool examples.
- ☐ Calculate your cash position and net worth.
- ☐ Set up your first automatic and regular savings or investment.

- ☐ Make a grocery list from a well-thought out meal plan for the week ahead.
- ☐ Write a handwritten letter to an important personal or professional contact.
- ☐ Schedule times in the coming week to take care of yourself. Working out, reading, learning, resting. Put them in your calendar!
- ☐ Do something great for someone else. Volunteer, donate, or simply lend a helping hand.
- ☐ Assess your current job. Determine what workplace differentiators you can use. Figure out what you want your next annual review to say about you!
- ☐ Call your parents or other loved ones and tell them you love them.

Ending Strong

Earlier in the book I talked about the great sport of boxing and how starting strong in a bout is an important factor in winning. Perhaps as important is *ending strong*. At the end of each round of a fight, the timekeeper beats the ring with a mallet, telling the combatants that there are ten seconds left in the round. When I was fighting, this was go-time! Ten seconds to let it all out. Time to leave everything I have out in the ring to win the round. Attack, hit the opponent with combinations, and don't stop until I hear the bell.

This is how you should treat life. Start Strong. Finish Strong. Enjoy everything in between. Life goes by fast. Before you know it, you'll be forty-eight years old and thinking things just began. Tell those you love that you love them. Live life without regret. Don't waste a single God-given day.

ACKNOWLEDGEMENTS

I've imagined creating a curriculum to share my life lessons for many years. As time went on, that vision turned into this book. I want to thank my wife and love of my life, Gretchen, for encouraging me to follow that dream. She lives with my idiosyncrasies and loves me anyway, and for that, I'm blessed. I cannot imagine my life without her and I love her dearly.

I'm deeply thankful for the unending love and support I've received from my parents, Camilla and Tony, who have always encouraged me to give life hell. Thank you for sacrificing your own wants and needs to raise Matt and me. Your love and influence helped prepare me for the world and helped make me the person I am today. You always taught me to start strong, to swing away, and never back down from a challenge. I'm forever grateful and love you very much.

Our three children, Adrian, Joe, and Madelyn, continuously teach me in new ways with their unique perspectives on life. They inspire me every day and have bright futures ahead of them.

Thank you to my brother, Matt, and his wife, Hiedi, who have always had my back.

I owe much gratitude to my Uncle Frank Pecoraro, whose letter to his nephews dated 12-12-19 served as a real inspiration for this book.

Thank you to my in-laws, Jean and Chris Stromwall, for raising my wife, Gretchen, to be the amazing woman that she is and for always being there for support for both of us as a couple.

I'm so grateful for all of the coworkers I've spent time working with and learning from at both Honeywell International and Metro Mold & Design. It's a blessing to have had the opportunity to work at two world-class companies.

Doug McLean and Dave Dube, my best friends, have played such a huge factor in my personal and professional development. The discipline and creativity I learned from Dougemac are priceless gifts. Dave, who I've known since I shared a football backfield with him at age eight, has been there whenever I've needed strong arms around me.

So many other friends have made me wiser, including the DMS Roto Crew, who I connect with daily; the St. John's University football gang, who took me in as their own; and the Kerins, who have been so warming to Gretchen and me. I'm very thankful for all my brothers of the Sigma Chi Fraternity who remain willing and able to help me whenever needed. There are ideas in this book that came from all of them.

A special thank you to the important mentors and teachers in my life, including Br. Paul Lauze, Fr. Michael Reding, Paul Orzeske, Ralph Carter, Stan Marshall, Paul Cote, Joline Girouard, Jeff Martin, Dennis Davey, Niels Jensen, Melissa Albers, Greg Heinemann, Greg Ulberg, Lester Lee, and Paul Zemanek. All of these individuals have taught me more than they probably realize in many different ways.

I'm very thankful for all of God's blessings which have made my experiences possible. I'm hopeful that you are able to make good use of some of the Lord's gifts I have shared in this book.

ABOUT THE AUTHOR

Ben Lampron has enjoyed a long career in industrial engineering and manufacturing, has toured the globe both personally and professionally, and has a strong passion for coaching. Ben has a bachelor's degree in chemical engineering from the University of Maine and a master's degree in business administration from the University of Wisconsin–Oshkosh. He spent the first twenty-three years of his professional career with Honeywell International in a variety of engineering, sales, and general management roles. Today, Ben leads the commercial and industrial division of Metro Mold & Design in Rogers, Minnesota.

Having raised three kids, visited forty-nine of the fifty states, and been to 153 professional baseball stadiums, Ben has some tales to tell. He has spent over a decade coaching youth sports, has been the president of a boosters club, and has mentored several individuals professionally. Ben finds personal value in sharing his successes and failures in ways that are easy for people to relate to and leverage. To that end, he's available for speaking engagements regarding the topics covered in this book.

Ben lives in Edina, Minnesota, with his wife, Gretchen; three children, Adrian, Joe, and Madelyn; and their chocolate lab, Callie. You can follow Ben's adventures on LinkedIn or Twitter @benlampron. Visit his website www. benlampron.com.

DEDICATION

For Juan and all our love and *aventuras*.

Cover design by Anna Torrey

CHAPTER

1

————

Julie's lips press towards my face and mark a soft glow of *raspberry glacé* on the window glass. "I'll be right there, Mom," she's saying, "I love you, you're the best." Rhododendron blossoms form two mounds of color on the car's back seat and I can feel the car pull away from the house. Are they *raspberry glacé* as well? Not really. The flowers are more of a fuchsia color, sharp and bold, the color of the bridesmaids' dresses.

My friend América, I remember, wore her fuchsia blouse all the time. That must be why I planted the rhodies this color, to honor that blouse somehow. It was all so long ago. Now here I am with all these picked flowers to fill the baptismal font at St. Andrews. Any that are leftover I'll tie to the church candles.

I don't want a florist. I don't want you to marry him. That's what I want to say. What I don't say, at least don't say twice. I do say it once. Then she turns her head to look at me from the left side of her face. She smiles and looks just the way I looked at about her age. *My Julie, my namesake, my sweet mommy dream of hope, I'm telling you to live the story right.*

"He is, no, he seems to me bossy, honey. Don't you think?"

Are you thinking? He's handsome and he makes a lot of money. Jonathan Miles Douglas and now all of a sudden he decides to change his name to Miles. He could be Jonathan like an apple if he doesn't like John anymore, but why Miles?

"But he's not English, Julie, not born in England."

She just smiles some more and shakes her head at me. It's hard to believe she's past twenty-one, and all these flowers are for her, and then she is off to California. "I won't even need my raincoat in Palo Alto," she told me last night, "it's so beautiful there." "Oh, take your raincoat, sweetie. Believe me, it can rain anywhere."

I think about what I did when I was twenty-one, and how it turned into a permanent scar by the time I was twenty-four. At twenty-one I went off to Chile with all my things and with my raincoat. My mother got me the blue raincoat for a trip the family took to Mexico the summer I was twenty. It would rain every afternoon, she said, and I'd really need a raincoat.

It did rain in Mexico City. Truth be told, I never realized how strange, how out of the ordinary, I looked in that blue coat. It was a sky blue, a clear sharp blue. Later, I'd realize it was also a *Virgin Mary* blue. The Virgin Mary is always wrapped around with a white veil framing her face and has a blue cloth to cover her head and body. That exact color of blue is seen all over Latin America. Teenage girls and young women never ever have coats that color of blue. But I did. I did because I didn't know, or rather my mother didn't know any better. How would we know such a thing? We were from Kansas City. This was our first and only trip to Mexico.

I remember clear as day that right after I got off the plane in Mexico City I thought to myself, *this is for me!* I loved it. I loved the colored tiles running up the walls of restaurants and the long-haired children waving trinkets in my face. It was 1967. I ran around the city in my blue raincoat feeling very bold even though I was there with my parents.

Barely a year later I packed the blue coat with its two rows of buttons and big lapels into a fabric suitcase that had a zipper closure. It was the last thing I saw as I zipped the suitcase shut. I had two of those suitcases—one a little bigger than the other—and a low, black, camp trunk with my grandmother's flat silver and two sets of new towels.

There also was a brand-new husband I'd met barely six months before. The husband with his cinnamon colored eyes was from Santiago, Chile, and that's where we were headed. I had just turned twenty-one and thought Chile was better than a trip to Mexico, better than going into the Peace Corps. After a few months of dates and kisses I turned my young life over to this fellow I hardly knew. I said to myself that I was going to walk, or rather fly, right out of Kansas City, Missouri, and have an adventure down in South America. The very cute Carlos Escala was my ticket. Foolishly I thought I could just up and leave my girlhood behind me.

Colleges and universities all over the country must have had them, mixers they were called. They were parties to meet the foreign students, make them feel welcome, and then make them feel at home. In the 60's most of the foreign students were young men, so naturally cute girls like me were right there at those parties and ready to be friendly. I met Carlos the night the foreign students were supposed to come dressed in their *native costume* and tell us about their countries. I spotted him right away because he was wearing a blue blazer and gray pants.

"It is," he said with a half-smile, "I swear to God, this is the *native costume* in Chile. It's what I wear. It's what my father wears."

He also wore thick, horn-rimmed glasses. His eyes were reddish brown. They made you think he had red hair, but he didn't. His hair was dark. He started shaking his head a bit by this point and began to look over my shoulder.

"What? You think I ought to have come more *nativo?*

Then he asked me, "Is your long hair part of your *native costume?*"

I did have great hair.

Carlos was getting a Master's degree in journalism and planning to go back to Chile. He was handsome with his curly, dark hair and his cinnamon eyes. He fiddled with his horn-rimmed glasses a lot and insisted he wasn't going to be part of the Latin American brain drain. Change for Chile was coming and he would be there for it. That's what he told me as he danced me around the floor at the college mixer. All I did was smile and listen to him. He was going to work for a copper mine. Copper was Chile's big export. He told me all about it.

A month later I told my sister that, of course, I was in love with Carlos Escala, and I thought she was being plenty insulting for even asking such a question. All I ever told my family was how much in love I was, but a lot of it was the dancing. With a slow dance Carlos had this way of putting his hand just a hair below the small of my back and pressing his left thigh along the inside edge of my right leg. It wasn't nearly as vulgar as it sounds. Actually, I don't think anybody watching us would have even realized quite what was going on.

"So, is this *nativo*?" I tossed my head and tried to pull away a little. "Is this how all the guys in blue blazers dance down in Chile?"

My parents said I didn't know what I was doing.

"You're running off to marry some Chilean boy you hardly know." My father's voice was sharp as glass. "What are you Julie? Crazy? They're all socialists down there. They're not like us. This Carlos boy, *he's not like us*"

But that, of course, was just the point. Didn't they know there were too many echoes of *young lady, you come here* and flashes of my father's hand reaching for the paddle?

The fraternity paddle from his college days sat, flat and with its chipped paint, on the ledge over the dining room door. As children we were often spanked right after dinner, just after the dishes were cleared. Three licks for being sassy to your mother, he'd say without even looking at the child being punished. I learned to bite the soft inside of my cheek. We got two licks for coming home late, but the worst punishment was for talking back. If I talked back, argued that I was sorry, or that Mother hadn't understood that it was meant as a joke, he'd make sure I tasted blood in my mouth.

At twenty-one my mother pled with me, "Julie, Julie dear, how can you do this? He says he is a radical. He said it to me himself. I asked him about his politics and he said, 'I'm a radical.'"

"He's a *radical*. *Radical*, Mother, it's a political party in Chile."

I paused for a minute. "Not everyone in the world has to be a Republican, you know."

My mother said I'd be divorced within the year.

Chile in 1968 was a long, skinny country getting ready for a change, and Carlos said we were going to be a part of it. I didn't know anything about Chile then, but I remember my first drive from the airport into Santiago. Wherever I looked, the mountains hung in the sky behind the city. Their snow formed the impossible horse's heads or fish I'd seen in clouds as a child.

"They aren't far," Carlos told me, "they look far away, but it's the haze. The haze from the city distorts the view."

The mountains are less than an hour drive from Santiago. We'd go to the snow on Sunday, my young husband promised. Out the window of the moving car I saw long stretches of squat, wooden shacks that were built right up to the side of the road we drove along. They couldn't have been more than six feet high. Each little shack was about the size of a child's garden playhouse. Of course, my sister and I never owned a playhouse, but Kathy did. When we were little, Kathy lived two blocks away from us in Kansas City. There was a square playhouse in her backyard. It had three windows. There was one on each side of the door and one on the back wall. Her father built it from a kit. As the car passed the rows of little houses there in Chile, I had a fleeting image of Mr. Carlson hammering nails into their walls just like he had done to the playhouse walls on 68th St. Terrace in Kansas City back in 1954.

"Lots of people live there," Carlos started to tell me, "It's horrible, but not for long. No government should allow this." He turned his head to face me even though he was driving. "It's those people, Julita, it's those people that always pay the price."

He sounded like a civil rights worker, and I thought, *wow, this is amazing.* He waved his left hand out the car window and pummeled the air with his fist.

"They'll be moved soon. They need to be moved, moved to where there's potable water and, and..."

Still smiling at Carlos, I pulled the collar of my blue raincoat up around my neck. It was July. It was winter in Chile and rainy, dark. My hands reached way down into the front pockets of my coat. My fingers ran up and down the seams made by the coat and the patch pockets. I fingered an old movie ticket stub and a loose button.

It was cold that whole July of 1968. It wasn't cold like Kansas City winters, but it felt colder and damper to me because Carlos's father's apartment, where we were living, had no heat. That is, it had no central heat, no heat that you could depend on. You had to light kerosene stoves, or gas stoves, to warm things up. The stoves were metal, about the size of my smaller suitcase.

You'd light the *estufas* with a match to make the fuel swish into flame. Two years later I would burn up the baby diapers I had drying in front of such a stove. I always have thought those *estufas* were a false promise. Even after the three years, the three winters I spent in Santiago, I can tell you, you never feel really comfortable in a room heated by an *estufa*. Either you are too near to it and hot, with a dry, searing kind of a heat that you instinctively know isn't meant to last, or you feel raw. After my first month in Chile I wore sweaters and wool stockings. Often, I even wore my blue raincoat at the dinner table. My legs itched sometimes, and I thought about radiators and how dumb my father-in-law was not to put them in, no matter what they might cost.

My in-laws were separated, had been for many years. It's hard to imagine it now, but that was a scandal in Chile in those days. There was no legal divorce at all. People with money would get unhappy marriages annulled, and then run off to some other country to marry again. It all seemed ridiculous and inexplicable to me. My family, particularly my father, was stalwart Midwestern Protestant and loved telling *dumb Catholic* jokes. Daddy would have loved knowing about the annulment foolishness of my new in-laws and their country. I smell the punch line of a good joke in that… He said that sort of thing. I wrote my parents about once every ten days, but I never mentioned this separation business to them. How could I?

"You should go to nursing school, young lady, go to nursing school and stop all this wildness, all this running around with that *pinko chileno*—or whatever he is,"
is what my father told me two days before I got married.

The letters I wrote my parents were masterful in their falsity. In them I was shadowed by majestic mountains, eating wonderful sticky buns, and learning Spanish. I told them that I'd found a street in Santiago that looked like the Country Club Plaza in Kansas City. The Plaza is a wondrous shopping area built in the 1930's that they say looks like Seville, Spain. Nothing I ever saw in Santiago looked a thing like the Plaza. I wrote that Carlos's parents were *absolutely great* and Dolores takes me to all her favorite pastry shops. I reported via letter that Dolores and I had gone to the movies the week before.

Despite their separation, Dolores—my mother-in-law—always said she and Tomás loved each other. Her hair was always in a bun or a French twist, and she usually dressed all in one color. She was a severe looking woman who was plain, but well-turned-out, as my grandmother would have said.

"*Somos católicos* and we love each other." It was that simple. "That is the truth," she said in her matter-of-fact voice.

She always looked me right in the eye when she repeated the phrase. Of course, even at twenty-one, I knew that it wasn't true. It was like the shacks about to be renovated, or the warmth from the *estufas*. It just wasn't so, but she said it, and came to my father-in-law's for lunch every Wednesday and Sunday. I guessed that she believed in that love and in being a Catholic.

For more than several months Carlos and I lived in the back bedroom of his father's apartment. It faced the garage of the building and was quiet. The room was big enough, but it didn't have a closet. We hung our clothes on hangers that were then hung on large hooks that stuck some ten inches out from the wall. I always had my blue raincoat on the first hanger so I could see it hanging there. It looked pretty. The blue seemed light. Next to our bedroom there was a sitting room large enough to hold a sofa, chairs and an old mahogany desk with carved feet. The desk was large, so large in fact I wanted to use it as a dining room table for us. We could pretend we had our own apartment, I figured.

"*No, Señora, no.*"

In this land where everybody else got to affect the reality they chose; I was told by a maid named Melita that Carlos and I were always to eat in the front dining room. Melita, mind you, was maybe five years older than I was, but she was the one who scooped from my arms the pale red carnations Carlos sent me for our six-month anniversary and arranged them in a vase by the front door. I remember when she grabbed the flowers, I just leaned against the hallway wall and watched her place one stem and then another in the terracotta vase. I felt silenced by her authority and almost instinctively searched for the place in my left cheek that I could wrap with my teeth.

Carlos plainly had no interest in arguing with her since he didn't care where we ate. After her edict, there we sat in the front dining room for every meal in his father's apartment. At the dining room table politics were the main topic of conversation. That was, in fact, one of the reasons I wanted to be able to eat with Carlos alone. When we were courting, we talked politics, but that had been different because it had been just the two of us. Carlos would push his dark rimmed glasses up on his head and hold them there. *You have no idea Julie.*

His eyes, flecked with red and brown, seemed soft then. He was older than I was, he'd say. I had no idea about barefoot girls who washed their babies in dirty water and had them chew seaweed because they can't afford to give them meat. When it was the two of us talking, I was dazzled. I agreed that, yes, Chile needed to move forward. What did I know? Carlos knew. He'd put his glasses back on and talk on. That's why he'd wanted to see the USA and how it worked and then go back to Chile. Conversations always ended with that he was *un Radical.* It had seemed clear enough to me in Kansas City, but now I yearned to talk about something else, anything else.

I arrived in Chile knowing no Spanish, not even enough to talk to the chickens, as my mother-in-law would laughingly remind me. After just two weeks in Chile I was going to classes three hours a day and finding out how slowly one learns another language. But even I could figure out that *lo político* in Chile was life and death for people. Anything and everything a person did was *político*. My mother-in-law told me, and she was dead serious about this, that *señora so-and-so* was *una comunista*. She knew this because the woman wore French clothes, or rather she had her dressmaker copy French design dresses she saw in magazines.

"The French are notorious, notorious *comunistas*, *izquierdistas*," she'd say, smoothing her dark skirt that matched her dark blouse. "They all think they're superior, and then they just dream up all these terrible *comunista* ideas. They really do want to see the world ruined. The French are all over Cuba, you know."

Her eyes would squint up whenever she said things like this, giving her face a pained look. You knew the *comunistas* were causing her actual physical distress.

Cuba. Cuba was the topic all talk headed towards. Carlos had gone to the States, but his best friend Alfredo was in Cuba in 1968. Tomás, my father-in-law, admired Alfredo's daring, his courage to go off and experiment with his ideas. That was the phrase he used. His voice hushed every time he'd ask Alfredo about Cuba. He longed to hear every detail. I thought Alfredo—actually his name was Alfredo Cristian—was romantic in a way that had nothing to do with his political ideology. He was tall and looked thin because his clothes were always slightly too big on him. To me he looked like a bohemian university professor. Actually, thinking about Alfredo now, I think he looked like an actor trying to look like a university professor, but in 1968 I thought he was divine. It was amazing to me that people we knew, a friend of ours, had actually been to Cuba.

My grandmother went to Cuba when I was seven years old. It was the talk of the family for months. All the way from Kansas City she had gone alone to Cuba, as, I guess, an act of defiance. She was widowed that year, the year she was 58, and going off to Cuba was her signal to the family that she wasn't going to just sit around and be miserable.

I adored Grandmother with all her stories about trips, and I wondered what she'd think of me being all the way down in Chile. She died right before the vacation to Mexico. In fact, that's why we went to Mexico in the first place. We went to calm down, to rest up after all the strain of those weeks when she was so sick. The last thing Grandmother ever did was tell my mother to give me the blue raincoat she'd seen in Swanson's front window. Mother just had to do it. You couldn't argue with Grandmother or boss her around even when she was sick and about ready to die.

Of course, no one bossed Alfredo around, but I did think leaving his wife in Santiago to worry about him night and day while he gallivanted around was terrible. Cuba was a dangerous place in 1968. Alfredo's face beamed as he told Tomás his stories. Tomás would lean forward, his shoulders down towards his heavy stomach, to hear him. Alfredo was like a brother returning to the fraternity house after the big night out. I couldn't follow the Spanish, couldn't feel the impact of the minutiae he recalled, but I knew the body language. I knew he was proud of the risks he'd taken.

Tomás was not actually a communist, he said himself. He even swore it to his ex-wife. Swore it to his separated-from, but not divorced-from, wife. I knew Carlos wasn't a communist either. He had told me that, and I had told my mother that. He was *un radical,* and that was a different political party in Chile. It was the communists that made a lot of people nervous. For Dolores it was worse than a disease.

"The communists," Dolores said, her plain face taut and earnest, "they will take the furniture, our clothes. They'll grab the land, the good schools, *la iglesía.*"

That image of communists taking my furniture, my pretty clothes, stuck with me. It was a concrete dread that persisted for the three years I lived in Chile. It made my stomach hollow out the way the fear of a spanking did when I was a child. It was something I could never talk about. Does my Julie carry fears with her? Will they silence her?

CHAPTER

2

———

Salvador Allende and Tomás Escala were friends. They were very good friends. They were Freemasons together. Allende—he was called by his last name, which I thought made him sound like a race horse—came to a very elaborate party Tomás threw for himself not long after I got to Chile. At the time it seemed strange to me, Tomás giving himself a birthday party, but that's what he did. He planned the menu, invited the guests, even told Dolores which dress he wanted her to wear. Funny, I thought, a man wanting to be in charge of everything like that. He even imported a special Italian cheese from Argentina for his guests. Seven couples were to be at the dinner, and I knew we'd never fit around the dining room table. It was a table for twelve at the most. Dolores fretted.

"With *Doctor Allende* coming, we can't possibly split the group up into two tables. *Sería un insulto.*"

She fretted so, and it wasn't even her house really. She and I spent the afternoon setting and resetting the table to make the fourteen of us fit. First we eliminated the regular bread plates in favor of little silver coasters that were only about three inches in diameter. They didn't look like bread plates to me, but Dolores thought they would do. Then she decided that Carlos and I could sit very close together, and I mean very close. She pushed our chairs so that the front leg of his chair crossed neatly in front of the leg of mine.

A seven o'clock, maybe even later, I heard Melita slam the kitchen door. She would not work in a kitchen with *esa mujer* she spat out in a high screech to no one in particular, and then she stomped back towards her room. Dolores never cooked so I couldn't imagine for the life of me who Melita was talking about. Standing close enough to the kitchen door to swing it inwards, I looked past the rows of pans out on the counter and saw a woman in a bright fuchsia blouse standing next to a small pile of bricks. There must have been seven, maybe more, of these old looking bricks stacked one on top of another. She didn't see me, and then proceeded to empty a bag into the sink. Dolores pushed past me with her arms open in an embrace.

"América, I am thrilled you could come. Now, don't you worry about Melita. She'll settle down." I swear these are the first words I ever heard América say: "For fourteen I charge extra."

Her voice was open, relaxed, but in a way that penetrated the listener as they filled the room. Of course, of course, we would pay extra, Dolores said nodding her head as she motioned for me to come into the kitchen. América was here to prepare the *cordornices*, the quail, she went on in a stage whisper that rang with excitement. So special, so large, so amazing were these *cordornices*, and only América knew where to get them, and only she knew how to cook them.

"Bricks?" was the word I said

América, silent, turned her back to me to face the sink and started to unwrap the quail and lay them out, still wet, on the counter. Dolores shook her head to indicate I wasn't to ask any questions. She then put a hand on my back to guide me out of the kitchen. Once Dolores was ahead of me, I turned and took two steps back into the kitchen. I didn't even say the word out loud. I couldn't have. *Ladrillos* wasn't a work I knew.

"There're very clean, you know." América didn't turn around.

'Oh my. I mean, oh yes. I'm sure they are. I never thought they were *dirty*."

"Well, that makes you special *señorita,* or rather *señora.* You are a *señora* I understand. Most people just presume the bricks are dirty, and that I must be a crazy country woman to carry them around."

She had a long thin knife and was cleaning the little birds. All I did was look at the back of her blouse and notice the fan-like pattern the wrinkles made in its bright color.

"But what are they for? Aren't you here to cook?" She very slowly turned around, still holding the knife, and put the other hand on her hip, "That is," she paused, "a very direct question. A good question."

I stood there and held my breath.

"I'm very busy now. I'll tell you another time," and she turned back to her work.

As we all sat down to the table that night of the party, I suddenly remembered about the way we'd pushed the chairs together. Soon I felt the length of Carlos' thigh press up against my own. A short curl of his hair rested on his shirt collar. I saw the edge of a smile and he pressed his thigh harder up against me. He never turned his head my way. From time to time during the party I let my left hand stray in back of the tablecloth. It also brushed my leg, and I hoped to find Carlos's hand to hold, but I never did. When we were alone we held hands. Actually, even walking down the street he'd catch my hand and tell me I was his pretty girl, his garland of birds, his *pajarita*. I loved it then, loved it at twenty-one being treated like a pet.

A doctor friend of Tomás sat to my right at the table that night in 1968. Naturally it made me nervous to try and speak Spanish to perfect strangers, but I did try. After a minute or two I turned my shoulders to almost faced the doctor, and then, with one long breath, asked him if he worked with Allende. Dolores had referred to *el doctor Allende* the whole time we'd been setting the table, so I felt confident that this was a reasonable question. This other doctor turned down the corners of his mouth a little as he smiled back at me. *Oh no,* he cooed. Allende didn't practice medicine anymore, although, he had been Minster of Health in a previous government. Then he leaned into the table and spoke in Spanish to Allende. I guess he must have been translating what I'd just asked him. The doctor laughed. Salvador Allende laughed. The slight pressure of the leg against mine eased, and Carlos laughed too. *Julie,* was all he said and turned away from me to speak to his father. A shiver of embarrassment ran through me.

Politics, I thought after a few more minutes went by. The whole dinner conversation would be about politics, and Allende would be the center of attention. For a while I tried to follow the conversation, but I knew it would be impossible. Voices rose and fell. More laughter. One man offered a toast. I could hear the music from the record player in the living room. Someone mentioned Cuba and *senadores*. I nudged Carlos with my leg. I even tried rubbing his ankle with my foot, but he wouldn't be distracted from his conversation.

One of the women did ask me how I liked Santiago. She had that shouty kind of voice people use when they know you don't speak their language. Other than that, I just sat there at the table and tried to eat as slowly as I could. I felt like a child forced to attend her parents' party. My tongue played over the inside of my cheek, and I felt just like the child meant to be seen, but not heard. I knew Allende was important, Carlos had told me that much about him. He wore glasses not unlike the ones Carlos wore. Staring at those dark, heavy glasses I realized I couldn't understand a thing Salvador Allende said.

Once we were all settled at the table Melita brought in the first course. In amazement I stared down at a whole artichoke and a tiny little crescent-shaped dipping dish snuggled up alongside of it on the plate. Of course, I did knew what it was. I'd seen pictures of artichokes, just never ever had eaten one.

Dolores was the first to slip one leaf of her artichoke free from its flower, and, holding it with just her thumb and forefinger, dip it into the dressing. She didn't eat the leaf though. To me it seemed as if she just sucked on the stem end before she put the leaf down on the edge of her plate. She repeated the gesture over and over, forming a neat pattern with the leaves around the shrinking flower. After sucking two or three leaves myself, I quickly figured out to let them scrape up against my top teeth. The moist, cool pulp was delicious with its vinegary sauce. The music from the other room and the conversation I couldn't understand flowed together to make one sound. I kept my eyes down and was fascinated with my artichoke. I felt vaguely like a naughty child being able to play with my food like this.

Once I had eaten nearly all of the leaves, I glanced up at Dolores again. It appeared she was using her knife and fork to eat the remaining center on her plate, I did the same. My fork piercing the thistle center of my artichoke, I cut off one small piece after another to eat. I ran out of dressing, but ate anyway. It was something to do. It passed the time.

Finally, it was the doctor who said, "What on earth are you doing?"

Then, with a broad smile crossing his face, he looked from me to my father-in law.

"Tomás, Tomás this child has eaten the whole artichoke."

Embarrassment rose up from my toes as my face turned as red as Santa's suit. With that, Carlos reached an arm around my shoulders and bent his head towards my ear. I thought he was going to say something, whisper to me, but he didn't. He was still talking to his friends, to Allende. He talked about about *mi gringa, mi gringuita* little bird and everybody laughed some more. My eyes burned and I tried to catch Carlos's attention, but I couldn't. Then, sitting as still as I could, it felt as though my father were in the room, and it had been him laughing at me. Wariness crept over me, as I realized I had been betrayed.

After Allende was president, the first thing Carlos told people as he introduced me was that I ate the whole artichoke the one time I had dinner with Salvador Allende. Cf

Whenever he told that story, I imagined I could still hear the laughter at the table, and it pierced me like the thistle center of the artichoke I'd eaten that night.

After the merriment at my expense the room went silent. Slowly I looked up to see América standing in the doorway dressed in a starched black uniform that shown like her black hair. She had wide, straight bangs that cut across her forehead. Amazingly her white apron was all lace. I'd never seen anything like it. With extended arms she held out a red platter with what I knew were the *cordornices*. I thought the guests were going to applaud but they didn't quite. Instead they gave out the subtler, appreciative sighs of people thrilled by anticipation. They knew her, I realized. Maybe people all over Santiago had her come and fix quail for fancy dinner parties. With the same regal voice I had heard earlier in the kitchen, América spoke only two words: *Damas y Caballeros.*

You would have thought she was starring in a play. Then América stepped majestically between Dolores and Allende and stood totally upright as Dolores served herself to one of the birds. Each quail took up most of a dinner plate. They were flat with a wing and a leg reaching out to each side as if they were trying to desperately take flight. When it was my turn, I took some of the parsley my quail nestled in, leaving the platter redder and more exotic than before.

Son deliciosos. Everyone said it. They said it over and over. The *cordornices* were nearly blackened with pepper that just barely burned my lip. Juice squirted, filling my mouth, as I bit into mine. I thought about the bricks, and couldn't for the life of me figure out what they had been for.

After dinner Tomás poured Scotch whiskey for those who wanted it and sat down to open his birthday presents. The big present, the one everybody wanted to see, was a set of double Old-Fashioned glasses. This was the gift from Allende. They were cut glass with etched initials on them. Such an elaborate present, I remember thinking, and strange. I knew no one drank Old-Fashioneds in Chile. Probably no one ever had even heard of them. They are an American bourbon drink.

My parents drank Old-Fashioneds on special occasions. They drank them the night before we all left for Mexico. My father served them with orange slices and maraschino cherries. In Chile you drank *pisco sours* in little shot glasses. Later, those glasses from Allende became a strange kind of family heirloom. Carlos's mother, who hated Allende because he wanted to ruin the country, set them apart on the shelf in the hall cupboard, and, as far as I know, Tomás never used them. She finally gave them to me right before I left Chile. I loved those glasses because they were beautiful and had the weight of importance.

CHAPTER

3

I wrote my parents a long letter that Carlos and I had rearranged all the furniture in the back rooms of Tomás's apartment where we lived. I even wrote that we bought a huge poster of the *Santa Lucia* hill and had it hanging over the window that looked out onto the building's garage. I always wrote on the thin, almost transparent airmail paper that self-folded to form its own envelope.

The hill, the real *Santa Lucia* hill is just the other side of the *Alameda* boulevard that runs at the end of our street. The hill is circled around and around with walkways and staircases. This hill could be right in the middle of the Plaza in Kansas City if it weren't for the mountains you see in the distance. Anyway, the poster is really great and Carlos and I can lie in bed and pretend that we are looking out at the real *Santa Lucia*.

Love,
Julie

None of this was true. None of it except that there is a Santa Lucia hill right near where we were living. The heavy, old furniture stayed right where it had always been. The pictures in the room were of Italy, I think. Carlos knew I didn't like living with his father and promised me it wouldn't be for long. The truth was that we often lay on the bed and looked out the window straight at the dreary garage. Carlos would push his glasses up over the curls of his hair and pass a hand over my breast, or caress my hair.

"My little bird, *mi parajrita,* you flew all the way here."

I almost cried one night when he called me *parajrita* and talked about me flying all the way down to Chile. He kissed an eyelid. He whispered in Spanish. I didn't understand a word he said, but I felt his breath against my ear.

"Little birds should never be alone."

He tossed one of the pillows on the bed to the floor, and laughing, put his glasses on the bridge of my nose.

"Little birdie, you see how handsome I am?"

His whole face blurred in front of the glasses propped over my eyes.

"If you fly right over here, I can make sure you never feel lonely again."

We both giggled and I knew that Carlos loved me.

In March of 1969 I got pregnant in that back room and dreamed about babies and the life we would all have. Carlos told me stories about the volcanoes in the south of Chile and swore we'd go there some time. We were very happy when we were alone together. When we weren't in the back rooms, Carlos and his father went off to work every day.

Tomás was a retired journalist but still kept an office where he worked on political articles he sold to various papers around town. Carlos was a journalist too, but, odd to me given how liberal his politics were, had given up the idea of working for a paper and did public relations for an American copper company.

The new mine was being built way up in the Andes near the Argentinian border. They hired Carlos because there was a controversy about displacing mountain families in order to build the mine. He was supposed to keep articles about that sort of thing out of the papers and off the TV, but what could he do? It was a great story: poor families, generations in the high Andes, displaced by a greedy American copper company. One article ran a picture of a withered woman pointing a long stick, or maybe it was a cane, at where her little house had been. In the grainy photo you could see that a long scar crossed her left cheek.

With Carlos off at work, I passed the months we lived with Tomás by going to Spanish classes and ducking in and out of movie theaters. Since Melita wouldn't let me do a thing around the apartment, the movies were a godsend. Most films were imports from the States blaring English to my great delight. The Spanish sub-titles that floated at the bottom of the screen were the only indication that I was in Santiago and not Kansas City.

On weekends Santa Lucia was crowded with parents taking children to sit atop stuffed ponies and to buy treats. During the week the park was quiet and I could sit on a stone bench and look down at the Chileans rushing around below. They're all talking about politics, dreaming that one of their pals is going to be president, I'd think to myself.

Late one sunny morning I looked out across the Alameda and spotted a bride standing on the far side of the street. For one long breath of a moment I saw her white dress, her lacy veil being blown against her long hair as she stood there on the sidewalk all by herself. Before I had completely stood up to move closer to the hillside edge of my perch up there on the Santa Lucia hill, two women and a man rushed towards her. They spun her around and gave her kisses. Then the four of them started walking down the block towards the San Francisco church.

She will, I sighed to myself, she will get married. I was on my feet by then and almost running down the park path to keep the bride in my view. I wanted to see her at the door of the church, wanted to watch her smile at her friends and family. I couldn't though. It was all going on across such a wide street, and soon the bride and the church were out of my angle of view. When I told Carlos about the bride he didn't really listen to me, then he pushed some hair behind my right ear.

"*Te quiero, Julita.* I love your long hair."

He tried to run a hand between my neck and my shoulder to make me laugh, but it didn't work. He knew I was sad because we hadn't had a wedding. I might as well have *run off with a Mexican*—that was my father's attitude when I first told him I wanted to marry Carlos Escala. A family wedding was all I really wanted. I tried to explain it to my father, but he wouldn't listen.

"You're telling me you want to marry a kid you've known for fifteen minutes and run off to Chile?" That's exactly what he said. "Not on my nickel, you won't."

I think it made him furious that he couldn't paddle me or lock me in my bedroom without dinner.

"Don't you raise your voice to me, young lady, don't you talk back."

That was pretty much the end of it. Mother didn't want to fight about Carlos, and my father didn't want even to discuss him. I couldn't turn to Grandmother for help because she was already dead by then. There was no wedding, no party. We just got married at the county court house and made our plans for coming to Chile. I moved my things out of my room on a dank Wednesday morning when I knew no one else would be in the house and told myself it was cooler this way, more *hip*. It was the 60's after all.

After seeing the bride I sat up on the top of Santa Lucia hill and daydreamed about what it would be like once Carlos and I left Tomás's apartment and started living on our own. Alone on that hill I could rub my belly and think I felt a roundness caused by the baby growing inside of me. Was the baby's head up or down? Even with blue sky over the mountains, days seemed gray.

My sister sent me a book about pregnancy and childbirth. I read it over and over and consoled myself that with a baby Carlos and I would be a family even if I hadn't had a wedding. We'd be fun parents. Children would never be afraid of us. I desperately needed for us to be a family to fill all the folds in my brain that were empty. With a baby I wouldn't ache for friends, I wouldn't forget to eat lunch.

Even if I was lonely, I did have monogrammed towels. That, and I had my grandmother's flat silver I'd brought all the way from Kansas City. When I was not more than seven or eight years old my grandmother told me I was the one to get her silver. This was very important, she assured me, getting the silver. My sister would get the good china, and Mother would get the furniture and the money. Mother already had silver and china. Grandmother would tell us stories about all the wonderful dinner parties she'd had with her silver and china and how anything eaten off a silver fork tasted better than food eaten off stainless steel.

You girls always have to let people know you're stylish was her advice about life. A good character was fine, but it didn't mean you had to live like a frump. Then she would add a little dig that our mother hadn't taken much heed of this.

I didn't see Mother as a frump, but she didn't have Anna Bolini come in to make individual lemon meringue tarts to serve at her dinner parties. Anna would spend the whole day of a party in the kitchen at Grandmother's and create the most wondrous biscuits and rib roast with four kinds of vegetables. All of it got served up on bone china and dished out with silver.

Of course, Anna wasn't like América. She didn't bring her own game fowl to cook, or bricks, or Chinese red platters. Anna was a cook and a waitress. I didn't know exactly *what* América was. She seemed to be more like my Grandmother in a way. The fact that people scurried out of her way or held their breath when she spoke made me envious of her self-confidence.

There I was in Chile, pregnant, with the silverware, and wondering how long before I could use it. By late April of 1969 Carlos and I finally moved from my father-in-law's apartment out to what had been his weekend house. It was way on the outskirts of town in an area called *el Arrayán*. An *arrayán* is a kind of myrtle bush. I'd voted for us moving to a little apartment where we'd really be independent, but Carlos didn't agree.

"Oh my *gringuita*, believe me, we'll be on our own. We just won't have to pay rent."

He wouldn't even talk about getting our own place. It wasn't that he didn't listen to me, it was more like my words were lost in the air, blown aside by his words. There was such a familiarity to how he did this. *You're not going to camp, young lady.* Why? Because I say so. With my father I never got the breath out to answer him back.

Does my Julie, my baby girl, let John, or Miles, or whoever he is, boss her around? John's the one who told her not to have Jessie be a bridesmaid, and she said *fine*. He's the one who planned the move to California. Doesn't Julie want to stay East? Will Julie start to talk to herself? Start to plan her words, clever phrases, and then wait and wait until they slip away?

***

By the time we were moving out to where *God lost his shoes* everybody knew Salvador Allende was working his magic to put together a political coalition and make a run for the presidency of Chile under the banner of *Unidad Popular*. I was pregnant and busy figuring out how to save a nickel. Nearly every day I'd go off looking for ways to make do with what I could find in the outdoor markets and little shops. A maid up the street from us had told me all about pickpockets, so I made a button closure on one of the pockets of my blue coat. My wallet, keys, even my gum, was always in that pocket. I bought cheap vegetables at street markets. Carefully I took the apples and fish wrapped in old newspapers home in a net bag. In my blue coat I must have looked very foreign. *Chilenos* favored dark clothes, especially in town. You'd see navy blue, gray. One morning a vegetable man said to me, "Miss, Miss, where are you from? Are you from *Hollywood?*" He was laughing before he finished the question.

It was at about this time that meat began to be a real problem in Chile. Chileans considered eating beef a status thing. My mother-in-law boasted that Carlos ate meat twice a day as a child, *just like in Argentina.* That was why his bones were strong, why we would have healthy children.

In the 60s I can tell you the Chilean beef wasn't like the beef in Argentina, or Kansas City, or, for that matter, like anywhere where meat is good. *It was tough* and pretty much tasteless. Unless you got the most expensive cuts, it was stringy and a funny dark red color. It looked as if it had paint on it. When I was first keeping house a political turn or other caused beef rationing. First it was just on Fridays that you couldn't buy meat. Then it was two, often three days a week. We ate chicken or fish, and if I do say so myself, for twenty-one I was a great cook. Carlos, though, started in that I needed more beef because of the pregnancy. One warm evening he ran his hands over my belly and murmured, "*Carne, carne, carne,*" in a low sort of growl and opened his mouth wide, like a monster. He got me laughing and finally I promised to buy steaks for a cookout we were having that coming Saturday night.

It was the very first time we'd invited anyone but family to come for dinner, and I was elated at the idea of entertaining friends. On Friday, off I went to the butcher shop, but once I got there, I stood frozen in front of the meat case. It all looked very dead: *posta negra, entrecot,* I didn't know what anything was. It was a woman in a stained white apron that told me to buy whale meat.

"It's better than this, *m'ija,* escúchame." She waved a red stained hand in the direction of the meat case. "It's tough. It's all tough. The whale meat is fresh and sweet and tender, créame."

"No, No," I told her, "I don't want fish. My husband wants me to get meat. We're having a little party."

The woman in the apron called to the butcher,

"You tell her, Gino. Tell her the whale *is* meat." Then to me she said, "Whales should be grazing the *pampa, m'ija,* instead of swimming around. Gino, tell this girl they aren't fish."

She was very emphatic and then reached into a separate case and picked up a whale steak. Gino never said a word to me, but I figured I'd give whale meat a try. It did look rosy and had a fair amount of fat on it. It looked like meat to me.

By evening the next day there were scalloped potatoes with onions and grated cheese, an apple cake, and even a caramel sauce. I used 12 lemons to make the *piso sours,* which is what Carlos had promised to do, but didn't. He also didn't put the meat on the grill and let the smoke drift through his hair. I did all of that. At dinner one of the women, a blond girl about my age, announced that the whale meat was odd, sort of cloying. Since I never saw her put even a taste of it in her mouth, I didn't know how she knew this. After hearing her comment, Carlos waved his fork around and asked me why on earth I'd bought whale meat instead of *carne para asar.*

Then, turning to the blond woman he said, "Julita must have been confused, you know, her Spanish isn't very good yet. I bet she misread the sign"

From what he'd said I couldn't tell if Carlos was on my side or not, but I'd seen the fork and heard a sharp tone to his voice. *You just try buying meat, mister*, that's what I wanted to say, but didn't. That night I slept with my coat wrapped up in a ball like a pillow, and I bit my cheek for hours. The buttons rubbed up against my face and left their marks by morning.

Chapter

4

It was over three months before I wrote my parents that I was pregnant. One of the last things my mother said to me before we left Kansas City was, "Marrying this boy is bad enough, but I swear to God, if you have a baby down there you will *ruin your life.*"

Mother was such a hornet and always thought I was about to ruin my life. She was counting on me leaving Carlos, or as she said it, *coming to my senses* within a year and undoubtedly thought a baby would be a horrible encumbrance. I didn't put it past her to tell me to have an abortion, even though abortions were even more illegal in Chile than in the United States.

Alone, I ached to at least call my sister and talk and talk and tell her I was pregnant, but I didn't. On a cold, dank July day I wrote my parents one of my long, windy letters full of lies and half-truths about going to the opera and finding a place to buy *Time* magazine. Only the latter was true. At the end of the letter I said I'd also just bought four yards of lavender cotton and miles of white lace to decorate a *Moses basket*. The word pregnant wasn't used. Included in the letter were just details about how I was making a ruffled skirt out of the lavender cotton for the baby basket. I even said the sun hood was to be edged in lace and that I'd put lace on the baby sheets.

Everyone knew I could really sew. My grandmother taught me when I was about ten. We made aprons together. She'd guide my hands as I pulled double threads taught to make gathers. My mother hated sewing. The baby might be born on New Year's Eve and we were all thrilled, was how I ended the letter.

Probably the happiest Carlos and I ever were together was when I was pregnant. I was his little bird and he was so handsome. He'd rub my belly with both hands and say,

"This *guagua* will play *fútbol* and chase pretty girls like you." We'd laugh.

I wanted a boy too and hoped he'd have Carlos's dark, curly hair and cinnamon eyes. Before Charlie was born Carlos and I had the effervescent confidence of the very young. We were sure our baby would be healthy and perfect. We promised we'd be cheerful parents who would never criticize him for being bad or threaten him with spankings. My obstetrician spoke such good English that I remember thinking he might as well have been from Kansas City. As a matter of fact, he had done an OBGYN residency at the University of Michigan, which made him sort of an honorary Midwesterner. One office visit, as I lay on the examination table with my legs in the stirrups, he told me all about a *gringa* nurse in Ann Arbor he'd almost married. Then he went on to tell me I'd have a midwife with me at the baby's delivery. A midwife? This was very cool, a midwife, I thought at the time.

Baby Charlie couldn't make up his mind about being born. Carlos and I were sent home from the clinic twice before the midwife let me stay. After my second rejection Carlos went back to work and I, huge with child, with no real friends, and speaking bad Spanish, went to the movies. It is what I knew how to do. I went to see *Easy Rider*. My sister had written me about *Easy Rider*. She'd written me all about James Taylor and *Flying Machines* too.

All by myself, I sat in a nearly empty movie theater that afternoon a few days before Christmas and held my belly against the labor pains I felt. Dampness marked my skirt by the time Peter Fonda was killed. It was two hours before Carlos got to the hospital. The midwife clocked my contractions and taped a twisted magazine to my arm to splint it for the IV the doctor was to insert right before delivery. For some crazy reason the clinic was out of proper wooden splints. Except for Carlos standing outside the labor room door, I felt even more isolated than I had at the movie theater. Baby Charlie was born four hours later. That night was the first time since I 'd been in Chile that I called my parents on the long-distance telephone. Shouting into the phone, I heard my words echo as they went up the underwater cable all the way to Kansas City.

"It's a boy. We have a baby boy." Just saying the words made me cry. "He is beautiful."

My parents were both on the line, their words jumbling with the echoes of mine as we spoke. Congratulations and they were fine. My sister was fine. What did the baby weigh? Was he Charles or Carlos? At the end of the three minutes, I asked them when they were going to come to visit us, to visit their grandchild. After a pause my mother said, "Now Julie, you know your father won't fly. You knew that, honey, when you went to Chile."

Chapter

5

The presidential elections were in September of 1970. The funny little man who sold newspapers at our corner told me three kids paid him to paint political slogans on his kiosk. He had made more for that sign than for selling three days of papers. Slogans were on every wall. The Christian Democrats, the party in power and the friend of Uncle Sam, were in trouble. It was a lot more than meat rationing-and selling whale meat-that had made people mad I figured.

What I did know for sure was that my dream baby, my Charlie who had been so perfect, was nine months old by then and was very sick. That whole September he had a staph infection in the bones of his left check. His round little face was swollen enough to close his left eye. He screamed all the time, and I was terrified.

Charlie's infection had been building up for weeks by the time we went to the doctor's that September. He was put on two kinds of antibiotics by mouth. Still the infection raged. Finally, the doctor said we'd have to put the baby on injections of penicillin every four hours. *Un practicante* needed to come to the house, the doctor said, every four hours around the clock to give the injections. Carlos and I couldn't handle that, I thought.

Our house, actually Tomás's house in *el Arrayán*, was way outside of Santiago. With the baby needing all those shots, staying with Tomás at his apartment downtown made much more sense. I, naturally, had no idea what *in practicante* was. A visiting nurse is what I envisioned. She'd be a nice woman in a white uniform, have a neat black bag, and carry disposable syringes.

The pediatrician gave Carlitos, my baby Charlie, the first shot right there at the office. Then I took him in a taxi over to my father-in-law's. *Señor Dávila* would be there in three hours to give the next shot. When I answered the door, at first I thought the man I saw was selling milk, or bread. I kept looking over his shoulder out onto the landing to see if someone else were there. This mister Dávila man was dark looking. He had on one of the worn, threadbare gray suits modest Chilean men wore. His shirt collar was frayed and he wore an out-of-shape, out-of- style necktie. He waited for me to introduce myself and then he spoke to me very slowly, very deliberately. I understood exactly what he said.

"I'll need to use the stove, *Señora*, and after five minutes, a full five minutes, I'll ask you to take the baby over by the window."

The window? *Why the window?* He needed the daylight, he said,

"You can see better in the daylight. Naturally, at night we must rely on electricity, but daylight is better.

Standing in the doorway I watched the needle and glass syringe go into a little saucepan to boil. Carlos was somewhere in the other room. Later he said he knew what *practicantes* were; he didn't need to see all of this. Sitting on a straight back chair, I held my little son face down over my knees. Light came through the glass while this perfect stranger shot penicillin into Charlie's bottom. It took time, a good three minutes, to give the shot.

"The more slowly you inject, the better the absorption," Dávila commented.

We spent the four days before the presidential elections marking the comings and goings of señor Dávila. We were in our back bedroom, and my coat was on the same funny hook we'd used two years before. Our baby, with his cinnamon eyes like his *popi* and his light hair like me, improved.

The actual day of the election felt like a party in Santiago. By law registered voters were required to vote in Chile back then, so most everyone was out and about that Friday, September 4th, 1970. Wagers were placed, and all over town working-class people held three fingers up to signal an Allende victory. The U.S. Embassy thought Tomic, the Christian Democrat, would take the prize. Chile was too developed, too European, to be suckered into a serious engagement with the *Unidad Popular* the *gringos* said. Since I was a *gringa* I believed them, but Carlos told me to wait and see. I never asked him how he voted, figuring it was a toss-up, seeing how he worked for an American owned mine and had all his ideas about do-gooding and social change.

Even with the election, my focus was squarely on baby Charlie and how sick he had been. Carlos and I were going with Alfredo, the guy who had gone to Cuba, and his wife Silvia to hear the election returns at the apartment of young Swedish diplomats we all knew.

In the 60's the Swedes seemed to think that they could advise Chileans on how to develop their resources. Like the good socialist he was, this young Swedish diplomat threw the election night party because he thought it was great that Chile was flirting with electing a socialist as president. I was all dressed up. It was the first time I'd ventured out to do anything fun since baby Charlie had been sick. There I was in a green wool dress, my long hair all piled up on top of my head, and I had on my blue raincoat. We headed out to have a good time, but as soon as we walked in the door at the party I sensed things were terribly wrong. I remember my fingers running along the seams of my coat pockets. Erwin didn't even say hello to us. A man pulled Alfredo over to a phone. Carlos kept saying, "*¿Qué?*"

Five or six people were talking at once, and a radio was blaring in the background. There was so much excitement, but I couldn't understand exactly what people were saying at first. *Tomic wasn't winning.* Having it a three-way race—Tomic, Allende, and Alessandri—had thrown everything off.

"No one," a man said, "can see the road now. Everything will change."

I knew he used the true future tense when he spoke, *todo cambiará.* It sounded very formal, very definite. An hour passed. We drank *pisco sours* and ate *empanadas.* At about 10 p.m. Carlos said he was going over to one of the newspapers to find a journalist friend of his in order to get more definitive election results. He and Alfredo were out the door before I was able to get my coat.

Several other people abruptly left as well. With Carlos gone, I did take the time to say goodbye to Erwin and his wife, and then threw on my coat. It was a fairly warm night so I didn't really need a coat, but I even buttoned it up. A group of us walked across the street and began looking for cabs. It was well after 10 by now, but it wasn't late, not in Chile.

I always felt safe at night, because no matter when you leave any place it is always just after dinner. Even when we'd eat at 11, I'd feel that somehow it was only still early evening. The other women got in a cab going east. I told them not to worry, an empty cab would be right along, and I'd head downtown. Despite the dark, the street felt like the afternoon because of the elections and all of the excitement. Since I was right there on *Providencia,* one of the main avenues of Santiago, I decided to just go ahead and take a bus. In high school I had always come home by bus, but in Chile I was the only person I knew who regularly took them. People we knew took cabs or walked places when they were in town. I figured once I got back to the apartment, I'd check in on the baby, have a cup of tea, and wait for Carlos to get back and tell me the election news.

It's funny how memory is. I have such a clear memory of getting on that bus. Stepping up from the curb I felt like a child. The step seemed high, out of proportion. The bus hadn't quite pulled up to the curb I suppose, and that forced me to swing my leg way forward to pick up the first step. As the coins fell through the slot into the fare box, I could hear the loud conversations and singing. Usually people don't talk on buses in Chile. If they do, they almost whisper. I'd tell Carlos I thought Chileans were all telling secrets or were all out with their lovers. He'd laughed and said I was probably right. But the night of the election everybody on the bus was boisterous and waving their hands around. My eyes darted down the center aisle looking for a seat. The movement of the bus made my feet lurch forward making my joints feel oversized.

A man looked up at me from his seat. At first I thought it was señor Dávila and started to speak to him. Before a word was out of my mouth, I realized that it wasn't señor Dávila. It wasn't anyone I knew. His eyes motioned to his seat as he got up. He followed that gesture with a little sweep of his hand. As I moved across him to sit down, I think I heard him whisper, *Señora, you should take off that blue coat.* I didn't need to look up at him to know that he continued to stare at me. His voice, what he had said, hung in the air around my head and filled me with dread.

It would have been too awkward there on the bus to stretch my arms out, but I knew I'd take the coat off just as soon as the bus stopped at *calle Carmen*. I'd let my left arm slip free of the sleeve as I stepped down the bus steps to the street and then fold the coat inside out over my arm as I walked the two blocks to the apartment. No one would see its blue color, no one would see how foreign I was, how out of place. The talking, the noise on the bus menaced my confidence by being unexpected. The bus passed a group of Allende supporters wildly waving election posters. Two men behind me shouted something out the window, mixing their words with hilarity. I didn't turn around or look up again.

Once I was in the front hall of the apartment I could hear a fretful little whimper of a cry. The dim hallway framed Melita. She must have been in a dark dress, because I only saw her face as she spoke, "*Señora, Señora* the baby is worse. He's been crying all evening."

Crying all evening? Charlie always cried so much. Melita was right behind me still talking as I hurried down the hall.

"Let me make him strawberry tea, *Señora*."

Charlie was just sitting up in the crib as I opened the door. He had both of his hands by his left hip to push himself up. His cry turned to a wail as if this movement had filled his lungs with all the air in the room. The very loudness I heard relieved me. I knew that scream. It was his angry scream, his *I'm hungry, I'm wet* scream. At not even a year old, Charlie had attuned me to his entire language of cries. Fine, blond hair stuck damp to his forehead. As his cinnamon brown eyes caught mine, he relaxed and stretched out his arms to be picked up.

"Don't you cry, baby Charlie, don't you cry."

Swaying back and forth, I nuzzled his neck and felt its warmth. He smelled of talc but didn't feel feverish. All those shots, all that medicine, he couldn't be sick again, I pleaded with I didn't know what. Carlos was standing right behind me before I realized he was in the room.

"Is he alright?"

Alright? So much of the time this child, this Carlitos, this baby Charlie with his yellow hair and smooth fingertips, was not alright. We never seemed to have the jolly, healthy child of those months of the pregnancy. He always seemed to have a fever, or diarrhea. He threw up, or he had the swollen face, that terrible swollen face caused by the staph infection.

"He's fine." I told Carlos. "I think he missed us. He must have woken up and realized we were gone, that's all. He'll settle down now."

Carlos wrapped his hand over that small head up against my chest and kissed the top of my brow. I swayed more from side to side to rock the baby to sleep. Carlos kissed my cheek and then stepped back from the two of us to speak.

"Sweetie, it's chaos outside, really *loco* with people running up and down the streets like they're crazy. God, right at the corner a man has a microphone hooked up to their car is yelling, *Ganamos, ganamos*—we won, we won." With that a grin crept over his face, " I can't believe it Julie, I just can't believe it."

"He's won, Allende's won? I thought he *wouldn't* win."

Carlos's smile broadened enough to show all of his front teeth, and his head shook from side to side. The grin was for himself.

"No, I didn't either. I didn't think he'd win, but he did." He stepped away from me a bit. "This will be it, *pajarita,* this is the change."

It sounds crazy, but the first thing I thought was that maybe we could invite Allende for dinner. We knew him, after all. We could have a party for Allende, and this time I wouldn't eat the whole artichoke. América would come and fix *cordornices,* and I could find out what she did with the bricks she carried around.

"Dinner? Are you crazy, Julie?"

Carlos sounded dismissive as he walked towards me again and reached out to hold Charlie. I just stood there and felt my tongue pass over the inside of my cheek.

"Allende is going to be e*l Presidente*, Julie, this whole country is going to change. *Todo cambiará*, like that man said at the party." What I read as an odd, solitary look crossed his face, and, for just a moment, he looked like my father.

"Allende's not going to have time to come to our house for dinner."

Carlos handed Charlie back to me and turned his back as he moved towards the bedroom door. My eyes shifted from the back of Carlos' head to the top of Charlie's. I stopped rocking and moved over to put my sleeping baby back in his crib.

CHAPTER

6

The next morning I dressed Carlitos in tan, hand-knit cotton leggings and a blue sweater. He didn't have a fever and his face seemed fine. Dolores and her sister were at their apartment. I knew I would much rather spend the day there than at Tomás' hearing about the election results.

We didn't have a baby stroller, so I carried Charlie as I walked the eight blocks to my mother-in-law's. He wrapped his legs around my waist and held on to my neck. I just had to lock my arms together under his fanny, and away we went. It was very practiced this position, this way of going places. Charlie always wanted up on my left side because that way he knew he could fiddle with the top buttons on my coat. The buttons were off-white and about the size of large bottle caps. They were sewn to the coat leaving a little leg-up of thread. This slack, this quarter of an inch, meant that Carlitos could twist them around, or even get them in his mouth.

Dolores and her sister lived in a fourth-floor walk-up apartment overlooking *Plaza Brazil*. In its heyday *Plaza Brazil* was grand with palm trees and lovely cast iron benches, but by 1970 it was *venido a menos*, that's what people said. The whole neighborhood had the same down-at-the-heels look. The apartment Dolores shared with her sister Asela sprawled, taking up nearly the entire floor of the building. The front windows looked out over the *plaza,* and to me that living room felt like a place where people had lived forever.

Over-stuffed chairs, dozens of family pictures, and what Carlos called *chucherías,* were everywhere. I saw them in every house I ever went in Chile. Little silver ashtrays, pillboxes, mementos from a first communion or a wedding lined every flat space. One woman I met had three braided hair necklaces with tiny silver clasps out on her coffee table. She told me they were her mother's. I didn't know whether that meant they were made from her mother's hair or just belonged to her mother. Of course I didn't ask her.

Dolores had three of Carlos' baby teeth in an enameled box. That little blue and gold box was one of the treasures she had brought back from her only trip to Argentina. It wasn't the table ornaments that fascinated me in that room as much as the family photographs. Carlos never told me much about his family, but if I asked about a photograph Dolores could talk for an hour. It was like listening to the radio. She would go on and on, piling detail upon detail about the person.

That morning, after the maid whisked Carlitos off to the kitchen, I pointed to a rather faded picture of a young woman. It was in a large, heavy, silver frame with relief work on all four sides. The picture stood alone on a round table next to the sofa. I noticed the picture the first time I ever went to the apartment because the young woman in the photo looked about my age. It was a formal portrait done in sepia tones of a young woman with long, dark hair all done up on the top of her head. She wore a high lace collar fixed by a pin. She didn't smile and seemed to have her gaze fixed in the distance.

All I said was, "Who's that?"

Dolores, who had been straightening up magazines on a table across the room, turned, looked at me for a long moment, and sat down next to the photograph before she spoke.

"That is my sister. That is a picture of my sister Rebecca."

Rebecca? There was no sister Rebecca, not that I knew of anyway. There were just Dolores and Asela.

"No, no, Julia, you won't ever know Rebecca. She died a long time ago. She was the oldest, you know, the oldest and the most lovely, but she wasn't meant to live." Then Dolores said the oddest thing. She said, "Rebecca had no destiny. She was a sweet girl, a beautiful girl, *pero sin destino.*" Her voice trailed off before she spoke again. "There was a warning about it, after all. Before our mother had that picture taken she already knew something terrible would happen."

Rebecca was twenty-three when she went to Viña del Mar to *Fotografía Elegante* to sit for her portrait. A month later she fell off a horse and smashed her temple against a fieldstone.

"But that wasn't the worst of her dying young." Dolores said, her voice eager and intense. "Asela and I thought it started with the baby. That's what did it, I suppose. That's what cut her life off. It's what let her die even before she cut her hair. We all cut our hair in the 20's. It was fun. I remember I came up to Santiago to have my hair cut into a bob. But not Rebecca, she was gone before then."

Dolores wasn't talking to me. She was sitting on the edge of the green velvet sofa, staring at the photograph, and talking to it. And on that morning the day after Salvador Allende was elected president of Chile, Dolores volunteered this story that she had obviously told many times before. It was like hearing someone tell a bedtime story.

"Naturally to you, Julita, it would seem young her getting married at 18, but it didn't seem young to us. Most of the young girls we knew married at 18 or 19. I was only nine years old then. To me she was grown and he was a charmer and he was from Santiago. He had been sent to manage his family's *fundo* just outside of Linares. Not a big *fundo*, but *perfecto*. Mother was thrilled. 'They will have country life while they have their babies, and then they'll be off to Santiago to get them all educated. Perfection, girls, *la perfección andando*.'

Mother was happy about the match. Nevertheless, she must have been worried because of the forewarning of trouble for Rebecca.

Asela and I were all in the wedding in our light blue dresses. When she got pregnant, I used to pretend she was my mother. I longed to have a baby sister to dress up and fuss over. Mother would let me spend days and days over at Rebecca's house. I was the one who got to help her lift things, or do her hair. Being pregnant made her tired, she said, so tired. The baby was due in November and was born right on time. I was there. I saw everything. Pedro rode to town to get the doctor. The maid rushed all around. A midwife came. Luis Andrés was a beautiful, beautiful little baby. It's just that he had this funny problem. That's why the doctor said it would be best to circumcise him.

Pedro didn't want it done, he argued with the doctor. Rebecca was tired. How could she have known? She was very young and very tired. Nobody could have known what would happen. When he came back the next day, the doctor made Pedro look. 'See, the baby is fine, perfect, but the foreskin doesn't come together on the underside of the penis. I'd circumcise him if he were my child, Pedro, I really would.'

I've never known if Pedro and Rebecca talked about it first. Did they talk it over and make a decision? The doctor had the maid boil up his instruments. Then he told Pedro and the maid to take hold of the baby's arms and legs to hold him down.

Standing just inside the doorway, I saw the doctor's wrist and forearm make one quick half turn. The baby screamed. He screamed and screamed. The doctor did something else as the maid wrapped the baby up in a cotton blanket. Then the two men walked through the doorway where I had been standing and went towards the front door. Before Pedro had swung the door fully open, the maid's voice rose in a wail. '*Doctor!* Dolores, get the doctor. He's bleeding, bleeding. The baby's bleeding.' The doctor pushed his way into the room before even Pedro got there. Rebecca was in the next room shouting to be heard. I remember wanting to get Mother there. She would get ice. You get ice when you bleed. You press hard, and the blood stops. The maid had no ice. It was 1915, I think, or 1916. We didn't have ice, Julia, not in the spring, not in November.

Our mother did not come. Rebecca got up out of her bed and ran shouting into the yard. The Doctor said *no, no,* she couldn't be up, even for a minute. She could start to bleed too. They took the baby into Rebecca's room in order to make her come back into the house. The doctor stayed, then he left. Then he was there again. I didn't have any lunch that day. I didn't have one single thing to eat. By evening candles were lit in front of the cross on the hall table. By morning the baby was dead.

After her baby died Rebecca had very little ahead of her. Mother said not to worry. There would be lots of other babies, lots of happy times. But of course Mother knew she lied even as she spoke the words. Pedro ran off to Argentina. He stayed for eleven months. Rebecca was dead at twenty-three."

Dolores didn't look at me or look back at her sister's picture. Once she had finished telling her story, she stood up and walked back into her bedroom. She returned with a tiny, embroidered baby bib.

"I made it for him when I was ten years old. Why don't you use it? You could use it for Carlitos." She stretched out her hand to further reveal the bib wrapped in a bed of tissue paper. I didn't want to even touch it.

"Oh thank you, thank you very much, but Carlitos is too big, he's way too big to use that now."

After lunch I carried Carlitos the distance back to Tomás' apartment. Gazing down at his little blond head pushed up against my chest I realized that he'd fallen asleep in my arms. He felt very substantial, very solid. Even before I opened the door I knew Carlos and a group of his father's friends would be sitting in the living room talking about the election. Getting through the room to go and put the baby in his crib was easy. No one even saw me.

Later that evening I told Carlos I wanted to go home, back to our house. The baby was better, I explained. He reminded me we had another doctor appointment on Monday, so staying in town did make sense.

Then I tried to tell him about the Rebecca story and how it had given me the creeps.

"The creeps Julie, I'll say, *the creeps*. I've heard that story about a hundred times. All about the blood and poor Rebecca running out in the yard, or wherever it was, screaming for her baby." He waved his hands around in imitation of poor Rebecca.

"Mother's full of stories like that. She loves all that *hocus-pocus*. God in heaven, I just can't believe you spent the day listening to that crap. What about the elections? Didn't you all talk about the elections?"

I told him no, that actually we hadn't. He wasn't mad precisely, but bemused or dumbfounded because, I guess, everyone else in the entire country had been talking about the elections. Then I asked him why it was that Dolores thought her mother knew from the beginning that Rebecca wouldn't live long.

"Your mother said, 'She didn't have any destiny,' and your grandmother already knew it."

He gave me a soft, indulgent kind of a smile and said, "A fortuneteller no doubt. That's who it would've been. They all love *brujería*, reading the cards, you name it, Julie, and those women will pay for it. My grandmother was the same way. Hell, she raised them all to believe in burying toads and taking moon baths. Ha."

"Your mother goes to a fortuneteller?" Dolores with her neat, slick hair in a French twist, with her navy blue wool crepe dresses flashed to mind. Dolores with her good pearls on actually goes to a fortuneteller. "I don't believe you. You're joking, you're kidding."

How can a grown woman go to a fortuneteller, I thought. When I was seven, maybe eight, my Aunt Frances dressed up as a fortuneteller as my birthday surprise. At first I didn't even recognize her. I never saw her drive up or saw her in the house, just suddenly there was this incredible woman standing out in the middle of the backyard. She had on a long, gauzy skirt with gold threads running through it. Her hair was tied up in ribbons that held jingle bells and she must have had on all of her jewelry.

Actually, it was all of her jewelry and all of my mother's jewelry. Necklaces of shells, blue stones, even something that looked like popcorn, swung as she walked. One arm had bracelets all the way up to her elbow. That is where I saw mother's elephant. Mother has a silver elephant bracelet that I knew she would never lend to anyone other than her sister. Once I spotted the bracelet, I knew this wondrous woman with the painted face and funny accent was my very own Aunt Frances. To tell our fortunes she took us one by one into a tent my father had made by stringing big sheets between two clotheslines. She had candles lit and had a crystal ball in a silver stand. She gave us all chocolate candy wrapped in gold paper to look like coins.

"These are gypsy coins, *my dearrrrrrrrrrs*. You do not spend them, you eat *themmmm*."

It was the very best birthday party I ever had. Aunt Frances had fixed forever my notion of fortunetellers. But, of course, it wasn't just Aunt Frances. In Kansas City everyone, at least everyone I ever met, knew that fortunetellers were a joke. They were a party trick. The notion of a serious woman, a woman with a velvet sofa, paying a stranger to tell her about when a person might die amazed me. I guessed Carlos' grandmother had been a countrywoman, maybe that had been what made her so gullible. But Dolores, how could Dolores take fortune-telling seriously? Carlos explained to me that they weren't exactly credulous, these women. He talked about Catholicism, and saints, and how I was supposed to see how fortunetellers fit in with all of that.

CHAPTER

7

Carlos forever made it clear that he was not like his mother, not neurotically afraid of the Communists. He was surprised when Allende actually won the election, but he didn't think the Communists would close the churches and steal our furniture the way Dolores did.

From his reaction to the Rebecca story, I presumed he didn't believe in fortunetellers either. On the other hand, Carlos wasn't exactly like his father. We had just lived through the 60's after all; young men didn't want to be stuck in the mud and old-fashioned like their fathers. Also, Carlos had spent a year in *los Estados Unidos*, and he was married to me.

Even before the elections I saw Allende slogans painted all over newspaper kiosks promising *lo chileno para los chilenos*. I didn't know yet just how it would affect us, all of us. What I did know was that I was worried about Carlitos, my baby Charlie. I then thought about Rebecca. As I turned the Rebecca story over and over in my mind, I superimposed the face of señor Dávila for the nameless doctor of Dolores' remembrance.

Sometime that Saturday after the election, the Saturday when I first heard the Rebecca story, Tomic, the Christian

Democrat candidate, ceded victory to Allende. I thought that would be the end of politics until the November transfer of power, but I was wrong. Monday morning by 6:30 the phone was ringing. Doors banged, and I heard a muffled kind of a shout. I thought maybe the building was on fire. Seeing me in the hall in my nightgown, Carlos turned.

"They're not going to open *la bolsa* today. It's closed. The market is closed

His voice rang with high excitement.

The *bolsa*?

"The stock market, Julie. They've decided not to open the stock market."

I couldn't figure out what he was talking about. The stock market was in New York was all I could think. He had the morning newspaper in his hands and turned his back to me as I said something dumb like,

"I don't get it. *The stock market?*"

"Julie, this is major. This is, honey listen, this is the first time since '38 *la bolsa* hasn't opened. People are gonna be shitting in their pants, *cagando bolas!*"

Then he slowed down his speech in a way that reminded me of my foreignness.

"There'll be a run on the banks. Do you know what that mean? Everybody will want their money and the banks don't have it, see? This is how it starts, Julie."

He didn't say anything else, but it seemed as though he looked different, taller maybe. He had his glasses on and the hair by his neck looked damp. I wanted him to smile and make a joke so we could laugh together, but he didn't.

As I turned and walked back down the hall I could hear him placing a call to his boss to say that, yes, he could go In early. That meant I'd have to go alone to take Charlie to the doctor. Carlos always said he'd go with me to the pediatrician, but when it came right down to it, he rarely did. I'd go alone and hope the news I got was good.

Dr. Schmit was the grandson of German immigrants and, like most of the Germans I met in Chile, it seemed as though the Schmits did everything they could to remain as German as possible. Eric had been sent to the *Deutsche Schule*. He and his wife spoke German at home. For all I knew they ate sauerkraut every day. His office was on the fifth floor of a building that looked out over the *parque Forestal* downtown. It was a lovely park, and I always went there after doctor visits to buy Charlie ice cream from a funny man who sold ice cream and sewing supplies out of a cooler he carried slung from a wide strap that crossed his back. Such a random combination: *chocolitos*, silk thread, and needles.

Eric was about thirty and spoke English, which was a blessing for me. My Spanish was getting better, but when it came to doctors I needed to speak my mother tongue. Because he spoke English, and because he was nice to me, I always felt that Eric was a friend. He lowered his eyes a bit and gently shook his head as I told him the señor Dávila story and the business about boiling up the needles.

"I'm sure it upset you, Julie. Things here aren't like in the States, but," and his voice dropped a notch to sound more comforting, "believe me, boiling for five minutes is an effective way to sterilize." The main thing though, he said, was that Carlitos seemed fine.

"No swelling, no fever. That's what you want."

The rest of the visit was spent talking about vaccinations. Since Charlie had been sick off-and-on he hadn't had all of his shots.

It seemed ironic, all the talk about how Allende was going to *socialize everything*. To me it seemed that medicine in Chile was already socialized, at least getting vaccinations was. From the time Charlie was born he'd had all of his regular baby shots given at a *policlínico*. Apparently, this was the government's effort to get well-off people involved with the national health care program.

All over Chile young mothers with pearl earrings and, in my case anyway, blue raincoats, lined up at public clinics next to poor women in dark, worn dresses. You often waited for an hour or more for your turn to see a nurse and have your baby stuck in the arm or the buttock. In the waiting rooms there were no amenities. Never did you see a Coke machine or magazines. The only adornment was always a large poster warning that infant dysentery was the biggest killer of children in Chile. *Diarrea!* It could dehydrate a child in less than a day, kill an otherwise healthy child in less than a week. The posters were all the same. They showed a pudgy-faced, dark-haired baby about Charlie's age wearing a dirty undershirt and sitting on a plastic potty seat. You knew it was meant to be a poor child because there were no toys in the picture. The child's face twisted around his own scream.

Every time I would see that poster I would think to myself, that's just exactly how it is. I knew all about diarrhea. Baby Charlie had severe diarrhea five, maybe six times before he was a year old. Of course, he didn't die. He didn't even come close to dying because we could call Eric. I learned all the tricks about making rice water, about giving the baby liquids one tiny spoonful at a time. That's what keeps you from getting dehydrated. It keeps you from dying.

For a girl like me, going to a *policlínico* was the government's lie about us all being equal. The other women who sat on the benches with their squirming children knew that I was just there for the vaccinations. They knew that when my baby cried with a fever I took him to a doctor's nice office, or the doctor made a house call. Other than the whole awkward thing about going to the public clinics in the first place, I worried about the needles they used to give the injections. Even before my encounter with señor Dávila Dolores had pushed me into a worry about needles. "Hepatitis, Julita, hepatitis. You can't trust those government clinic nurses to clean anything, sterilize anything. They are *gente muy ordinaria.*"

To Dolores, to be *ordinario* was to be shiftless, unreliable. She branded whole groups of people with the term. I don't think she did it to be mean or elitist. I imagine she thought she was being informative. There I was, her young daughter-in-law from Kansas City, and she wanted me to know that suspicion of others was protective. *She ionsisted don Ricardo* was the only fruit vendor who didn't weight his scale. There was only one place that made *empanadas* with fresh meat. If I brought her a bag of cookies from a bakery she didn't patronize, she'd say,

"Lard, I'm sure they use lard not butter. You can't trust them Julia. Just don't trust anyone, *m'ija*."

When she told me she didn't think the public clinics sterilized their needles, I worried, but I didn't panic. Eric was the one who told me where to buy my own disposable needles and take them with me to the clinic. That Monday after the elections he'd told me Charlie needed his smallpox and measles vaccine and that I should take my own needles when I went to the *policlínico*.

CHAPTER

8

———

Twice that afternoon Carlos called from the office to say he'd be delayed. Both times I told him we had to buy needles and both times he asked me if I had seen the headlines in the afternoon papers. There was now *pánico*. The world saw Chile balanced on the blade of the knife.

When he walked in the door Carlos' face had the pinched look of apprehension I had seen on people's faces all day. I said something inane about us not really having all that much to worry about because we were young and didn't have any money in the stock market anyway. Now, I yearn to wrap that younger me in mercy and caution her not to be too literal, too naïve. Back then I thought the thing to do was just push along with my handsome husband and my sick baby and keep my parents behind me. That Monday after the elections seemed normal enough to me.

"Julie, I swear to God, I don't think you quite under-stand."

His tone wasn't condescending the way it had been in the morning. This time he had his glasses up on the top of his head and was giving me a kind of flirty look.

"What?" A furrow crossed his brow, but I saw the edges of a smile, "You think it's only about getting needles for baby shots? You've got to read the papers."

By the way he said it, I realized he was getting ready to pull my leg since everyone knew I didn't read the papers. He stretched an arm across my shoulders and I could nearly taste the scent of his cologne. It was like lemons.

"You've lived here for two years, *pajarita*. Haven't you been listening to Alfredo? He's one of Allende's advisors, you know."

I moved away to pick up one stray sock, then a toy. His eyes followed the bend my body made, and I swung my fanny in his direction laughing out loud as I shook it around just a bit.

"All that going to Cuba wasn't just a vacation. And," wagging a finger in my direction, "and I know what you're thinking—it wasn't to run around with *cubanas bonitas, bonitas como tú*. Don't you know what Allende wants? The very *first* thing he wants? It's the mines. He wants to nationalize the mines."

His voice was still light, airy, but as soon as those last words registered they made me go rigid. Right then, right there in his father's apartment, I knew we should worry because Allende would take over the mines and Carlos would lose his job. I even flashed to what I would write my parents. What story could I make up? I'd write *Carlos is taking a better job*-a job at a paper or a job with a bank. Did Allende want to nationalize the banks?

Without saying anything else Carlos bent down to help me finish gathering up all of our stuff. Once the sack of toys and fabric suitcase were in the car, I wrapped Charlie up in my blue raincoat. It was a going-home game we played. He would sit on my lap, then I'd cover his head and face with the coat and let him peek out as we drove around the *Plaza Italia*.

"There he is," I'd say, pointing at the statue, "There's Baquedano."

If we saw a man walking a dog I would say, "There's old *Pedro de Valdivia* -Chile's *conquistador*-with his famous dog." That, like the artichoke, was another family joke.

Because I had little patience for Spanish classes, the Spanish I learned, I learned by ear. Chileans tend to speak at a high pitch and drop final consonants. It was inevitable that I, with my *monkey-hear-monkey-say* approach to language learning, would hear *perro* de Valdivia for *Pedro* de Valdivia. I chatted away with Carlos' boss at a dinner party the fall I was pregnant with Carlitos. With my big belly sticking out and trying to conjugate all the verbs in the sentence, I quite seriously told this man how interesting I thought it was that Valdivia had a *dog* so worthy that Chile had named a street after him.

"A dog?" he repeated.

"Oh yes," I rattled on, "*avenida Perro* de Valdivia."

By then three, maybe four people were laughing.

I'd seen lots pictures of the great founder of the city of Santiago, and-and anyone can see it-along with Valdivia and his horse there often is a dog. It's always a large dog. Some kind of a Great Dane I suppose. I still think of that dog and smile. Charlie would shriek as he'd spot a dog, and then he'd bury his face back in the coat until we drove past *Coppelia,* a pastry and ice cream shop. Santiago, like a lot of cities, was set out along one long avenue. Downtown the avenue is called *Alameda.* Past the *Plaza Italia* the name changes to *Providencia. Coppelia* is on

Providencia and is still there. If we couldn't stop for an ice cream cone, we'd roll down the window and Carlos and I would shout, "We'll get some tomorrow. Give me *chocolate* tomorrow."

We shouted this in English. Charlie would clap his hands to see his parents horsing around. The last peek-a-boo stop on our long, straight drive from downtown to our house out in *el Arrayán* was *el Stadio Italiano*. It was a pretty little tennis and swim club right at the corner where *avenida Las Condes* branched out from *avenida Apoquindo*. If we caught the red light, Charlie could wave and shout to the gatekeeper. The gatehouse was no more than two feet from the street. You could see him, always the same man, sitting or standing there no matter what time of the day or night you drove by. Such a slight, formal looking man, he always wore gray trousers and a blue jacket and opened the gate for the club members.

Once you passed *el Stadio* the city quickly thinned out. Within a mile the neat, substantial houses and two-story shop buildings yielded to blocks and blocks of low-slung wooden shacks. Shacks just like the ones I had seen two years before on that first drive in from the airport. They were all the color of wet wood and stood very close together. Chileans called these clusters of houses *callampas*-mushrooms.

"They do," people would say, "they do just spring up like mushrooms. One day you have a nice little vacant field and a couple of days later all these filthy people. Where do they come from? They come in so fast."

It seemed that way to me too. I drove this road all the time and thought it was like seeing a cornfield in Kansas. Suddenly it's just all there: rows and rows of huge corn stalks. Except this was rows and rows of little houses with half-naked children peeing in a bucket in the yard. You saw dogs fighting. There were always lots of dogs. Carlos said the people came from a lot of places. Some were from other *callampas* that had been razed by the landowners or the municipality; others were poor people up from the south ready to try for a better life.

The sky could be blue, but *callampas* always looked as though you were seeing them through rain. They were that dark. At night, of course, you realized many of the homes didn't have electricity. But even during the day they seemed dismal. You rarely saw any flowers or grass in these places. The shacks were never painted. There were always lots of children and women. You'd see children running around playing and women with their heads down and their bodies pitched slightly forward sweeping. They swept the dirt in front of their little houses. Later I'd find out they swept the dry dirt floors inside those same houses. I never did know where the men were. Once I thought to myself maybe the men were at work and that was why I didn't see them, but of course I was wrong.

As we drove by the first *callampa* that night, I took a good long look at it. It was maybe the size of four city blocks. Charlie, tired from all of our shouting out the car window, was sleeping on my lap. I leaned towards Carlos and for some reason said, "You know, for all the world, that looks like a crop."

"A crop?"

"Yeah. Like something is growing over there. It sure doesn't look like people."

Carlos let his head drift over to the left a bit and then turned it back to the road. From the set of the edge of his lip I could see his smile, even in the dark. The smile was threaded with a slyness I didn't recognize.

"Oh sweetie, they're people alright, and I'll tell you every single one of them knows the name Salvador Allende."

We drove on past six or seven *callampas* scattered between the odd truck farm or orchard with a pretty house. It was that way in Chile, slums were right alongside a block or two of nice places. By any construction site, any office building or gas station going up, you would see it too. Ten, maybe twelve shacks would spring up. The construction workers, their kids, dogs, all would be right there at the job site for as long as the job lasted. At least those men had jobs.

Forty-five minutes after we'd left downtown, we were turning into our driveway in *el Arrayán*. By that night, that third night after the election, I did know our lives were going to change. As I got out of the car to open the gate, it occurred to me that the man on the bus Friday night, the man who had told me to take off my blue raincoat, could have been from one of the *callampas* we had just passed.

I lifted the latch from its hole in the driveway, and the wrought iron gate swung free. The rust in the hinges muffled the sound of the car engine as Carlos pulled passed me. The night air was cold. Without ever dropping the gate latch, I pulled first one, then the other side of the gate closed. Glancing down to reposition the latch, I realized that there was a connection between señor Dávila, the man on the bus, and Allende. I thought again about why the man on the bus had told me to take off my coat. Señor Dávila was in the day-dream as I stood there in the dark watching the car taillights move in front of me. He was holding Rebecca's dead baby. Minutes went by and I heard Carlos call to me for a second time to come pick up Charlie. After I did it, I used a foot to push the car door closed.

CHAPTER

9

We had a pretty house out there in *el Arrayán*. It was a one-story fieldstone house with a red tile roof, and, like a lot of things in Chile, it was pretty but impractical. At least it was impractical for us. It was too big and it didn't have any heat. Tomás bought the original house in 1944 when it was a country farmhouse down by a river. It had faded green painted siding and a big fireplace-a real *casa de campo*.

As soon as he bought it though, he set about adding on to make it into his idea of an elegant weekend retreat. He even called it *el Weekend*. Dolores said the first thing they did the summer of 1945 was to add a kitchen big enough the refrigerator didn't have to be in the dining room. Having your fridge in the dining room or the hall was a fairly common practice in Chile even when I lived there over twenty years later. I never could figure it out, why people would do a thing like that. It wasn't always because of the size of the kitchen either. Some people just wanted to show off their refrigerators. I figured.

Once Tomás had a kitchen big enough to suit him, he added a living room the length of the house. From its inception this was a risky room. With a stalwart kind of grace it catapulted out from the house and hung overlooking the muddy *Mapoche* river as it ran down from the mountains on its way to Santiago. The river was full of waste from a copper mine upstream so you couldn't swim in it, but it was lovely to listen to.

The way the living room reached out over the river always amazed me. Perched all by itself like that it defied Chile's threat of earthquake. I never saw another house not squarely sitting on its foundation. Two of the bedrooms had been enlarged and windows added. The third bedroom, right off the front hall, was so small they decided to leave it as a little *estar.* It made for a lot to clean, and, typical, there was no central heat. I bought three of those damn kerosene stoves. During the winters I carried them from room to room. If I thought ahead, I'd put the *estufa* in the living room, or wherever, an hour before I planned to go there myself.

That night, with Charlie all bundled up in a blanket, I walked towards the front door and remembered the maid wouldn't be there to let us in. Carmencita wasn't a maid, really. She was just a country girl, maybe eighteen, who had come to Santiago to stay with relatives and wait for her miracle. I never knew what miracle she hoped for, perhaps a husband or an education. But whatever it was, it didn't come along and she ended up working for me.

She didn't wear a uniform or know how to cook much. Both were things Dolores said I should insist on, but Carmencita was pleasant and adored us. I taught her my grandmother's recipe for pot roast and how to make shortbread cookies called Mexican wedding cakes. During our cooking classes she'd stare at me wide-eyed with her lips parted revealing her cracked front tooth. She'd nod her head. She understood everything I said. I looked up all the words for those cooking classes. *Freir, batir, hornear.* Teaching Carmencita how to cook *gringo* food was one of the ways I learned Spanish.

Since I usually gave her the days off that we went to Santiago, I knew the house would be chilly before I even opened the door and that it would stay that way. There was no point in turning on the stoves late in the evening. You can't sleep with heating stoves on because they aren't ventilated to the outside.

While Carlos brought in the bags, I paced up and down to stay warm and sent up secret prayers that the baby wouldn't wake up as I changed his diaper and got him under his bed covers. With the baby asleep and the house to ourselves, I thought Carlos and I could eat something and cozy up. Just as I walked into the kitchen from the far bedroom I heard Charlie begin to fuss. That faint sound provoked a physical feeling of dread the way an alarm bell can. I knew the fuss could turn to a cry, a scream.

"I bet he's kicked off the blanket. That's it. He's fine, you know, okay. Eric said he is fine now. All he needs is to get the rest of his shots."

Charlie must have cried for forty minutes. I tried feeding him. I walked up and down the room. I even went to the doorway and flipped the light switch off and on six times to get his attention. *Off and on, off and on.* I flicked the switch so fast it made no noise. This was a trick my sister told me about. Sometimes it worked, but not that night. Nothing worked. His cry became a holler. You would have thought he was a four-year old, all the noise he was making.

"Baby Charlie," I told him, leaning over his crib. "I am worn out. I have been worn out all day long and you better shut up, little baby. Just please, please, please shut your mouth." Of course, I was talking to myself.

"Tomorrow you're gonna get all those shots Eric talked about and then you'll have something to cry about."

I just didn't know what else to do. Twice I'd been a camp counselor. The summer I was fifteen I babysat for a woman with four children. Before Charlie was born I thought I knew all about babies. I thought I understood how to take care of them, how to make them hush up. I loved my baby, loved his blond head and his eyes that looked just like his daddy's, but his crying hollowed out my poise. I straightened up, pulled my arms away from Charlie and out of the crib. As I left the room I slammed his bedroom door and swore to myself I would not go back in no matter how much he wailed.

Carlos already was in bed and looked up from the paper as I walked in the room. His eyes ran up and down me for a split second as he started to fold the paper.

"How can he do it? How can he scream that long?" I said as I walked into our bedroom. I could still hear Charlie through the paneled rough walls of the house. "I've tried everything. He's not sick again. I don't think he's sick. Why does he cry like that?"

I suppose this wasn't really the conversation Carlos had planned on.

"Why does he cry? Oh, I dunno. He likes to use his lungs, I suppose. It must be good for his lungs." Then a sly smile lit up his face. "Maybe he's crying because he's worried about *la democracia en Chile*. You come right in under these covers, and I'll tell you all about it." I stared right down at him as I pounced to slide under the blankets, hoping his body had warmed the bed.

"Democracy in Chile? Will you give me a break?" The bed was warm as Carlos's legs quickly moved up against mine.

Carmencita arrived the next morning before we were even up. She tried to sneak silently in the side door, but the hinges creaked and gave her away. I never knew where she went on her days off or what she did. She never mentioned seeing a movie, or a friend, or anything. It was as though she disappeared as a rest and then reappeared when I needed her back to work.

That morning Carlos skipped breakfast. He was in a swivvet about getting in early to the office because he had to read the papers and go to the Ministry of Mines. He'd take the car. He knew it was my day for the car, but he really needed it, he said. There was no *I'm sorry*, just his abrupt requisition of the car. It was the kind of thing my father would do. Not having the car stuck me with the bus for the trip to the *policlínico*. It meant what could have taken maybe an hour would now take the entire morning. I always got the car on Tuesdays. It was my day. That was our deal. Tuesdays were my day to run errands, my day to visit a friend.

"Is this *change in Chile*?" I called out the door at Carlos as he drove towards he gate. "This *Allende thing* means I lose my car day?" I don't think he heard a word I said

When you learn a new language the turn of a head or the wave of a hand can give meaning when words fail. I always surveyed the faces as I got on a bus in Chile. It was like seeing a snippet of a play.

The buses out in our neighborhood were small. They didn't hold more than twenty-five people and, unlike the big city buses, rarely had standing passengers. In Kansas City you just got on a bus, paid your farem and sat down and that was that, but not in Chile, not back then. Where you sat on a bus clearly articulated your status and your preference. More than anything, where a person sat revealed determination. Men more than women moved around on the buses, angling for a favorite seat, but women did it too.

I'd watch an old, white-faced man come up the bus steps, watch him pay his fare. Then I'd bend down my face over Charlie, sitting in my lap, and whisper to him in English, *Where's he headed, that old man?* Where does he want to sit? Charlie's big cinnamon eyes would dart towards the ear I was whispering into and he would screech with glee. He loved whispers. The man might settle for an aisle seat in the middle of the bus if that were the best he could do. The same man might migrate from the aisle to a window, from the middle towards the front, back to the aisle again. Many people coveted the seat right behind the bus driver. Women with children often favored the long seat in the back that ran the width of the bus. Their children could play back there. It seemed to me that the poorer people were the more they moved around on the bus.

It was a forty-minute ride to the *policlínico* by bus. Even though the clinic didn't open until eleven I left home early. You had to get in line before they opened if you hoped to be finished by two when they closed for lunch. It was a pretty September day. Not a bad day to wait around outside the clinic I thought.

Once we lumbered off the bus in front of the clinic, I quickly surveyed the group of standing women to see where I ought to go. People didn't make lines to wait for the doors to open; they bunched together. The young mothers milled around as they saw their friends. After I had gone to the *policlínico* once or twice I realized being first through the door wasn't everybody's goal.

"Come on, baby boy," I said as I jiggled Charlie up and down in my arms, "let's get in line behind that other little nipper."

A few feet in front of us there was a cute little boy sitting on a blanket. He held a wooden truck. Charlie loved seeing other children and wiggled to free himself from my arms. I had a floor blanket too. That's what you needed to make an instant play space. I smoothed the blanket out over the ground, and Charlie crawled across it to the smiling face and toy that he saw.

"*Se llama Miguel.* He's my youngest and my last baby."

"He's very cute." I said, quickly turning my head to locate the voice. "Your last? How many children do you have?" As I spoke I realized I recognized the voice of the woman talking to me.

"*Plenty.*" Plenty was the only word she said.

Her voice was full and strong, direct. It made me look up at her face. I saw the round, open face framed by bangs and straight long hair. She wore the same bright fuchsia blouse I'd seen before. It was tucked into the waist of a bright blue skirt.

The colors were so vivid. They were kind of Mexican looking is what crossed my mind. These were not the colors Chilean women wore at ten in the morning.

"*Me llamo América.*"

I know was all I could think to say. It is embarrassing to not quite understand what you are supposed to say to someone. It makes you nervous.

"Oh, and I'm from America. I'm from the States," I chatted on, knowing I was saying the wrong thing. "But not the baby. The baby was born here. He's my *chilenito.*"

"*Me llamo América,* I am *América,*" she said again. "That's my name, *América.* It is not a Christian name."

"Dolores is my…" I wasn't able to finish my sentence.

"I know who you are, *Señora.* You are the daughter-in law of señora Dolores, and you, Carlos, and Carlitos live in that pretty house down by the river, don't you?"

Looking back down at the little boys, I was dumb-founded. How could she know where I lived? How did she know Charlie's name when she'd just seen me that one time at the party way before he was even born?

"I'm the *empanada* lady. You've seen me, you have. I'm by your house every Saturday morning with the best *empanadas* in *el Arrayán.*" After a pause to say something to another woman, she went on, "You never buy from me, I'm sad to say. You should, you must *Señora.* They are *lo mejor,* the best, my *empanadas.*"

The *empanada* lady, yes, I had seen the *empanada* lady. Everybody saw her, but I had no idea she was the América who fixed *cordornices* all over Santiago, even for Salvador Allende.

The *empanada* lady was always dressed in a long white dress that made her look like a flour sack. That was the whole idea I concluded after about a year in Chile. The white outfit was supposed to make you think of flour and baking. She even wore a white scarf wrapped low around her forehead so you couldn't really tell what she looked like. She always carried her *empanadas* on a large wooden tray pushed up against her midriff with a heavy strap over her shoulders. She shouted out with every step she took, "*Empanadas. Empanadas calientes. De queso, de pino. Empanadas...*"

To tell the truth, I never had bought from her because she always seemed to be down the street by the time I heard her call. There never was enough time to put down what I was doing to look around for my money. This woman in her fuchsia blouse definitely did not look like the *empanada* lady. She looked way more like the grand woman who impressed all the guests at Tomás's birthday party.

I told her I often wasn't home on Saturdays, which was a lie, and then said I hadn't realized who she was. She then told me to come to her house to buy *empanadas* there. She would sell them to me while they were still in the oven. She lived right in front of the little plaza where the taxis were, she said, in the little house with the tile roof. Even though I had never done that kind of thing—gone to someone's house to buy her home cooking—I decided I would. Why not? Then I asked her again how many children she had. I decided I wanted to know what *plenty* meant.

"Six." She spat out the word like a chicken bone you've bitten off by mistake. "I have six children. You can just imagine all the babies I didn't have."

Then, feeling slightly nervous, I realized I finally had a chance to ask her about the bricks.

"They're the weight, *Chica*. You split the birds up and pound them flat."

"You pound them with the bricks?" I didn't understand what she was explaining.

She smiled at me like I was a true innocent.

"No, no, no. The bricks sit on them while they cook. That way the quail skin pushes hard up against the bottom of the pan. It's what makes them crisp and tasty."

She traveled around with as many bricks as quail so she could cook them all of them at once. They she told me the older the brick, or rather the more it had been used, the better the flavor of the *cordornice*.

"It lets you taste generations of *cordornices*," is what she said.

We stood there in what passed for a line for forty-five minutes and talked first about cooking and then about our little boys as they played together at our feet. She knew I was there for the vaccines and asked which one. As soon as I told her, she seemed surprised that I'd let Charlie have that vaccine. The measles and smallpox vaccine would give Charlie a fever. She was sure of that. *Oh well*, was all I could answer. Her baby had an ear infection, so once the clinic opened she and I went through separate doors. She went to see a doctor and I took Charlie to the nurse for the vaccine.

Meeting América happened the Tuesday after the Allende election, and I fully intended to go to her house that coming Saturday. As things worked out it was well into October before I saw her again.

CHAPTER

10

———

As I walked through the front door of the house early that afternoon I heard the telephone ringing. We were very lucky to have a phone; the waiting list was over a year in Chile in those days. Getting a phone was like getting into a country club, it seemed to me. You had to sweeten a phone company employee up to convince them to push your application along. Anyway, we had done all of that and did have a phone. It rang and rang those days after the elections. I even called my parents.

"Allende is a Communist through and through," my father barked over the long-distance phone. "He'll be as bad as Castro, just you wait."

The sound of his voice made him materialize right there in the narrow hall between the kitchen and the bedrooms, the hall where we had the phone. His cheeks pulled down as he said the words *bad* and then *just you wait*. My shoulder turned, recoiled almost, from the phone and I was afraid I was going to be hit. It was like being eleven and living on State Line Rd. I was convinced that my father was pressed up to a keyhole of my brain and could hear the things I wanted to say. Quickly I ask him to put my mother on so I could tell her about Charlie.

As soon as I cradled the phone it rang again. This time it was an Embassy wife I knew named Janet. I wanted to tell her about the *empanada* lady I'd met as a way to get my father out of the room, but she just started in.

"The Embassy is in a panic," I heard over the phone line, "Tomic was their call, now all of us look like idiots."

She said her husband heard through the grapevine that Ambassador Korry had even been dumb enough to tell Washington that Alessandri could win. She said Every U.S. businessman in Chile was sweating bullets about having his business expropriated. Before she hung up she said there were rumors. She wouldn't specify, just rumors. Then she mentioned taking home leave early if there were any disruptions.

"God," I groaned, "you sound just like Dolores. Are you guys lighting candles to *la virgen de Carmen* and calling in the fortunetellers?"

She claimed not yet, but it didn't seem like a bad idea to her. If the diplomats, or at least the diplomats' wives, felt taken by surprise, the socialists' wives sure didn't. What was left of the afternoon I spent talking to Alfredo's wife Silvia. She called me and then came over. It was wonderful to have a friend drop by like that. By then I knew other Chilean women and could chat it up with them at dinner parties or the movies, but Silvia was my first friend in Spanish. In one way it was very difficult to have a friend in Spanish, but in another it was liberating. As far as Silvia knew I had been born in 1968, the day I stepped off the plane in Chile. She knew nothing about Kansas City, or my sister, nor did she want to. She didn't even want to hear stories about Charlie. Silvia was not cozy. Other than bits and pieces I never learned much about her childhood or family either.

Early on I figured Silvia didn't have a stylish family name because she used Alfredo's surname. This was unusual in Chile. Many women used their maiden names-that meant your paternal surname followed by your maternal surname—and then the tagged-on *de Martínez*, or whatever, for formal occasions. With three last names in the mix, chances were one of them bought you snob value.

Silvia was just plain Silvia Lorca, never Silvia *de* Lorca, and we saw each other once every couple of weeks. Sometimes we went out to lunch, but usually we got together at my house and talked about politics. Probably in some ways Silvia saw our friendship as a kind of an educational project with me the one who needed educating.

I think maybe she had been to Paris once as a teenager, but she had never been to the States. She hated the States; it was *la gran puta*. That was her pet expression. I don't remember anyone else using it, but she used it all the time. I never figured out why the States was a whore and not a bully in her lexicon. It seemed to me we were the bully in Latin America, at least in Central America, what with all those Marines running around the Dominican Republic. *Puta* had more of a ring to it I suppose. It sounded better than *el gran valentón*. As an epithet *el gran matón*, another Spanish translation of bully, was harsh even for Uncle Sam. If asked, however, for sure Silvia would have said the States was *el gran matón*. But hatred of the U.S. aside, I usually thought she liked me.

Silvia was a bit older than I was, had no children, and always wore loose cut pants that swayed as she walked. She wrote movie reviews for the left-wing newspaper *Clarín*. Other than our husbands being best friends we didn't have much in common except that we both loved the movies.

Funny, at twenty-three I was naive enough to ask her why a left-wing paper would even have movie reviews. The paper didn't have the social pages or sports coverage that dominated the bigger papers in town. Before I met Silvia I never considered the idea that a film could be political. To me the movies were supposed to be all about entertainment. *Everything is political,* she told me as a matter of fact the first time I met her. She threw her arms out wide and circled them around as she said it. To Silvia, wallpaper, the kind of tomatoes you bought, it all meant politics.

"Julie, you know those Western movies from the States? Entertainment? They are not entertainment, *chica*, they are made to pretty up the American genocide of the Indian peoples."

She said things just like that. She'd stride around in her pants and say World War II movies were made to justify U.S. involvement in Vietnam. Police thriller films were *anti-urban*, or anti-black or some-such. Silvia never could give it a rest. Her claim about the Indians I agreed with, though. My Girl Scout troop in Kansas City went to visit the Indian mission out beyond Prairie Village, Kansas when I was ten. It was all rows of impossibly dreary one-story buildings with no trees to soften the harshness of the landscape. There was no *America the Beautiful* out there.

Other things she said sounded too far-fetched for me. I honestly didn't think *I Love Lucy* was about the exploitation of *Latino* culture and told her so. Looking back on it, I guess she saw me running around in my blue raincoat and living rent-free in my father-in-law's house as an unenlightened *gringa*. To her, I embodied *el imperialismo yanki* and she speculated on my conversion.

That afternoon, that first Tuesday after the elections, she called to tease me.

"*Gringuita,* how does it feel? *You were wrong, wrong, wrong.* All those Embassy reports were wrong. Admit it, *chica,* admit it."

She allowed as how she would be out in our neighborhood in an hour and was going to stop by. Could I make her cinnamon toast? I laughed a bit as I hung up the phone. I'd have to pay her with cinnamon toast to tell me how great Allende was going to be. The phrase she repeated that afternoon was *súbete al bote-*get on the boat. She paced up and down the living room, looked out at the river, and took bites of her sweet toast. I never had seen her as wound up over anything. This was the moment to switch allegiances—she waved her toast at me—it was a *new day* in Chile. As she got going her voice took on the tone of a news broadcaster. I knew she was trying to be informative and not preachy, but still in all a lecture is a lecture.

The strike last June—June of 1970—of the *CUT (Central Unica de Trabajadores)* defined the new worker. That was Silvia's topic as she talked at me in my living room. The workers now had political power, and Carlos should declare his support of the expropriation of the mines. Her voice rose and fell with her perfect modulation.

I remembered the *CUT* strike. In my memory the strikers' taut faces mix with the acid smell of Charlie's vomit as it spreads over the floor of a taxi. Charlie was feverish before we even got to Dolores's that morning. He'd had the throw-ups, really had the throw-ups by noon. When he spit up even a teaspoon of chamomile tea Dolores insisted I get him right to the doctor.

The taxi man didn't know about the dehydrated babies in the pictures at the *policlínico*. Once Charlie vomited, the man just screamed for us to get out of his cab. I fumbled for my wallet, but he didn't want to be paid. He just wanted us to disappear. I carried my poor, sick baby through throngs of resolute demonstrators for a full ten blocks. My own face pulled as tense as those other faces I saw on the street. For me that was the day of the strike.

"He's *chileno,* Julie," Silvia argued with me, "the copper belongs to the Chilean people not the American businessmen. *Hijos de putas.*"

Silvia wanted Carlos to *subirse al bote.* After our drive past all of the *callampas* I suspected Carlos was already climbing into the boat, but I didn't say anything to Silvia about it. She shot out that the agrarian reform under Frei was such a joke. There was no way I could argue with her because I had no figures. I had no facts.

Communism is bad was the only simplistic phrase that came to my head. Mother wrote that in nearly every letter she sent me. *What about all those Cubans in Miami?* she'd write. Silvia talked about the entrenched oligarchy, the corrupted clerics. I felt myself grow physically tired. I heard Charlie's happy, shouty little voice in the kitchen with Carmencita and wished I were in the kitchen too.

CHAPTER

11

Dolores was the one who told me the next day about the Alessandri plan. I called to tell her about meeting América and that she lived in *el Arrayán*, but Dolores didn't listen to a word I said and just went on about Alessandri and what he was up to. Carlos said his mother didn't know what she was talking about, but since she lived not too far from the Congress and heard things, I always listened to what she said. *I heard from very reliable sources;* is how she began. Carlos once said Tomás separated from her because she embraced as gospel things like the Alessandri plan.

"Julita, my dear, now listen to me," she went on. "You must know Allende cannot possibly become president. It is plain as day. Without a majority he can't, he simply can't." Then she gave me the details of the *noble* plan. "Since there were three candidates and no one got over 50% the vote simply must go to the Congress and they, the good ones—they are mostly good ones except those Communists who want to ruin everything—, will vote for Alessandri." All I did was stand there and nod my head at the telephone. "He, *un gran caballero* like his father before him, once elected *he'll resign* you see. See that." You would have thought she was describing an old boyfriend and defending her taste for having known all along how cute he was.

"He is just like his father *el León de Tarapacá*. Such a gentlemen he is. There will be new elections, Julita. New elections and this time Alessandri will win, you'll see. These days have just been a trial for Chile, a trial." Her voice soared like a soprano hitting a hit note.

The elections certainly had been a trial, but she was wrong about the Alessandri plan. It never materialized. She was right about another thing though. On that Wednesday after the election she also told me on the phone that *señor* Pablo Rodríguez Grez was organizing a movement to save Chile from the communists. Not only the communists, she told me, but all the *fuerzas anti-católicas*. This would be great, she assured me, and finally Chile would return to peace and civility.

Carlos didn't even look up from his dinner when I told him about this new group. He washed down a half a meatball with his red wine and said, "My mother's crazy. I think she just dreams this stuff up." He started to smile. "I thought you just talked about Carlitos with my mother. *Mi pajarita*, can it be? Are you getting interested in politics?"

I was, actually. You couldn't help but be interested in politics in Chile in 1970 because it floated all around you. Looking there across the table at him, I thought about how much more Carlos knew than I did. He would have stayed on the phone and talked back to my father and said, *what?* Chile wasn't Cuba. Staring at the oval platter rimmed with red sauce left from the meatballs I heard the irritation, the slight superiority of tone Carlos would use with my father as he explained all about

Chilean politics. In these daydreams everything about Chile was well arranged, just like the letters I wrote home describing perfect weather and my pretty new clothes. Clothes I didn't have.

I don't recall whether or not there was any mention in the press about the Pablo Rodríguez Grez group or if they just started marching around. Carlos swore they didn't exist until we actually saw them one night about two weeks later. It was around the end of September 1970. We were driving up *Providencia* towards home. Out of nowhere we saw a group of six or seven young men marching, stopping traffic, egging on the crowds to follow them and hear their speeches. The marchers towards the front carried large medieval type banners with the words *Tradición, Patria, Libertad* in gold letters. It looked like they lived under rocks, those guys. They were pale. They had on white shirts, dark pants, and no smiles. They didn't look Chilean to me. They had that look Jehovah's Witnesses have, or used to have. How Dolores had known of their formation none of us ever figured out, but it did make me mad that Carlos hadn't listened to her.

It was easy to get sick of seeing the *Tradición* people because of the traffic messes they always caused. On that Friday evening not long after the elections we were caught in rush-hour traffic for twenty minutes because of their nonsense. Our car was at a dead standstill and I couldn't resist rolling down the window and calling out to the tall stick of a boy with the banner. Charlie was in the back seat and immediately started clapping his hands. He must have thought this would be like the *shouting at*

Coppelia game. The fellow with the banner walked quickly over to our car as soon as he heard me call out to him.

"Just which *Tradición* are you promoting?" I asked this fuzzy faced kid about seventeen, wanting to razz him about hobbling traffic and making little boys miss their dinnertime. It was Carlos who stole my thoughts and finished my question.

"So, you defend the *Tradición* of your father letting you screw the maid? Or the *Tradición* of your father screwing the girlfriend while your mother goes to Viña in the summer?" Carlos asked him with a very straight face.

Chile had what I considered an established tradition of *summer bachelors*. The wives and kiddies went to Viña del Mar, the beautiful city on the Pacific, and *Papá* stayed in Santiago and did as he pleased. Well, this *Tradición* kid didn't smile. He just stared right at me and inquired very solemnly,

"*Señora,* are you a foreigner?"

I never have had any idea why he asked that. After all it was Carlos who was really talking to him, but I decided that as long as we were stuck in traffic, I'd start playing the game Carlos had started.

"*A foreigner*? What makes you think I'm a foreigner? My accent, my blue raincoat?" I was really having fun now. "Actually I am. I'm with the *Washington Post* newspaper and I'm here in Chile on a Fulbright doing a big story on Allende and your *Tradición* business, I mean, *organización*."

"Julie," Carlos nudged my side and whispered in English, "a Fulbright? Ha. Honey, the press doesn't come down here on Fulbrights, for Christ's sake."

I thought Carlos was going to tickle me we were having such a good time. The cars were beginning to move a bit as the skinny kid backed away from our dusty red FIAT 500. Carlos waved a hand bye-bye out the window of the car at him and said to me, "You know, Julie, you terrified him, but it was funny. A Fulbright and *The Washington Post*?" he was laughing out loud and looked so handsome to me. "Where do you come up with these things? I bet Pablo Rodríguez is calling the Embassy this very minute."

I had never even read the Washington Post, but I read about the Post in Time magazine. Time was the only English language publication I could get in Chile and I read it cover to cover every week, even the ads.

"*Time* should run a picture of that kid with the banner." I said, feeling proud of myself. "I swear to God the *gringos* wouldn't believe it. Those people, those *momios*, really don't want any social progress at all, do they? All they want is to march back to the 30's."

Carlos laughed again, "Yeah, the 1830's, maybe even the 1430's… That's what Alfredo's crowd says."

The rest of our drive home I kept thinking about how serious people had gotten. The *Tradición* boy hadn't even thought we were funny. He was supposed to laugh at our jokes. Instead, with his pinched, tired face he had asked me if I were foreign. This kid, I thought, wouldn't laugh about meat rationing or the downtown hotels where you could rent a room by the hour. Probably all he did was worry about *constitutional compliance* and the new government. That was what was wrong.

After the elections, after it was clear that Allende really would take office, the fun went out of things.

I stared out the window at the *callampas* spreading out in the twilight as we drove by. What about them, I wondered to myself. They just have dirt floors, no jobs, but they have the *Unidad Popular*. Maybe now they are telling the jokes, I thought.

"You know," I said talking into the early dark of evening. "We could have a dinner like the ones your father has. We could invite some Embassy people, Alfredo and Silvia." I went on thinking out loud. "You know, mix it up. It'll be fun. People have gotta' lighten up about this whole Allende business. God, everyone's so heavy duty, Carlos. A lot of *pisco sours*, meat on the grill. We'll have América cook something famous and use grandmother's flat silver."

I chatted on a bit longer about my plan to bring a little fun back into people's lives and Carlos wasn't buying any of it. He just shook his curly head and fooled around with his glasses and gave me a fako voice query.

"*Señora*, are you a foreigner?" Didn't I understand this was not the time to be talking about parties? By then there was a quip to his voice that made me furious. I understood plenty. I'd been in Chile over two years. I'd had a baby there. Maybe I didn't read more than the headlines in the papers, but I went to the *policlínicos*. I rode the bus, I thought to myself.

"*I ride the bus,* you know. I shop at the street markets," I finally said, my voice straining a bit.

Of course, I was thinking, *you, Carlos*, steal the car on Tuesdays when it suits you so you don't have to ride the *bus*. I even stand in line like a good little *chilenita* to buy the whale meat your friends won't eat. My anger wound around me. I know what's going on. Just because I don't read the papers every goddamn day doesn't mean I don't know what's going on here! My words all backed up on the inside of my head. I'm just talking about having a party, for Christ's sake! Just planning a party to have a little fun.

He didn't say anything else, but I saw the hard edge of his mouth shadowed by the night sky. To me it seemed as though there was another Carlos who had come to stand in front of the Carlos I knew. The jokes we'd made while sitting in the traffic jam suddenly were like a daydream. They were as made up as all those letters I had written to Kansas City about the *Santa Lucia* hill and the pastry shops I went to. As the picture of the *Tradición* boy and our laughter drained away, I realized the only thing left for me to do was to go ahead and plan my party, my *soirée*, and then bring up the idea later. There was no point having a huge fight right then in the car. That's what I decided as we headed home in our little red car with darkness now all around us.

CHAPTER

12

———

The next morning after Charlie was fed and was playing with his painted building blocks on a blanket on the floor in the kitchen, I called Dolores. I told her I was planning a party. I omitted the part about inviting potential political enemies and just focused on whether or not I could borrow her two good tablecloths and some extra silverware? She said yes, of course, and then said something vague about how she hoped I wouldn't have this party until late October. It was around the end of September by then. I didn't need a month to plan a party I told her. It wasn't going to be that big a deal.

There was a hollow silence on the phone, and then she finally said, "Carlitos, Carlitos might need your attention."

Charlie, with a happy shout, slammed one block on top of another and let out a puff of air.

"What? What are you talking about? Need my attention?"

She at first wouldn't answer me. Then she danced around about Carlitos having been sick so much.

"He's such a marvelous baby. He's really a little boy now, isn't he? Then she, without ever taking a breath, snuck in, "We just hate to see him not totally well. Not just *himself*, you know what I mean? Of course you do, dear. He's delicious when he isn't in a sinking spell."

I hated it. She should have just said we all knew Carlitos was sick a lot and left it at that. Then she went on about all the stomach upsets he had, all the diarrhea. I should be very careful with him just now was the warning. That's what her sister said; that's what her sister had been told. The worst thing about a second language is speaking it on the phone. The words were detached from her face which meant I couldn't fix their meaning. What about her sister I wanted to know? Then Dolores's voice dropped a tone, and she told me not to worry, just to be very careful with Carlitos.

Her sister meant Asela, I was sure of that much. Asela was the sister Carlos and I called Mrs. Bates—as in the movie *Psycho*—because she was really wacky. She was the paper-thin *soltera* sister who always hung around just out of sight whenever I went to Dolores's. The entire family kidded her about never leaving the apartment-not exactly true—but she sure didn't have much of a social life. She didn't have any kind of a life that I could figure out.

I was in Chile for nearly seven months before I even met her, even knew she existed. After all that time my meeting her was almost by accident. I remember I was pregnant by then and Dolores invited me to come over for tea by myself. We would have a real ladies afternoon she promised. When I arrived at the apartment, Dolores opened the door and then crossed her arms and just stood there. She looked the way my mother looked when I didn't make the bed. *You should have called, Julita*, she scolded. Then she said I was an hour late. In the second or two it took to glance down at my watch I felt a panic. I wasn't late. It was 5 o'clock. I had left home at 4:10 and now it was 5 o'clock. The melted cheese sandwiches were burned, the tea was cold and my Chilean mother-in-law was fuming mad. I told her the time, showed her my watch. After a few minutes I even turned on the radio so we'd hear the time announced. It was just after 5 o'clock.

Asela had changed every clock in the apartment and then excused herself to go out to run errands when I hadn't shown up on time. She had gotten up from the velvet sofa and told her sister she wasn't about to wait around for *una gringa mal educada* even if I was married to her favorite nephew. Carlos thought the story was hilarious, but I didn't. I felt like I'd fallen down a rabbit hole. Why couldn't Asela have just said she didn't want to meet me?

"Oh Julie, that's no fun." Carlos said, "Asela likes to have a little fun. When I was a kid she'd hide my toys and then say, 'Truck, what truck?' I thought I was going crazy. She did this when I was six, seven. I thought I *was* crazy."

"Well," was all I could say, "They ought to stop her."

The afternoon of the tea party Dolores never apologized to me. She just chatted about how clever Asela was to change the clocks without anyone taking notice. Had she done it before lunch? After lunch? She talked about Asela the entire time I was there and practically applauded when she walked in at 6:30. What I hated the most about Asela was how she lurked around listening in on conversations. She'd listen and then let her disembodied voice float through a crack in a door or a wall to comment on things you didn't realize she'd seen.

Thinking about Asela and how she gave me the creeps, I continued my phone conversation with Dolores. I really just wanted to talk to her about my party, not about Charlie, but she'd snared me. The phone cord coiled around my wrist as I leaned down to pick him up. I got him to babble into the phone at *Abuelita*. He said *hola* and a work that sounded like *cookie* and then slipped down my leg back to the floor. I determined I couldn't end the conversation until I knew what Dolores was hinting at.

"Asela talked to someone about Carlitos?"

Not exactly, was Dolores' reply. Asela had consulted with a man, a man *muy astuto* in these matters. We, meaning the two of them, were, after all, concerned about Carlitos getting sick, she confided, as if this were new information for me. Once she said that the whole conversation suddenly clicked for me. Asela, my mother-in-law's skinny, weirdo sister, had gone behind my back to a fortuneteller to find out things about my baby, and now Dolores was giving me all these *indirectas* over the phone. Anger, a fury, rose up in me. My tongue pressed hard against the back of my front teeth, but I couldn't find the words I needed to fight with her. We left it that I'd see her in a day or two to talk some more about my party, and I hung up the phone. Looking down at Charlie, the photograph I'd seen of Rebecca slid behind my eyes. If I hadn't been so incensed about what I'd just heard, I might have spent a long time thinking about Rebecca just then, but I didn't.

There was no one I could talk to about this fortuneteller business. Carlos had been raised hearing stories about Rebecca. After all, he'd been raised with Asela around. Evidently, if you weren't going to take these things seriously you had to distance yourself from them, and that's exactly what he did. I could have talked to Janet, asked her advice, but what would she know? Silvia was out of the question. To her, fortunetellers inhabited the same terrain as priest and private school headmistresses. They were all *functionaries of an oppressive class system*. Those were her exact words. When I finally went to see my mother-in-law a few days later I was alone and didn't know what to expect.

Why hadn't I brought the baby? That's what she wanted to know. I couldn't say I hadn't brought him because I thought she was crazy and didn't want him upset hearing his mother yell at *abuelita*, so I mumbled words about having come by bus. I said the buses were crowded lately. I had been afraid I might have to stand, I offered. All a big lie, but I figured why start off being confrontational? After the usual pleasantries, after tea was poured, I leaned back against the velvet sofa and let my eyes shift from object to object around the room. There were many things in this room tight with presences. All the photographs and pill-boxes, the leavings of lives I'd never known. It all heightened my feelings of foreignness. Until I came to Chile I had never seen a room like this one. It was complete with furniture and things.

I wasn't to worry, that's how Dolores started off. I wasn't to worry, but I should be very careful about Carlitos not getting sick. He had a weakness that could prove *muy grave*. That is exactly what Asela had been told. Dolores put this information out as simply as she served the silver plate with ginger cookies. Did she really think I believed in stuff like this?

"We use a very good doctor, you know. Eric is very good, very well respected."

Clearly her warning was not about doctors, but it was all I could think to say. Sitting there, looking at my teacup, I realized this was going to be like other encounters I'd had with Dolores. Before with her, simple exchanges had spun from the ordinary to the bizarre, or at least what I considered bizarre. Dolores knew I wasn't a Catholic, but she never missed a chance to scatter mention of a saint or a *virgen* as, I guess, an enticement for me to ask her more about them.

Once when I was with her at a dressmaker to get a skirt shortened, she made an off-hand comment about dressing s*anta Bárbara* and how hard it was to get her hem to hang straight. It sounded to me like *santa Bárbara* must be a woman's name, a child who needed dressing is what I figured. I agreed that hemlines were difficult, particularly on full skirts. With that, Dolores's smile faded, realizing I wasn't going to ask her about the saint. I'm sure she couldn't fathom a religious expression that lacked the cast of characters she was devoted to.

My Protestant girlhood was filled with sharp denial of divine visibility. You were supposed to focus on God and Jesus and do it with words. That's what I had been taught. Our church didn't have statues or fancy paintings. We certainly didn't have any little *santa Bárbara* dolls at home to dress up and light candles to.

Around the time Carlitos was born I in fact discovered Dolores and her sister had converted the coat closet in their front hall into a homey little family shrine. They were all quite proud of it and told me all about how they had put it together during the last three weeks of my pregnancy. It fulfilled a *manda* the two of them had made. In spite of all the elaborate talk about the *manda,* I guessed it was their part of a deal they'd struck with God. "Let Julita have a great pregnancy and we'll build you a shrine right here in front of *Plaza Brazil.*" It was that kind of thing. To keep their part of the bargain the entire closet was stripped of shelves, painted the color of my raincoat, and then three small tables with saint dolls were arranged around.

When I first saw this home shrine, I couldn't believe my eyes. I knew better than to laugh, but it was hard not to. Her shrine, after all, was the coat closet. Dolores was past fifty and these were all just a bunch of fancy dolls was all I could think. *La virgen de Carmen* and *santa Teresita de los Andes* were her favorites, she confided. They were *chilenas.* After she showed me the dolls, she went on to explain how they lit candles there every Saturday afternoon and let them burn late into the night. She defined any prayer offered during those afternoon hours as more reverential. How could I argue with her over the logic of this? These saints were her accomplices in life. Making their dresses, having them run through with gold thread, having the hems straight, were all acts of devotion. Whenever the subject of the shrine came up, I'd be pleasant. Be pleasant and try to change the subject. That was the advice Carlos gave me.

Pulling my thought back to the fortuneteller and knowing the shrine was on the other side of the closet door, I imagined she was connected with the saint business. I thought maybe the fortuneteller prayed to *santa Teresita* and then the saint beamed back the information about who would get sick, or get the handsome boyfriend, or whatever.

Later I found out my guess was about right. All except the supplier of information from the great beyond was Manuel Rodríguez, and the fortuneteller was a man who had left a perfectly good job with an insurance company to go into the fortune telling business. Dolores rejected the irony and the humor in this connection even when I pointed it out. She was, though, enraptured when it became apparent I didn't know who Manuel Rodríguez was. *Chile's greatest patriot*, that is who he was. She said this bending slightly to pour me more tea. He fought for the independence of Chile in the early 1800's and now worked with Abelardo the fortuneteller.

She could have been explaining who Tomás's new business partner was or describing the owner of a wonderful new shop. After the first mention of Manuel Rodríguez, when she had hushed her voice and dropped her eyes slightly, there was absolutely nothing out of the ordinary in the manner in which she recited the story of how Manuel Rodríguez died in an ambush—willing to die for the glory of Chile. It seems that after all his sacrifice for Chile he was finally betrayed by another patriot, José Miguel Carrera. He was forever after immortalized in song and in the hearts of women like Dolores. And, she went on, because of his love for Chile or his good looks, I couldn't be sure since her story got complicated, Manuel Rodríguez had been available to help those who could contact him. Those who wanted his help—and who wouldn't? she assured me—had to deal with just the right people.

Her tone was laudatory and matter-of-fact. Even though I couldn't follow every word of what she said I realized this was like saying George Washington or Patrick Henry was feeding information to the best fortunetellers in the United States. They were the top of their profession and the ones the smart people hired to consult about what to do in life. I listened to her talk on and on. The way she told the story it sounded reasonable because her emphasis was on how qualified, how superior Manuel Rodríguez and Abelardo were. It was like hearing my mother say she went to the best dentist, except Dolores was saying she went to the best fortuneteller. Once I shook loose from the spell of her sensible tone, I remembered Manuel Rodríguez was dead. The whole story was like something I would have heard at a slumber party when I was nine years old. Naturally I didn't say that to Dolores.

As she finished her story telling, I gazed around the living room again. Before when she told me about saints or even her political notions, I had always felt a funny little rush of superiority overtake me even though I was in my early twenties and she was a grown woman. I was used to hearing her and just not considering what she said as weighty, not thinking I needed to accept it as real. Now that I had heard the Manuel Rodríguez story, I felt threatened, even demoted. I knew that whatever it was Asela had heard from Abelardo, Dolores truly believed it. His advice and recommendations were for her a physical truth the way the saint dolls were. None of these ideas would be abandoned because of a girl from Kansas City, even if that girl happened to be married to her son.

That day when I first heard about Abelardo and Manuel Rodríguez, I remember Dolores stared over my shoulder to catch the view of *Plaza Brazil* out of the window. I felt an aching rise up in me like warm milk filling a glass. I was in such a foreign place, I thought. It wasn't just that people spoke Spanish and drank *pisco sours* instead of Old Fashioneds, or ate lunch at 1:30 instead of 12:30. It was that I saw a sick little kid and called the doctor and felt guilty that I hadn't sterilized the pacifier. Dolores saw the same child and sensed the entanglement of other presences.

Up until that very moment, that moment when I strained to find out exactly what some man had said about my baby getting sick all the time, I figured I could reduce the differences I had with Dolores to a surmountable problem. Even as a kid I had a knack for avoiding the head-on-position in a discussion. I never would have come right out and said, "Tell me this minute what this Abelardo guy knows." Advancing sideways and keeping quiet is more my style. I was the younger person after all, and I knew Dolores was intransigent in her beliefs. That, and now I knew she lit candles to saint dolls she kept in her coat closet.

At this point Dolores stood up from the chair where she had been sitting and took a step forward, and then another. She was not a large woman but had a look that caught the eye. Her hair was always slicked back in a twist. She had a straight back and always dressed in just one color. In the afternoons she almost always wore her good pearls and a small ruby ring Tomás had bought her years before in Argentina. Organized. That's how she looked. The pictures of Asela, the picture of Rebecca, they were all there on the tables in the room. Phrases from the Rebecca story echoed at me from the month before when I had first heard it. Dolores spoke deliberately; she wanted me to understand her. Her words formed a tight seal across my thoughts quieting them.

"You know, Julita," she began, "none of us want you to be alarmed. *No,* no worry. It's just with these things one should know, that's all. If anything happens, then you're prepared. We'll all be prepared. Don't you see?"

Dark blue wool. That's all I could clearly see as she stood there next to the sofa. I saw the fuzz on the wool of the dress and heard her voice talk about worry. I felt stunned almost beyond thought. What worry?

"Worry? Why do I worry? I'm not worried."

Then she started in. I hoped she would sit down, but when she walked over to the window I stood up too. I held my teacup in my right hand and crossed my left arm across my waist as a kind of protection against what I might hear. I sensed her apprehension as she began to speak again. Charlie's repeated illnesses were what everyone was worried about. Carlos apparently never had the runs except the one time when he ate all the cherry pits. I relaxed my arm. I explained about how common it was for children to get sick. That's what kept the doctors in business after all, I said, attempting half a smile. She didn't hear me and went on that the problem, the reason she felt she must mettle in this (and she was sorry to mettle, but how could she not?) was that Charlie's health revealed an intricacy that was cyclical.

Her voice had the same slow, measured pace she had used to tell me the Rebecca story. It wasn't the colds or the diarrhea or even the terrible bone infection that worried her. Many children were afflicted with these complaints, she conceded. But with Carlitos, with my baby Charlie, the nights of changing diapers made rancid in just an hour, or the days of coaxing a cfspoonful of rice water past his dry lower lip, weren't unconnected. She was certain of that. She and Asela were certain of it. Every four weeks they came. Asela had been the first one to begin to keep track. That's why she had gone to Abelardo in the first place.

So that was it. That was the secret or at least part of the secret. Her voice rose like an inhalation sucking at me, tempting me to move. The cup in my hand shuddered as if I had lost my balance. It was like the dread I felt when I was eight and had a black kitten named Velvita. My mother told me Velvita meant black velvet in Spanish. Of course it doesn't, but I had named the kitten that anyway. It snowed very early that year in Kansas City, and I remembered being out in the falling snow calling and calling for my kitty. Calling for my kitty to come into the house was the first time I ever felt fear. I looked down at my feet and saw snow swirling around them. I suddenly knew that my kitten would be a little black ball rolled in white snow and would freeze that way.

Fighting my dread, I gave Dolores a sideways look and then turned to face her as I put down the teacup. *Just let me tell you,* is what I wanted to say, but no words came out of my mouth. You should have talked to me first, you know. *If Asela thinks there is a weird thing going on with Carlitos she should have told me and not run off to the fortuneteller man.* All those sharp words were in my head, but all Dolores could see was the fear and anger as I stood there without the teacup in my hand.

"I can tell you, Asela did not talk to just anyone," Dolores said.

As she spoke the *you* was the formal *usted* in Spanish not the *tú* used among friends, the *tú* she usually used with me. That *usted* was cold and formal. It signaled a sudden, new barrier between us.

"Well, something went on." I finally managed to say. "Abelardo told Asela things about my baby, and he doesn't, doesn't even know him, has never even seen him."

This last observation made Dolores smile. I trembled, was furious, and all of sudden she had a big smile on her face. Abelardo, she offered, was not limited to the concrete. He didn't need to know either one of us. After all I should remember the source of any knowledge he offered was Manuel Rodríguez. Well, with that I thought I was going to flip. Here I was, I had spent the entire afternoon coming to town, drinking tea, and now I was hearing that a dead Chilean patriot knew all about baby Charlie's health problems. I told myself this was all looney-tunes and I didn't believe one word of it. Still, surprising myself, I blurted out,

"What exactly did he say?"

Looking across at the pictures on the table and not at me, Dolores finally spoke,

"There is very little resistance and many forces are working against Carlitos, Julita. Be very careful."

There was a funny hollowness to her voice as she spoke the words. There was nothing I could find to say back to her. My anger dropped inside of me. It was pointless to be further ensnared in this kind of hocus-pocus was all I could think. After all, I comforted myself, she really hadn't told me anything. *Many forces?* What the hell did that mean? Nothing, I thought. That's fortuneteller talk. I looked at the teacup and saucer down on the table next to the picture of Rebecca and noticed again how lovely her long hair looked. I had to get home I said. It was late. I had to get the bus, fix dinner. I longed to balance Charlie on my knee and see him smile as I swung my leg and cried, *horsey, horsey.*

CHAPTER

13

I felt myself slump into the bus seat feeling right then very disconnected from all the other people headed home on that bus. My face turned to the window, and I saw my face, my sweet young face, look back at me from the glass. I looked pale as I observed myself. Dolores now stood just separate from everyone else in my life the way the first biscuit round is the moment you lift the cutting ring from the sheet of dough. She hadn't meant to worry me. She had kept on using that word, but that was what she wanted or she wouldn't have told me any of this in the first place. I physically felt my sense of the normalcy of things thin out to a transparency. Every time Charlie coughed or ran a fever I was going to think about Rebecca. That is where all of this came from. It was clear as day.

The low houses and buildings bounced by on the far side of the bus window. I could see the mountains hovering up there in the sky, and I thought about Rebecca. Rebecca and her baby dying like that, blood all over. It was probably one of Dolores's earliest memories. She must remember all the blood, people screaming, and her mother not there. That must be why Dolores went in for all this stuff. Her mother had been told things about Rebecca. Her mother was a country woman, though. You wouldn't think her ideas would have rooted so tenaciously in her city daughters.

For sure I didn't believe her. I didn't believe for one minute that this Abelardo man was right in any of his guesses about my baby. That's what it all was, guesses. Things he made up to tell women who insisted that the central feature of their lives was the meddling of saints and angels in the minutia of the everyday.

As my own thoughts crowded me there on my bus seat I realized like all the other odd things I had come up against in Chile, this was isolating. Oh well. I was the one who flounced down here to Chile, after all, I thought to myself. My parents had warned me I was crazy to do it. My hands held each other in my lap, and I kept reassuring myself that Charlie was basically fine. He'd be walking any day, I figured. If I held him, even circled his wrist with my fingers, he could take four or five steps before he'd tumble onto his fanny.

Weeks went by. Charlie did start to walk by himself around the middle of October and he became the talk of the family, at least the talk of the women in the family. What the men talked about was politics. Men at Carlos' office said if Alessandri hadn't been such a *señora* (that's what the left-wing paper *Clarín* called him, *la señora*) Allende wouldn't have won in the first place and the *gringos* wouldn't be frantic about the expropriation of the mines.

Since Alessandri was single, it was easy to make jabs about him maybe being queer. Being queer was the very worst thing you could say about a man in Chile in those days. It was worse than being dead. Of course, I couldn't have cared less about

Alessandri's reputation because I was focused on baby Charlie. Women everywhere we went fussed over Charlie. There is something marvelous and impossible about a baby walking. Those big heads and big eyes riding up above their spindly little feet defy logic. Baby Charlie was only ten months old, which made his first toddling steps all the more remarkable.

I'd finally kept my promise to start buying *empanadas* from América and one Saturday I took Charlie with me to her house so he could show off his new trick. She baked from five in the morning until about nine, running heavy old aluminum cookie sheets in and out of her gas oven. It was a small stove not meant for this *empanada* enterprise, but evidently it worked perfectly well. A heavy, bright orange *balón de gas* fueled the stove. I knew about the gas tanks for heat and cooking. I used one too, but mine was installed outside of the house, and then we'd run a hose line into the stove. The first time I'd gone to América's house and seen her kitchen set up I had asked her. "You don't worry about that thing blowing up?"

It was an obvious question. There were tremors all the time, tremors big enough to make the dishes shake. Twice our electricity lines went down in tremors. Once the electric pole just snapped. The other time we never did find out what had happened.

"Naw, I don't worry about the gas blowing up, *Gringuita*. I worry about many, many things, but not that. If the good Lord wants to blow me up, he is welcome to do it."

She sounded so cavalier I thought maybe she didn't realize how dangerous a fifty-pound gas tank was. "Some little spark? Or one of the kids? What if Miguelito fools around with the connection on that thing?" I don't know why on earth I thought I knew more about how to manage her kitchen than she did, but I did.

She swung her head around to face me, "Do what? He wouldn't live to see another day and he knows it. He knows it for sure." She went on that Miguel knew to play on his blanket. He wouldn't dare move off of the blanket spread out on the floor any more than he would try and bite the cat. I avoided her gaze.

"I work here, *Gringa.* I have no husband who pays for the food in this kitchen."

She did have a husband and he did work, but I guessed he paid the rent and couldn't cope with much more.

That particular Saturday morning when I took Charlie there to have him walk for her, América had spotted us out her window. Charlie glided down from my arms and with just the slightest wobble started the last few steps up to the door. I hadn't even knocked when América pulled the door back and, with a capacity I have never known another person to have, shouted in a whisper, "¡*Usted camina! ¡Usted camina!*"

That *you walk* was the announcement of a miracle. It happened in Chile all the time, this wondrous reaction to the doings of babies. Babies were carried around endlessly. Every tidbit they ate someone noticed. I thought maybe it had to do with babies dying in Chile. There were all those posters of sick babies you saw at the *policínicos.* It also had to do with maids.

Everybody had a person to help with babies. You had a maid, or a grandmother, or a cousin, someone. América had her oldest daughter, a girl about 18, and the old woman who lived next door. I never met this woman, or even saw her, but evidently she helped the young mothers out. It was unclear to me whether or not she got paid for this babysitting. Judging by her house I'd say she didn't. From what you could see from the road the house was one room with a roof, a door, and two windows. It was painted. It didn't look like a *callampa* shack, but it was small. América said it was big enough. Rosita shouldn't even be living there, according to her. She should live with her daughter and help her out.

Once we had tried to get Charlie to give Miguelito walking lessons, I told América I was thinking about having a party. She listened to me ramble on with a polite but vacant, stare on her face, then she shook her head. *Empanadas* and steak on the grill wouldn't be nearly enough, not for a Sunday lunch. *Cordornices* were out of the question. Was I crazy? Ten was her limit, she said boldly. She'd only done fourteen for Dolores because Allende was at the party and it had been Tomás's birthday.

"Sweet thing, *el Arrayán* is the country for your friends. It may not be for you, but it is for them. Believe me *Gringuita*, those friends of yours are coming out for the whole afternoon."

It evidently was a *paseo* to come for Sunday lunch out in *el Arrayán*. She was amazed I didn't know this. She'd make the *empanadas*, but after the *asado* I better know everyone would stay until teatime. She could sell me a cream filled cake and some cookies.

"And you better be prepared," was her final warning. "They'll all want a drink of whiskey before they leave. They will. The Communists too, they'll drink Scotch whiskey no matter what their politics."

"Whiskey?" I was dumbfounded.

"And don't buy Argentine Scotch," she added. "It makes people think you're cheap."

When I had first had this party idea I thought I could fix lasagna and a couple of salads and call it a day. Janet was the first one to cure me of that idea.

"It's a formula." That's exactly what she said. In all her years as an Embassy wife she had learned that much. "You know how it is. People expect certain things. They want *pisco sours* the minute they walk in, and right now you've gotta have those new kind of potato chips."

Janet gave me the list of about five different kinds of salads. Carmencita would know how to do all of them.

"You would think it was national policy. Every *asado* in the whole country has the same food, trust me."

I imagined they didn't all have Scotch whiskey as the send-off. Scotch, at I bet fifty dollars a bottle. I figured América must have told me the Scotch business because I was a *gringa* and she thought I'd want to show off.

My other problem about the party was Carlos. Since the election he was in danger of becoming what my grandmother would have called a perfunctory husband. She said when a man started favoring paying the bills over smooching with his wife, the wife better watch out for trouble. Once Allende got elected it seemed Carlos barely warmed his chair at home, let alone the bed. He didn't even want to play our *shout out the window* games with Charlie in the car. In the mornings I'd wake up to see him already dressed and looking in the mirror combing his hair and cleaning his glasses before he put them on for the day.

One morning, still stretched out with my head propped up on both pillows, I looked down my body, over my toes, and asked him, "Why so early every day?" Then I added in as sultry a voice as one can muster at twenty-two, "This *pajarita* doesn't like being alone."

His back was facing me as he looked at himself. I could see the reflection of his eyes as his gaze went from his face to mine. He turned and stepped towards the bed with both his arms still raised and his two hands busy smoothing his rebellious curly hair. From where I lay, I didn't even have to sit up to reach the buckle of his belt. Two of my fingers slipped between the buckle and the gray flannel of his pants.

"They can't expropriate copper mines this early in the morning, can they?" I said.

Carlos started to sit down on the edge of the bed, then straightened his legs and just bent to kiss me. Both his hands ran over my hair and he smiled, glasses and all.

"I know, I know, I know. I've been too busy, I haven't..." he paused a minute, "I miss you *pajarita*. I promise we'll get away. What about next week? Next Friday? We'll go up to the mine." He was in the doorway by the time he'd finished saying this. I got out of bed, pulling the bed sheet along with me and wrapped it over my shoulders like an enormous shawl.

"You know I'm stark naked under here."

He laughed, "I promise, I really do. There's a lodge we can stay at up near the mine. We'll leave Carlitos at home." He kissed me again and then bowed his head to peak under the sheet where it met my neck and collarbone.

"No Carlitos, just us and, oh, did I tell you we're having lunch with Pepe and Silvia next Friday? We'll have lunch and then head up to the mountains."

As he walked away and towards the front of the house I called out to him, "We're having a big party here on the 25th."

I heard the front door swing shut and didn't know if he'd heard me or not.

That morning I started calling to invite people over for lunch on Sunday October 25th, 1970.

CHAPTER

14

———

Friday came and we went for lunch with Pepe and Silvia. By October the normal bustle of the political in Chile was very intense. Back in the middle of September Allende had made it perfectly clear that if the Congress didn't ratify his elections, he'd fix it so the entire country ground to a halt with strikes. He even made veiled references to land takeovers. It all sounded like the Black Panthers to me. They used that *We will liberate your money if we don't get our own way* rhetoric.

Before the Christian Democrats would sign off on the ratification of the general elections that had to pass the Congress, they came up with a list of guarantees they wanted the *Unidad Popular* to promise to adhere to. The reports of the power-brokering going on in Chile filled the papers week after week. It was what people were talking about, what we'd be talking about at our lunch with Pepe and Silvia.

As soon as we sat down for lunch in the dimly lit restaurant with silver trays and elaborate swords on the walls, Silvia launched into a defense of the new Buñuel film and how Chileans were too simplistic, too *vendidos a Hollywood* to appreciate it. After ten minutes Carlos and Pepe were both leaning way into the center of the table talking just to each other. Silvia and I might as well have been in Viña. The only reason I heard what Pepe said was he kept repeating it, *phrases about the Estatuo de Garantías.* Evidently, whatever this bill of rights designed to calm down the Christian Democrats was, it wasn't working. Or at least some people thought it wasn't enough. His voice strained not to be too loud against the dull noise of the restaurant.

"Property."

That's what I heard him say. That is what he whispered, really. The list of guarantees didn't say anything about property.

"He's got the votes in the Congress though. Twenty or 25 of the Christian Democrats are all lined up no matter what the *Garantías* lack."

Carlos and Silvia listened.

"When is the final vote?" Carlos asked.

"The 24th. They vote on the 24th," was all Pepe said.

I blurted out, "What do you mean? *Nothing about property.*"

An image of communists hauling away my furniture flashed in my mind. For two years I had been hearing Dolores say the communists would take away the Church, the good schools, furniture. Carlos always scoffed at her fears, but listening to Pepe I began to wonder if she could be right.

"The new government won't let us have property? Won't let us keep our *things?*" I couldn't help myself.

Silvia put the palm of her hand on her forehead and for an instant I thought she'd laugh, but she didn't. She really did think of me as her celebrated accomplishment, or rather my education as her accomplishment and never missed an opportunity to enhance it.

"Julita, my dear, not that, not your *things*. *Propiedad.* There are people in this country that have so much property you can see it from the moon. There are *fundos* half the size of entire *provincias*…."

Pepe reached out to take her hand before she could go any further. He smiled and gave her the *don't lecture the gringa look*. It was nice of him to do that. My cheeks felt hot with embarrassment, but I knew that even if my Spanish were perfect, even if I read the papers all day long, I would have misunderstood that word *propiedad.* Carlos buttered bread and mumbled words I didn't understand.

"Well," I began, anxious to change the subject, "We're going on a little trip. Yes we are. This afternoon we're driving up to the mine for the weekend."

As I said it, I realized that the weekend at a copper mine didn't sound like much of a vacation. Carlos put an arm around my shoulders and said to Pepe, "That woman I want to interview is up there, and it's beautiful this time of year. And, and this is amazing, the company has even lent me a *camioneta* to take."

This was the first I'd heard about *that woman* or the *camioneta*. A *camioneta* is a small, in this case very small, pick-up truck. I turned towards him and made a joke about him inviting me to meet his *other woman* and the four of us laughed. Then I remember I gave out a real child's wail and nearly shouted at Carlos, "Don't you dare tell me this weekend is *work*. I'll kill you if we're driving all the way up there for you to work."

"No, No, not much of it is work."

He said it with almost a twinkle in his cinnamon brown eyes, and I was gullible enough to believe him. Then he went on about what a great time we were going to have with the lodge all to ourselves.

Leaning towards me he added, *oh-là-là mon chéri*, and he gave me a big smack right on the lips.

Pepe and Silvia seemed to chuckle while Pepe waved to the waiter for the check. "You lovebirds have fun," Pepe said as we all walked out of the restaurant. Then he moved towards Carlos and added, "Take careful notes on what she says. It could prove important."

I knew the *she* wasn't me, but at that moment all I wanted to do was hold Carlos's hand and head off on our little trip.

The *camioneta* was tiny with barely room for the two of us on the front seat. We tied our suitcase, the same suitcase I'd brought from Kansas City, to the floor of the miniature open flat bed in the back. As we drove up the *Pan Americano norte* towards the mountains and the Chacabuco tunnel, Carlos explained that we'd stop the other side of the town *los Andes* so he could talk to María Pérez. María de los Angeles Pérez he corrected himself. She was the woman who had lost her home because of the mine.

"Wiped out, Julita. Generations were wiped out."

His voice sounded low, throaty. I remembered the story about the woman and how the company tore down her little house, her shack, to make way for the mine. The article and her picture had been in all the papers upsetting Carlos, to say nothing of Carlos's boss, because it made the company look villainous and greedy.

"What's different now?" I asked him, feeling our legs press together on the narrow seat of the *camioneta*. "I thought that was all over months ago."

I didn't want to hear an answer to this question. I wanted to talk about *us*, about did Carlos think I should get a new dress for our party? Wasn't Charlie adorable? Those were the questions I was asking him in my mind.

"Chile is different," is what he said.

I stayed in the *camioneta* when Carlos went up to the low, dark house with a tin roof. He stood in the doorway, his back to me, talking for the longest time. When María del los Angeles Pérez finally walked out her front door, it was like seeing a newspaper photo come to life. She was old and carried the same walking stick she held in the pictures I had seen of her. The scar on her left cheek glistened in the sun as though it were oiled. Carlos walked just behind her with both his hands a bit forward ready to steady her if she stumbled on the rocky footpath that led from her doorway up to the road where we were parked. He waved an arm for me to get out of the *camioneta* and then introduced me to her.

"This is my wife Julie. She is from the States but has lived here since 1968 and loves Chile." He spoke very slowly, very deliberately.

He told her all about me, for whatever reason. Explained that I didn't work for the mine. Said I was a good cook and loved *empanadas*. Stepping closer to me Carlos switched to English and said under his breath,

"Look sweetie, I'm sorry, but we need to take her up to the mine with us. I need her to show me things." He started walking me around to the back of the *camioneta* before I quite realized what he was doing. "It's not a long ride, I promise. Just sit with your back to the cab of the truck and hold on to the suitcase straps if you want to. They're bolted down, don't worry."

"That article was months ago," is all I repeated as I climbed into the back of the *camioneta*, frightened as a child.

As the little truck picked up speed in its travel up the mountain road I squared my back against the glass window of the cab. I pulled my knees to my chest and held them there until the first sharp turn made me reach for the near strap holding my dull cloth suitcase against the wind. I could hear Carlos and the old woman talking but their words carried off in the air. As we went faster up the steep road I saw bushes and stunted trees fall away from me like things tumbled out of a dresser drawer. I let one hand go from the strap and banged it on the window, banged it for Carlos to stop, to slow down. First my fist, then the flat of my palm struck the window. That noise too was carried off in the air.

By the time we got to where María de los Angles Pérez lost her house, a hillside that now was scared with deep trenches for the footings of new, more substantial buildings, my hair had come loose from its pins and swirled around my neck. Tears held hair against my face so I felt like a swimmer startled and bobbing out of the water. Carlos still sat inside the *camioneta* talking to his passenger. She was the one who finally heard me and said, "Your *gringa* seems to be crying back there."

Once Carlos swung the truck door shut and started walking back towards me. I shouted at him, "You wouldn't stop. I banged and banged and you didn't stop." I cried harder, holding my stomach and rocking myself the way an abandoned child will do.

The old woman, now out of the truck too, leaned on her cane with relaxed composure and looked at the hillside. Carlos looked at her and then back to me. "Believe me, Julie, this is important."

I watched him jam both hands into his pockets and begin to pace around in tight little circles. Clearly, he didn't want me to make a scene. The circles his feet drew made it meant he didn't want me to talk back either. It could have been my father standing there is what I thought to myself. That moment, that very moment was when I felt a tear between us. It was a strong sharp pull, the kind that parts a fabric dead straight down the line of just one thread. All the smiles and dancing and baby Charlie, all the silly games and learning new words were touched by that, ...*this is important. This* wasn't me, and it was as real, as looming, as the mountains that were all around us in the late afternoon sun. I wanted to howl, *I was terrified. I could have been hurt.* But instead I stood there and bit my cheek.

Will my Julie, my baby girl, ever be that way, I wonder? Will she ever swallow words she longs to spit at John and feel them make her sick?

By the end of dinner that night I knew that the displaced woman, María de los Angeles Pérez, had worked from 1966-1968 as a kitchen maid in the lodge run by the copper company.

Chilean and U.S. executives stayed there when they were up at the mine and the help overheard things.

For two years this woman heard tidbits about copper prices, a man's nephew who got a pavement contract, what the mine paid for dynamite. When she lost her house she told everything she knew to union organizers. Now she was telling it all to Carlos. After dinner, after he told me this part of the story, it was like being back in the truck again with things tumbling away from me. I wanted to say, *Carlos, Carlos you work for the mine. Why are you doing this?* His eyes didn't meet mine. *Why do you care if they pay too much for dynamite?* All I did say was, "And I bet she didn't own that land anyway." I knew he wasn't really listening to me. "You know it was just a *callampa* house, that house she lost. She can build one of those anywhere, can't she?"

Other words floated around inside my head and I ate little bites of cookie left on a plate. It clicked one-two for me. Carlos was *getting on the boat*, as Silvia said. *Lo chileno para los chilenos.* What does he do all day at work, I wondered for a moment. Then I thought of Carlos talking about lost houses while I banged on the *camioneta* window. I had been so afraid in the back of the pickup truck, and he hadn't even heard me.

That night in bed through the thin air of the mountains we could see stars out the window of our room. Carlos caressed my hair and told me about the stars of the Southern Hemisphere and how water south of the equator swirls differently down a drain. The faint starlight was just enough to outline his nose and mouth against the window. It was a softer face than the one I'd seen against the mountain sky hours before.

"You've got to trust me *pajarita,*" he murmured as he moved a leg up over mine and pressed his hardness into me. "Trust me."

I didn't know exactly what I was supposed to trust him about, because I never asked.

CHAPTER

15

The next day we drove back down through the mountains. I don't know where María de los Angeles Pérez went. Back home it was easy enough to focus on Charlie and see that he was learning to prefer walking over crawling. It was this slip-slide back into a routine that kept me from thinking too much about screaming in the back of the pickup truck as it went up the mountain road. The whole event became cordoned off from the rest of my life. Instead, I just smiled at Charlie walking all around and hoped this would make him less prone to catching cold since floors in our little house were drafty.

Carlos went back to work on that Monday morning, and I spent an hour on the phone inviting thirty people for lunch on Sunday, October 25th. I'd decided to make my party a real mix-up of people. Pepe and Silvia would be there along with Janet, her husband, and another Embassy couple. People from Carlos's company had accepted as well as a few of his old buddies from school days. Tomás and Dolores would come. Tomás was bringing several friends, one of whom had worked with Allende on previous campaigns back when he was a senator. It was going to be great. I was going to have a real *soirée* I told myself.

The weather was getting warmer that week before the party. Trees were beginning to leaf out. The papers were full of articles about the coming ratification vote and the coming installation of Salvador Allende as the first freely elected Marxist president in the whole wide world. And then on the morning of Thursday October 22nd, as I was ironing a blue skirt, the radio blared that a General Schneider had been shot.

The report was confused. It referred to *sources* and said *aparentamente* Schneider had been shot. His driver had driven him to the *Hospital Militar*. The news team was waiting for further information. Carlos hadn't heard anything about it before I called him, because he'd been working on a report all morning. He told me that since Allende's election General Schneider was the one to assure the Chilean people of the military's discretion. In a speech he'd given in September he promised all Chileans that their military would never move against an elected official. It wouldn't be constitutional he had said.

No one ever thought the shooting was a random crime, not for a minute. Dolores called me a couple of hours after I'd heard about it. She called me all the time, that wasn't unusual. What was maddening was she sounded so gossipy. To hear her talk, you would have thought she actually knew the entire Schneider family, which was preposterous.

Two of Schneider's four children had worked for Allende's election, she told me in that kind of hushed voice she got when she talked about serious matters. She determined the apples couldn't have fallen too far from the tree. Then she went on that, of course, the *comunistas* had done this terrible thing. It made no sense to me. As crazy as it seemed, though, it turned out that lots of people seemed to believe the same thing. The next day or two you heard other people saying the *Movimiento de Izquierda Revolucionaria*, the MIR, was behind the shooting. Why would the left go after one of its sympathizers? Dolores was predictably stalwart in her conviction that the attack had been carried out by the left and said it foreshadowed the chaos an Allende government would bring to Chile.

"You'll see," she repeated over the phone lines, "lawless-ness is what we are going to get here. Not since Diego Portales have we had a political assassination, not since then."

Schneider was still alive at this point, but gravely wounded, he wasn't expected to survive. Dolores's voice took on the weight of a lament.

"1833, Portales was killed in 1833. A murder in broad daylight, a murder in the street. It is *caribeño, tropical*."

For the next couple of days the press reports were confusing and contradictory. Over and over I saw a picture of the General sitting in the back of a large convertible limousine, waving at a crowd. He had on a heavy black coat. In the picture his head was bare as if it were then, that moment, when he had been shot. Of course it wasn't. The photograph must have been an old one from a parade or other happier day. There were many versions of the story. By Sunday, the day of our luncheon party, it was all anyone could talk about.

CHAPTER

16

Janet called and said they couldn't come to the party. There were emergency meetings at the Embassy. She wouldn't say more than that. Carlos made a snide remark under his breath - and in Spanish- about Uncle Sam and his diplomats being two days behind the news that was published in *la Segunda.* They weren't able to control the bugs they hatched. *La Segunda* was not even the biggest paper, so his comment was meant to be a real dig. At the time I didn't understand his comment about the bugs.

"O sure," I told him, "it's easy to poke fun at us *gringos* and our Embassy. They were worried about something happening and now it has."

Then I thought to myself that at least the *gringos* knew for whom they were working. I watched as Carlos turned and took a few steps. I read his action as his not listening to what I was saying about what was serious. Clearly though, this wasn't a time to get all bent out of shape. I just stood there and let my hurt feelings coil around me until they eased. It was easy enough to do. The smooth palm of his hand, the curl of his hair, they soothed me every time. Carlos bounced Charlie on his leg just like I did and rubbed his little-boy belly to make him laugh out loud. He even liked salt and pepper on cantaloupe the way I did. I knew it wasn't his politics that tied me to Carlos.

Even now, I have to admit I still don't know exactly what his politics were then. I simply couldn't tell you if he was ideologically committed to the Allende enterprise, or not. Maybe for him it was just the way to get ahead?

Another, younger, Embassy couple came that day for the party. América arrived at noon with the *empanadas* and three cakes. I went to the kitchen and saw her there. She charged me more for the cakes than I had counted on, but they looked fantastic. Actually, they looked like a child's fantasy. Each cake (they weren't cakes, actually, but rather meringue concoctions) was three layers high. They had fruit between the layers and were covered with whipped cream and decorated with an orange goo that was delicious. Never in my life had I seen a dessert like them.

Once I thought about it, I realized I had absolutely no idea how she had gotten them to my house. She didn't have a car. She couldn't have carried them. Carmencita thought she must have come by taxi, but she hadn't seen a taxi. She said América just appeared at the door with one cake in her hand, the *empanadas* in a large cardboard box balanced on the little wall by the door, and the other two cakes at her feet. I never asked her how she transported it all, but figured that's why she upped the price some.

I paid her and continued getting out extra glasses while I checked on the salads. She told me about heating up the *empanadas*, and then she asked Carmencita for plates for the cakes. She had even brought doilies to put them on. I left the kitchen because I heard Charlie fussing out in the dining room. Now that he could walk around, he did. Unless a person was actually talking to him, he'd wander off. My hope was to feed him lunch and get him down for a nap before people began arriving at 1:30.

My plan would have worked if Tomás hadn't arrived early with a wind-up doggie toy that clapped its paws and spun around on its tail. Charlie toddled over to his *abuelito* and screeched with delight. Tomás leaned way over to put the toy on the floor and was saying how the doggie was just like Chile.

"*Un perrito*, just like Chile, spinning on its ass."

"Well, here we go." I said to no one in particular as I walked out of the room. "People will even talk to baby Charlie about politics."

Before anyone else arrived, Carlos sat down with his father outside on the little benches near the front door. Tomás talked to Carlos. He never did talk a whole lot to me unless we were alone for some reason. When I first met him I thought this was because my Spanish wasn't good. Later I decided he simply preferred talking to men, that is unless he were flirting.

I pulled up a chair to join them because I was dying to know what Tomás knew about the Schneider murder. It was murder now. Schneider had died from his wounds and there were to be three days of national mourning. Unlike Dolores, who dressed up her personal bias as fact, with Tomás you felt like you might be getting inside information because he knew a lot of politicians. He must have heard things, I figured. When I joined them, he was saying, "Monsters. They wanted a monster so badly, you see." He was looking towards Carlos and then lifted his chin as though he were speaking to a crowd. "That's just what it was. That's all. They had to have a monster to attack. So kiddo, when none appeared they had to provide it."

Carlos asked him, "Who? Who provided the monster?"

I was confused. Who *was* the monster? Just then I could hear the bell ring at the gate.

If all of the guests had been *gringos* I wouldn't have had any trouble managing things. Between Carmencita in the kitchen and Dolores entertaining the baby, I would have been fine. *Gringos* will introduce themselves to each other. They'll get their own drinks. Chileans, on the other hand, act like stranded birds when they arrive at a party. You open the front door and they stand there until you say, *Come in, come in.* You always get the kiss hello, but then they plant themselves just inside the doorway unless you shepherd them along. You have to take their coats, indicate which way they're to walk. It is incredible, really. When you see them at a party it makes you wonder how they ever get anything done in their lives. There is such passivity about it, the waiting to be waited on. Carlos never agreed with me about this. He found it polite. It was, after all, the way he'd been raised.

But someone always does get you a drink, that's what maids are for, he'd laugh.

He always gave me that argument. It sounded spoiled to me, to say that sort of thing. The men were the worst. Not only did they look for maids to wait on them, they expected their wives to do the same. At every buffet dinner party I ever went to in Chile the women lined up with plates in hand, carefully selected the best meat, vegetables—or no vegetables—and then dutifully carried the plate to their waiting husbands. *You have webbed fingers?* I once asked a man as his wife served him. He looked startled, but I don't think got the joke.

Most of the people that afternoon knew each other or knew of each other, but they were surprised to be together since they clearly were not all from the same *group*. Fearing that perhaps I would commit an unpardonable social sin, Tomás quickly surveyed the guests as they arrived and set out to encourage conversational groups that would avoid obvious clashes. Clearly he didn't want Silvia right next to the young Embassy wife. It didn't bother me; I was passing olives and knew that before the afternoon was over lots of sparks would fly.

Funny, when I had originally planned all of this, the election of Allende had been the defining event for all of us. The *Unidad Popular* and their victory, their promise, made people reevaluate how they thought the country was going to run and where it might be headed. Whichever side you were on, though, I had felt like Chile was still Chile. Any dramatic shift was out in front of us, if only just. Now things had cracked. People started counting out time, not from the day of the election, but from the day Schneider was shot.

Carlos's boss obviously was obsessed with the entire story. Well he would be, after all. The copper industry stood to lose the most with any bad turn. He stood kind of over around the side of the house (we were all outside having drinks because it was a warm early spring afternoon) with a group of six or seven listening to him. They all held their *pisco sours* and looked first at him and then at each other as he described the killing. He sounded as though he'd been there, seen it all. He told the story almost as though he were Schneider.

"You all know the street," he began, "*Martín de Zamora*. A quiet street, the leaves are out on the trees now. Not a fancy street, you know. The townhouses, those small apartment buildings."

He painted such a familiar picture of the pleasant, but not pretentious neighborhood. *Not pretentious,* he kept repeating, as if pretense could have justified the actions. But Schneider was not pretentious. Every day the General left for work at the same time. Were they friends I wondered? How did he know all of this? The general's Mercedes car drove up *Martín de Zamora* and then stopped in the middle of the street. The general leaned a bit forward and looked out the back window of his car. There were eight men. He had been reading the paper, that's why he didn't notice the cars before. There were five cars. Four were in front of them, one behind. The general was in a trap.

"He turned his head from one window to the other and then reached for his gun just as a hammer swung and broke the car window." We all listened. "The gun was under his briefcase."

I had read that the gun was inside the briefcase, but what difference did it make?

"Three shots. One of the bastards panicked. Three times, they shot him three times. Once in the wrist, once in the neck, once in the spleen."

It was supposed to have been a kidnapping. A guy standing there that I didn't recognize, a friend of Carlos, said they had tried to kidnap Schneider the previous Wednesday after an official dinner. Later someone would say there had been two attempts before the botched crime of October 22nd. Carlos's boss clearly didn't want to lose control of the storytelling and waved his arm a bit as he continued giving details of the murder.

I was walking all around, saying hello to people, making sure the coals of the grill were getting hot. A good half-hour later I went back around to the side of the house and Carlos's boss was still there telling the story to another group of people. There were only three this time, but he repeated every sentence from the first version of the story and then added more about the *doctrina Schneider*.

That seemed to be it. Apparently Schneider had been killed because of his promise to keep the military out of politics. There were, though, and Dolores wasn't the only one, people theorizing that the left was involved. People couldn't stomach the notion that a person who voted for the Christian Democrats could also pull a trigger. They were hoping a MIR *terortista espía* was the one who actually shot the general. MIR would have done it to make the right-wing terrorists look bad.

As I walked on, looking for Carlos's face in our crowd of people, I grabbed at the idea that somehow María del los Angeles Pérez had known all of this was going to happen. Maybe, I thought, letting myself lock into daydream, she rubbed the scar on her long face and told my Carlos all about how union organizers were going to kill General Schneider. Maybe that's what they talked about in the truck while I banged on the back window for them to stop. I heard the *camioneta* strike rocks on the road and shoot them up under the carriage of the truck. *Rat-a-tat-tat. Had Schneider banged his hand against the car window too?* Carlos's hand on the back of my waist jostled me. I turned my head to him, and, after pausing for just a second, smiled.

"A great party?"

"Trust me," he answered, "this is a great party,"
He bent his head down just enough to kiss the side of my neck.

If the Chileans were animated that afternoon, the fellow from the Embassy, David something-or-other, was as stiff as a crinoline petticoat. The Embassy must have been giving lessons to all the junior officers on how to behave with the locals now that Chile was going to have a Marxist president. This guy arrived looking like he was dressed for church and never took off his jacket the whole afternoon. As far as I could tell he never even had a drink. I felt sorry for him in a way, felt like we'd cornered him, which we had. Janet and her husband were supposed to be there to help him out, but since they bailed out David and his wife were there all alone defending Nixon and the fact that he had failed to send Allende congrats for being ratified as president. Jesus, what was this David guy supposed to say? *Of course Nixon isn't going to congratulate Allende. Do ya' think we're idiots? The communists stink. Our government hates communists. Our businesses hate communists. We all really hate communists.* That's no doubt what he wanted to say, but didn't. He was a true diplomat.

Silvia, not to miss a chance to get her claws to prey, inquired about U.S. government involvement in the elections. She stood there in her bright blue trousers and bold as brass asked if the U.S. had funneled monies to Frei. *Had Frei been in touch with Nixon directly, or just with Kissinger?* Exactly how many millions had been sent to throw the election? I couldn't believe she was badgering this poor guy unmercifully. What was he supposed to say to defend himself?

"You just think we're all banana republics, don't you?" she spit out as her final flourish. "Isn't it true the U.S. will stop at nothing to protect the bananas?"

I swear to God, this David was maybe twenty-six, and all he did was stand there in his coat and tie and take the abuse. His wife had had her baby at the same clinic where Charlie was born and I knew her fairly well. Her name was April, and she taught second grade at the Embassy sponsored school, *Nido de Aguilas*- Nest of Eagles. It was a hilarious name for the U.S. school I always thought. Teaching was one of the few jobs an Embassy wife was allowed to have in those days. April said it made her feel much more in touch with home being with all those cute *gringo* kiddies. I was looking at the two of them and saw that she kind of waltzed away from David as soon as Silvia launched her attack. You couldn't blame her really. Being a diplomat is hard, but it was David's job, not hers. David had only been in Chile a little over a year. He and April were still taking Spanish lessons three afternoons a week, so you knew they probably didn't know much about the U.S. mucking around to keep Allende out of office.

Silvia, her shoulders back and her voice insistent, harped that Ambassador Korry had used more than just his influence to support the Alessandri plan. Hadn't he tried to buy Christian Democrat votes to block Allende's ratification as president? That was her question. David gave her a wide-eyed stare.

I stepped over to Silvia and poured more *pisco sour* into her little glass. All I could think to say was, "The movies, what's good at the movies?"

I was afraid her next question might be about Korry and the Schneider kidnapping.

A few people were sitting in the house and as I walked by, I could hear something else being said about Schneider and *Who had done it?*

Carlos had started to cook the meat so I needed Carmencita to get the rest of the food out on the table. After nearly two and a half years in Santiago, I had found what I thought was the only good butcher shop and didn't want our expensive steaks to get cold before anybody ate them. Dolores came in the kitchen with Charlie. There was no way he was going to take a nap with a party going on. Standing close to Charlie, Pepe started telling a story. Charlie's walking evidently was like his brother's walking.

"Pedrito had this same wobble. Come here Carilitos *hombre,* let your *tío Pepe* take a good look."

Then he went on and on about his baby brother, now in university, and how it was to grow up poor in Linares, a town in the near south. This, *I come from the destitute south, from the land of privation,* was a very popular line in Chile in 1970. Pablo Neruda had made it popular because he had done the same thing. Neruda hadn't quite won the Nobel Prize yet, but in 1970 in Chile he was a national hero. He wrote all about being a poor man from a poor little town. It sounded very good, very romantic, in the poems. But even I had been in Chile long enough to know that you couldn't come up from totally nothing and make it. You could, maybe, inch up from lower middle-class to middle-class. That, after all, is what made Chile unlike Perú. In Perú, Dolores told me your life was fixed two generations before your parents even met. In Chile, though, if you were brilliant and lucky at the same time, you could go from middle-class to star. Pablo Neruda was a star. His claim about being from such a poor family you had to take with a grain of salt. Or as Dolores said, *Tómalo con Andina -Andina* was a popular brand of mineral water. She and her sister knew Neruda when he lived in *Nuñoa* and she assured me he had always gone to the best bakery. That's evidently how she'd known he wasn't destitute. Neruda was young then. It was before he moved to *Bellavista* and made it the Greenwich Village of Santiago. Dolores summed up Neruda with her pronouncement that *Neruda was un grosero.* She obviously held his young-self guilty for his mid-life leftist leaning self, but as she went on the punch line of her story was,

"He couldn't have been from such a poor family, or how would he have been up at *la Universidad de Chile* in Santiago in the first place?"

Her point was well taken. You didn't come from the *destitute South* and go to university if you were dirt poor. Years later I read somewhere that Pablo Neruda, in fact, had his university studies paid for by Gabriela Mistral, Chile's other Nobel Prize winner. I knew that Pepe, for all his *when we were poor in Linares* talk, wasn't the son of sharecroppers either. Pepe went on cooing and gooing at baby Charlie as Charlie wiggled every which way around to get at his drink. Once Pepe realized what the baby was doing, he turned to me and said, "Can't this *hombrecito* have some soda? I bet he hasn't had anything to drink but milk and water for days." Pepe stood back up and turned to me as I walked by carrying plates to the table, adding with a wink, "You good *mamacitas* don't give your children anything fun."

Charlie choked a bit with his first sip of soda, but that was just because he was shouting baby talk words as he tried to swallow.

Pepe wagged a finger in Charlie's direction and to no one in particular said, "Don't choke little fellow. Now, if he were drinking Pepsi, we'd all know why it made him choke, wouldn't we?" Then he added, "Pepsi makes us all choke."

Three or four people were standing there and I started shooing them outside to get their lunch. As expected, the only people in line getting food were the dutiful wives. It made me feel compelled to make my joke about the Chilean tragedy of having so many men with webbed fingers. They could, after all, waste away and starve if it weren't for the tender care of the valiant *chilenas* always ready to serve them.

Pepe clapped, and as people laughed, he again said something about Pepsi. "She's right, you know. We're weak and only survive because you *lindas* are born to treat us well. Just don't serve us any Pepsi, *vino chileno*'s what we drink."

Everybody knew Pepe was in on things, he advised Allende after all, so the Pepsi comment brought a stir. People were talking all at once and I couldn't make out exactly what was being said. A few minutes later I caught Carlos as he came back out by the grill and asked him what all the Pepsi comments were about.

"It's a dig at Doony Edwards," he said and I watched a smile spread across his face. Obviously, he'd gotten the joke.

Doony Edwards was arguably one of the most important businessmen in Chile. That much I knew, though I'd never heard him called *Doony* before. To me he was *el señor Edwards*. His first name was Augustín. The family had been in Chile since the nineteenth century and originally had an immense tract of land. The kind you can see from the moon, as Silvia would have said. Evidently, once they tired of *fundo* life, they came to Santiago and got into banking and newspapers. *Banco Edwards*, the banks with the blue and white signs, were everywhere. Augustín Edwards owned *el Mercurio*, Chile's largest newspaper.

After the joke about Pepsi, lots of people started talking about Doony Edwards and saying he was such a conservative man. It made sense to me; after all, it sounded like he had a lot to conserve. From what one of the mine guys said, word had gotten out that Edwards left Chile about a week after Allende's election. People were saying his old buddy Donald M. Kendall, the chairman and chief executive officer of PepsiCo, offered him the job of handling all of PepsiCo's dealings in Latin America. It seemed the fortune Allende wanted to take from Doony Edwards, PepsiCo would replace if he could get more Latinos to drink Pepsi.

As soon as Pepe snatched center stage with his Pepsi remark, people perched lunches on their laps and started to *pelar* Doony Edwards. *Pelar* is to peel, as in to peel an onion. For someone who wasn't actually a politician or a movie star, Edwards was very high profile, Pepe said to the group still listening to him. This was meant to be funny because Edwards was as huge a man as he was a rich one. Overall, Chileans aren't nearly as tall as people from the States, and Doony Edwards must have been six feet something. He had a big head full of bushy hair that made him look even taller. A school friend of Carlos's told a rather vulgar *huge Edwards* joke about him gobbling up half of Chile and then shitting out turds of information for the CIA to feed to Uncle Sam. The thought that upper class Chileans would be giving information to the CIA was a new one for me, but it made sense. Doony Edwards had a lot to lose and no doubt thought Uncle Sam looked like a better bet than Salvador Allende.

Tomás said the ideological underpinnings of the elections were all a *Who's on top?* game. It wasn't that the left wanted to help the poor and the right didn't. He's used the refrain *Quítolo tú, para ponérmelo yo* -you take it off, so I can put it on. It was about who would have the power, and it sure wouldn't be the poor people.

By the time people finished eating and telling jokes it was cooling off. Inside you could hear the river more than you did on the patio. It was remarkable, people commented, so graceful to have a house with a living room hung right out over a river. I had grown used to it. To me it was a house with no heat, no insulation. Cold air seeped through every wallboard in the winter, but it was lovely that day. The living room and dining area were crowded once people moved inside. Charlie became the center of attention and did his tricks for the crowd. He waved *bye, bye* and giggled. Carlos's boss was still talking to people about the Schneider murder. As I brushed up next to him with a plate of cookies, I remember thinking how odd it was that we all knew so much.

The peculiarity I sensed wasn't exactly that we were all talking about the Schneider murder or making jokes about Doony Edwards, it was that most of the guests at our party knew these people, or knew somebody who did. There wasn't the impenetrable distance I expected to divide us from people like Schneider or even Allende himself.

After all, even I had met Salvador Allende. Dolores and I set the table for that dinner party. I sat right at Tomás's dining room table and ate the whole artichoke with Salvador Allende sitting right across from me. That had been in October of 1968. Now it was the end of October 1970 and Allende was president of Chile, well, almost president. Thinking now about the people at our house that day, we were all very young, all of us except Carlos's parents, and it didn't seem to me at the time that we were so important. The way I looked at it, we didn't even have piped-in gas for Christ's sake. But there we were in *el Arrayán* in our living room out over the river, and we were in on things.

I think more than anything, what I felt was a sense of bewilderment, bewilderment and a kind of specific betrayal of what I considered the natural order of circumstance. I grew up assured of an irrefutable separation between me and the people in the newspapers. Politicians, important bankers, they were supposed to be as remote as movie stars. During the whole time I was growing up in Kansas City only once had an event violated that separation. As our party wound down, I overheard more snippets about the Schneidner murder and saw people gather up their purses, cigarettes. It made me think back to another murder story where I had almost known some of the people involved.

When I was in the fourth grade a six-year-old boy was kidnapped from our school. His name was Bobby Greenlease. I didn't actually know him, but once the story was in the newspaper and on the television there was such a familiarity I felt for this little boy it was as though he could have been my brother.

On just a regular day while I was studying arithmetic, or going to lunch, a woman walked from the curb of Locust Street right into the school. The woman went to the school office and said she was Bobby's aunt. She was a very nice-looking woman dressed in a suit and carrying a handbag, its leather strap over her left wrist. Or maybe that was just the picture of her they showed in the newspaper, I don't remember. Bobby's mother was sick, very sick, she said. The mother had been rushed to the hospital and she, the aunt, had come to pick Bobby up from school to take him to the hospital too. She took Bobby's little hand, helped him on with his jacket. Bobby just stood there with his round face, his hair parted on the side. He did not say, *No!* The school principal was traumatized, but how could she have known? Bobby willingly went off with the woman. He got into the car where the man was waiting. He must have been confused and afraid. After all, Bobby thought his mother was sick and in the hospital. I could have seen it all. It happened right in front of the school, right outside the classroom windows. I didn't see it, but I could have. I was that close. There were pictures of our school in the newspaper, pictures of Bobby, his teacher, everybody.

His parents paid the ransom, but it didn't save him. Bobby Greenlease is buried right next to my Grandmother in the Abbey at Forest Hills Cemetery in Kansas City. It makes me think of him as almost a relative.

That evening in 1970, I gazed at the people in the rooms of our little house in *el Arrayán* and felt a sharp, sudden chill. *Who in Chile is Bobby Greenlease?* I let myself ask. *Who here is going to have something terrible happen?* I didn't have an answer.

América had been right about the whiskey. By 7:30 that evening every Chilean at our house had his or her fingers wrapped around a glass with J&B Scotch in it. I was too tired to drink anything else. I still had to get things cleaned up, but as I watched the other people sip their Scotch, I thought I could have bought a new dress for what it had cost me.

CHAPTER

17

After people left and I got baby Charlie to bed, I wandered into the kitchen and saw that Carmencita had washed all of my grandmother's silverware and put it to one side of the three doilies América brought when she delivered the cakes. I hadn't noticed them before. I had seen them, but I didn't realize they were cloth and not paper. They were sticky now with cake icing and cream and I thought soaking them in cold water would be a good idea before I washed them. As I scrubbed them by holding the edges with my fingertips and swishing soapy water through the thousands of tiny holes the lacy pattern formed, I wondered at the work to make such things. América must have made them herself, must have crocheted them from fine white thread. Why would she have done that? *Why make these when paper doilies are so cheap*? Then again, maybe these were cheaper because you could wash them and reuse them. They were beautiful the way snowflakes are.

América had probably never seen a snowflake. It snowed in the mountains, but never in Santiago. She was such an efficient woman, what with all those children and all the work she did, but it was a delicate beauty that slipped out in her white lace.

Once I'd washed the three doilies, I looked around for the big breadboard and got sewing pins from my repair kit. I carefully stretched each doily out and secured the edges around with pins to hold it on the wooden board. They'd dry flat this way. Once I'd done all of this I stopped, let my hands swing down by my sides, and felt a shiver go up me.

How on earth did I know how to wash and dry those doilies? I thought I'd spoken the words out loud, but when I looked over at Carmencita it was apparent she hadn't heard anything. She didn't tell me how to stretch the lace, pin it down so it would dry and hold its shape. As I stood there in the kitchen and considered what I had just done, I figured maybe my grandmother had taught me how to do it. Did she know how to wash hand-made doilies? She might have shown me when I was a little girl and then I had forgotten all about it until right that moment. What it felt like was that she'd taught me just then how to do it. But that was crazy because she was dead. She was dead and right next to Bobby Greenlease in Kansas City in the cemetery. Bewildered, I gathered up grandmother's silverware lying there now dry on the counter and started putting it away.

Naturally I needed to return the doilies to América and set out to do that the next morning. Before I could get out the door I knew I'd have to negotiate with Charlie. I wanted to walk down to San Enrique and used two cookies to tempt Charlie into his stroller. Now that he could walk, he screamed in rejection of his former means of transportation. I told him we had to take the stroller for the trip home because América's was all downhill from our house. Not convinced, he sat with his hands braced behind his hips and began a true tantrum. His heels pounded against the floor until I thought they must be numb.

I should have left him there with all his fussing, but off we went without the stroller. There's a skill to walking in the street. Not only did I face the traffic, which wasn't much, but I picked Charlie up every time I saw a car come because it was a narrow road and he was so little I thought the rush of wind created by a passing car might blow him over. Once we got down as far as the bridge there was a narrow sidewalk where we stood and dropped pebbles into the water. Every spring two or three *callampa* houses appeared down by the river near the bridge. Every winter with the heavy rains they were damaged or completely washed away. It was such persistence against inevitability. Everybody knew how bad the river could be right there at that turn. The even line of rocks that formed the riverbank in warm weather was covered by rushing water by late May. Carlos and I joked about these summerhouses when we'd drive by in our car. But gazing down at them, watching the chips of stones Charlie threw skip into the water, the shacks looked forlorn and sad.

América must have seen us come down the road because she was standing in her doorway as we approached her house. My expedition that Monday morning initially centered on thanking her again for her remarkable cooking and returning the doilies, but when she asked us to come in I was pleased. Our friendship was an odd one but one that meant a lot to me. When she came by my house it was always with a narrowly defined purpose and deferential treatment. I was *la señora* and she was selling *empanadas* or whatever. At her house, though, we could talk. She was always very frank and open if I asked her things. In a way she was my informant, the person I sought out to ease my confusion about life in Chile. Carlos told me things. He'd tell me anything I wanted to know, but he couldn't really do it very well because he, or rather people like him, was what I wanted to know about. América was the one who could catalogue experiences and people in ways that made sense to me. *Soy testigo ocular* to everything that goes on in this skinny country, she once told me. She was too. She went all around selling her *empanadas* and preparing *cordornices. From the kitchens of the finest houses you learn more than in any newspaper* was her claim.

I think she sat around and dreamt up stuff like that to tell me. She loved it, having pithy little sayings that implied her great knowledge of how things worked. She was a good judge of character too. From just hearing my comments, she'd described Dolores as a *católica profesional* because she lost her other job, that of being married to Tomás.

As soon as I went in the house, she glided around the kitchen to make us tea. Tea making was a pretty big deal if you made it the way she did. Instead of a tea bag, or even loose tea in a teapot, she first made an almost blackish brew from whole tealeaves and a small amount of boiling water. She'd pour just enough of this to cover the bottom of the cup, then fill the cup with clear boiled water. The tea drinker, in this case me, had to indicate just how much tea brew and just how much water were desired. You could have it as strong as you wanted, but she said you should always be able to see through to the bottom of the cup. Otherwise the tea would be bitter and cause *acidez.* Such a production for a cup of tea, but tea fixed this way really is delicious.

I didn't sit down until she motioned me towards a straight-back wooden chair near the ironing table. It would be rude not to tell her all about everything at our party, she made that clear. What about the people? The food? The flowers? Did I have flowers on the table? Charlie settled himself over by Miguelito on the floor to play, looking up only to query about the two cookies. Even though we hadn't brought the stroller, I did have the cookies. He clenched them for a time, but in the end it was Miguelito who unwrapped them. América went back to her ironing once the tea was poured out and I leaned against the chair back and began to tell her all about our party. She'd tolerate no vagaries. Who arrived first? What did they wear? I created a collage of the previous afternoon's events with intermittent evaluations of behavior and dress.

"April looks great, but she ought to cut her hair."

Those were the very words I had written to my parents before I'd left the house with Charlie. A lot of the letter sounded like news from the society page of *The Kansas City Star*. Silvia in her stunning blue pants, discussed the opening of the new Cary Grant film… Carlos's boss told Tomás what a fabulous job Carlos did representing the mine to the press…Such a talented young man… With people like him, we have nothing to fear with the coming change in government… Charlie is just great and so on. Love, Julie.

After rambling on to América for ten minutes and drinking tea, I blurted out, "Schneider, that's what the party was really about, América. It was all people could talk about."

Then I went on and told her the Doony Edwards joke and the whole story of how Schneider was shot three times. All about the cars surrounding his Mercedes. She ironed, stopping occasionally to delve into her laundry basket for another shirt or blouse to smooth across her board.

"I see you knew how to stretch the doilies? Smart girl." That was her first response as she looked up from her work and smiled. I explained that I hadn't *known* how, I had just done it. Then I confided my speculation that my grandmother had taught me about stretching lace, but she shook her head.

"Could be, but maybe not."

"How else could I have known?"

Discarding my question, América smiled again and added, "But you didn't come here to talk about doilies."

She was right. I had come to talk about the Schneider story. It seemed to me, and this is what I had been thinking about as I'd walked down the hill from my house with baby Charlie, that the young men who surrounded Schneider weren't some kind of an alternative Chile. Maybe they could be anyone.

"This doesn't happen in the States?"

That was her provisional answer, but it didn't satisfy me. The States was another story. I wanted to know about Chile. I wanted to know how a person decided to shoot someone like Schneider. América told me I was a still a baby in diapers if I didn't understand how people became terrorists. It was easy. It was simple. Any glitch, any snag in life can push you, she said, make you unpredictable and ready to take a risk.

Then after a long silence, she put down her ironing and began to tell me a story.

"You know, I wasn't confirmed the year I was fourteen. The bishop was to come just before Easter, but Easter was late that year and it rained and rained before Easter, before the Bishop came, so they canceled the confirmation," is how she began.

The intensity of her story-telling was hypnotic. I remembered being confirmed. It's a big deal. She was to have had a new dress. Her mother was going to give her a party and let her cut a cake. The following year she was already three months pregnant by the time the Bishop came back to confirm the young people in her little town. Her mother would not let her be presented. *No one even knows, no one at the church even knows,* América pleaded. Her mother was resolute. No white dress, no party, no cake. Having a baby at fifteen in Chile in 1952 wasn't unusual.

"I didn't have any other plans, really," was her comment.

The boy married her the following New Year's Eve and they moved with their daughter into a shack that had a corrugated tin roof and three windows.

"And here's what I did. I told him, I told Bernardo we weren't going to stay in that house for long."

A baby had gotten her into that miserable house, but more babies weren't going to keep her there. Her voice tightened. By the time her baby was eleven months old she was pregnant again.

"I was still nursing, such bad luck. I was supposed to be protected, but you can't trust anything."

Her first abortion was the worst. She grimaced as though she still felt the pain. For three days she drank an herb tea that made her throw up. Her uterus cramped, but not enough. The woman was a nurse or a *practicante* and didn't have any anesthesia when she'd stuck the long, cold instruments inside of her. *You'll remember this pain,* she'd said, *remember this pain every time you feel desire.* América said that wasn't what she'd remember. She'd remember the white dress and the confirmation cake.

América talked on and on. In nineteen years she had twelve abortions and six children. At one point she announced proudly, "I am exceptionally fertile."

I couldn't help but laugh, which made her laugh too, but it wasn't funny.

"*Bueno,* this is what happened," she bent close to me to pour some more tea. "Two months ago I thought I was pregnant, and Bernardo said he wouldn't pay. Here we are, I told him, here we are in this fine house with a tile roof, but he said he didn't have the money."

My stomach grew cold. Her tone of voice just then chilled the entire room. "I was ironing, *chica,* just like now. Miguelito was sitting right there on the floor. Bernardo was behind me, here, right here," she indicated the spot right in back of her left shoulder. "I said, '¿*Qué?*' and he said, 'I won't pay.' With that I picked up the iron and in one smooth movement pushed it right up against his right cheek."

She stood stock-still and said it had been as easy as ironing a shirt. Then her lips parted and I thought she was going to smile or laugh, but she didn't. I was stunned. The tea had grown tepid. Charlie and Miguelite weren't making a sound.

América added as an after-thought to her story, "I'd never done anything like that before, but what can I tell you?" With that her story ended and she turned back to her ironing.

"What did he do? Tell me, please tell. He must have done something."

"Oh, he did something alright. He cried out one piercing scream and huddled himself in the corner of the room. Then he beat me." She paused. "He thought he would beat me to death, but he didn't of course. And, you know, he's got that ugly old scar on his face forever."

That was it, she finally said. That was how people became *terroristas*. Burning your husband who won't pay for your abortion seemed pretty removed from planning to kidnap a general, but she said no, "It's about the same really." She moved around the room and I thought she was going to tell me another story.

"You know *tortillas*?" *Tortillas* in Chile are omelets. "*Tortillas* are just advanced eggs. They look fancy, but that's all they are. Well, *terroristas* are just advanced *huevones, huevones avanzados y enojados.*"

Huevón was one of those words you heard all the time. A *huevón* literally means a person with big balls, but the feel of it can range from *jerk* to *fucking idiot* depending on how pissed off the speaker is. América's take on terrorists was that they were just advanced and furious fucking idiots out to get what they wanted.

I slowly tipped my teacup to drink the last drops of sweet tea and thought to myself that María de los Angeles Pérez was furious when she went to the union organizers. That was her hot iron, her bomb. But what would Carlos be furious about? Or was he even furious, I didn't know and I was afraid to ask him. It was just like with my father, I always felt hedged in by an invisible something and I knew I shouldn't ask too many questions or talk back.

América offered me more tea, but by then it was time for me to get back home. As I collected Charlie's things, I groaned about probably having to carry him most of the way up the hill. It wasn't that I was fishing for América to help me, share the load as it were, but she had *recursos.* If you asked her to solve a problem, she always seemed to come up with an idea. Once, when I bought a wrought iron light fixture from a house two doors down from her (the family was moving back to the south and were selling everything they had to finance their trip) she'd scouted around, and out of nowhere nabbed a boy with an old red wagon to get it up the hill for me. I hoped maybe one of her older children was around and wouldn't mind the walk up over the bridge and the few blocks on to our house. I'd give them cookies, I thought to myself.

Instead of that, América made another suggestion. "Com'on with me and we'll look for a horseback ride up the hill." Her arm stretched towards the window. She indicated two horses tied to a post down the road a bit. "If I know the *huaso* who rides that mare, Carlitos'll have a fine ride home. Otherwise *chica*, it'll be good exercise for your arms." She laughed as she said this.

You saw horses around in those days. You still do actually, especially in *el Arrayán.* It was just far enough outside of Santiago that horseback riders mixed pretty freely with the cars and buses on the roads. There weren't lots of riders, but enough that you noticed them There were always men and many of them were old. They rode *criollo* ponies-small, heavy-boned horses, with rubber shoes on many of them. Carlos had told me that way the horses didn't slip up in the mountains.

Once a rider climbed over our fence and stole apricots from our front tree. I saw him out the window and shouted at him as he went back over the fence and got back on his horse. He was an old white-faced man on a white-faced horse and when I'd seen that I was sorry I hadn't let him take more fruit. Maybe, I thought, that'll be the man who will give baby Charlie a ride up the hill. It wasn't, but América did talk to a rider who was happy to go up our hill for 25 cents.

Chapter

18

América's story kept me company for the next few days. I couldn't decide whether or not to tell Carlos about the confirmation cake América never had. Should I mention the hot iron and how people become terrorists? Days passed and I didn't say a thing. I'd just listen to Carlos, listen to what he said about his day at the office and look at his shoulders, the curve of his neck. Marriage is so physical when you are young. What we ate, our smooth skin, our baby, those things wrapped around me much more than what Carlos did exactly. Not that I didn't think about what Carlos did or why, but as I remember it now my thoughts were framed always by a physical response more than words.

When Carlos talked about unions or terrorists, I'd feel my hand beating on the back window of the *camioneta,* and then I'd feel the coldness that comes with betrayal. It was the same coldness I'd felt as a child when I'd hear my father slam a door and shout my name. One evening Carlos said he was sure the union would favor the expropriation of the mines. In the end, he was sure, the *gringos* would have to walk away from their profits, like it or not.

"The union," I asked him, "Do you think union people could be terrorists and involved in the Schneider murder?" I could practically see the face of María de los Angeles Pérez floating there in the room.

Carlos pulled in his chin and pursed his lips as though I'd put something sour in his mouth. Then he rubbed his hands down my back and told me I was silly. The unions had won. Allende was their man, why would they kill Schneider?

He moved a step back and asked, "*Pajarita,* is dinner nearly ready? What's for dinner?"

By the time Allende was finally inaugurated in November there was a new effervescence to the political news. Rumors and hopes about what Allende would or wouldn't do flew around like kites in a March sky. The one thing I was hoping for frankly was to wrangle tickets, or whatever it was you needed, to go to the actual presidential inauguration. I had gone to President Kennedy's inauguration in 1961 and thought that being in the crowd when Allende was inaugurated nearly ten years later would make me part of a very select group.

In January 1961 my family drove east to Washington from Kansas City. The day of Kennedy's inauguration we stood for what seemed liked hours on a street near the Capitol. It was freezing cold and we couldn't see very well, but we could hear because of the microphones. Robert Frost read one of his poems. I simply couldn't believe my ears. I don't think I realized Robert Frost was still alive because I had studied him in school. I must have thought you only studied a person's work once they were dead. Frost's voice was weak against the cold January day, so you couldn't always quite make out what he was reading.

Even when I couldn't hear him, I could see him and his white hair as it glistened in the sun. I was enthralled. By the time Kennedy began his speech I was trembling a bit from the cold. By the time he finished I was in tears. All that talk about the *New Frontier* and putting a man on the moon, it just made you know that we were the greatest nation in the world. Later, my father said all those promises were just a Democrat's ploy to raise your taxes, but I knew my father hated Kennedy because he was a Catholic. As far as I was concerned the speech was inspired. Ten years later I wondered what Salvador Allende could say to inspire the Chileans.

As it turned out, Carlos and I didn't get to go to the actual inauguration, only Tomás did. He was invited as a personal friend of the president-elect. Overall, seats were very limited because the ceremony was held indoors at the Congress. By the time we'd finished watching all of the television news stories and hearing Tomás's account, I felt almost as though I had been there and seen it all. It was amazing. There were lots of men in uniform with all their braids and tassels gleaming, so many priests. Frei wore white tie and tails. Allende wore a suit and stood completely still as he was draped with a stripped silk sash from his right shoulder to his left hip.

For all the world, it looked to me more like the crowning of a prince than the swearing in of a president. There was no awareness of austerity and singleness of purpose that I had felt when I saw Kennedy, no Robert Frost. The speeches mostly sailed over my head. All that overly formal, elaborate Spanish was impenetrable as I sat there, staring at the television screen.

November 5th the new government put on a real show for
the people at the *Estadio Nacional.* All the foreign dignitaries
were there along with thousands of Allende fans. People waved
paper flags and shouted *Unidad Popular* slogans. Allende
shouted too. He shouted right into the microphones all about
his hero *el presidente José Manuel Balmaceda.* Carlos told me
Balmaceda committed suicide in 1891 when his reform policies
ran him smack up against the oligarchy. Thinking about it now,
I see that Allende was foreshadowing his own death, but none
of us realized it at the time. Maybe Abelardo, the fortuneteller,
knew what would happen to Allende, what would happen in
that *Estadio Nacional* in 1973, but on November 5, 1970,
everybody who listened and cheered didn't. Allende outlined
the reforms he'd carry out, and then over and over he promised
these reforms would be in *la vía chilena.* He would bring, he
promised, a true *revolución a la Chilena* with *empanadas y vino
tinto* and no guns.

That day I turned away from the television and said to
Carlos, "That's alotta *empanadas.* It'll make América a rich
woman if she gets part of that concession."

"You bet," was Carlos's response as he leaned over to give me
a kiss.

Then he swung his feet up onto the sofa and put his head
in my lap. He lifted one of my hands and began to run my
fingers through his hair. I watched his eyes close and then made
funny little braids out of his hair as he slept there in the folds of
my skirt. During those days we spent a lot of time sitting in
front of the TV watching the scenes of the inauguration over
and over. It crystallized for me that this was, in a way, what I

had come to Chile for. I was literally living on the upside-down part of the world—down *where God lost his shoes*—and I was having an adventure.

It was a gray, kind of damp Sunday afternoon when I sprung on my parents the fact that Carlos and I weren't going to live in Kansas City once we got married.

You better watch out Julie, it's underdeveloped down there. That's what my father

warned me. He pronounced the word *underdeveloped* like a schoolteacher entrusting the class with a new vocabulary word. I never knew if he thought it would make me not marry Carlos, not move to Santiago, or what, but he must have told me this ten times in the weeks before we'd left.

"Go back down *there*?" My father sounded bewildered before he sounded angry.

To him the United States was the land of milk and honey, and Kansas City, Missouri sat right smack in the beautiful middle of it. How could anybody get to the USA, get a Master's degree for Christ's sake, and then say they were going to leave and go back to a place like Chile? That was his initial reaction. It was after the shock wore off that he started in with all the *underdeveloped* business. For me, at twenty-one, that word was part of the allure.

I knew people backpacking around Europe and sleeping in youth hostels. Two friends were in the Peace Corps. Now I had seen the inauguration of Salvador Allende and could tell the story of the Freemason Marxist president in his jacket and tie who goes to a full-blown *Te Deum* mass at the cathedral right after his swearing in. "Chile is a country of such startling contrast," I wrote my parents right after the election. "The North American press has it all wrong, Chile won't be another Cuba." I even wrote, "Carlos says most people think the mines should be expropriated because Chile needs to change. As in almost all of my letters I also lied. Our weekend trip to the mine became a wonderful *aventura*. "Carlos even let me ride part of the way in the back of the pickup truck so I could better see the glory of the high Andes."

Who knows if my parents sensed threads of doubt in what I wrote them? If they did, they never said a thing. They wrote me back. Actually, it was usually my mother who wrote and filled me in about the good sale at Swanson's or the run of three days over 100 degrees summer weather. They missed us all. They worried about Charlie. Did he get enough orange juice, and maybe he needed vitamins? They did know that Charlie got sick a lot because I had told them that much.

In one letter home I wrote a page and a half longhand about what it was like to buy two pencils and a notepad.

I went into the stationery shop and walked right up to the counter and a very nice-looking woman with a head full of tight little curls got me just what I wanted. I handed her money to pay, but she smiled and looked away. "Oh", I thought, "pay the cashier," so I stretched out my hand for the merchandise. No go. In Chile, spending your money and getting your merchandise is a three-step process.

1. First the clerk gives you a slip of paper with the price of your purchase noted on it.

2. You wait in line at the cashier and pay.

3. You find the clerk again to exchange your now stamped slip for you package.

It all seems wildly inefficient to me. Carlos said it gives more people work, and anyway it means the store only had to worry about one person handling the money. Fewer sticky fingers to think about… Ha, ha, ha.

Love, Julie

P.S. Charlie can now say *up,up* and *nite, nite.* He's really cute. I'll send you more pictures next week" I never told then all the words he could say in Spanish.

CHAPTER

19

When I was young Allende and whatever he would do was really more than I could manage to think about most of the time. If I spun thoughts about him around in my mind for long, the image faded and then just vanished. What I really remember thinking about, think about even now, is how nearly every morning I used to wrap a towel around just one finger to clean the soap out of Carlos's right ear after he shaved.

"Carlos," I'd prod him in the abdomen with the draped finger, "What's with this right ear thing? What if I'm not here some day? You'll go off to work looking like you ran off without paying the barber."

He'd laugh and say that's why a man got married, to have a lovely woman to clean his ears. One morning, standing there in front of the bathroom mirror with just a towel wrapped around his waist, he grabbed my hands and tried to tickle me.

"As an Allende supporter I refuse to listen out of my right ear for political reasons," he bellowed, waving both hands, fingers out and wiggling. Baby Charlie toddled into the bathroom as Carlos's towel fell. He looked up at the two of us, his father stark naked, and promptly pulled down his diaper. We all laughed hard enough it made Charlie pee on the floor.

I still remember too how a flimsiness, a certain kind of thinness about many things in Chile, saddened me. Paper napkins were thin, almost transparent, and small enough you could barely clean two fingers with them. You thought they make them like this to save paper, but everybody used five instead of one, so what did they gain? If you bought a ready-made skirt, it had a hem of maybe only half an inch. Bakery cakes were sponge cakes made without butter, with artificial vanilla.

One afternoon I sat at América's kitchen table, her only table in fact, and asked her point blank, "Why's the wood of this tabletop only a half an inch thick? And why is this milk skimmed?"

It was a somber question really. I wasn't being rude, or at least I wasn't trying to be rude. She had offered to be my *testigo ocular,* and I was taking her up on it. In any event, the only milk I could buy was skimmed and awful. Her shoulders hunched up almost to her ears, which was her way of saying *honey bunch*... And then she said, "It took you so long to notice."

I told her, *no.* I'd noticed right away. It had just taken me a couple of years to feel comfortable enough to ask. I was, in a way at least, a guest in Chile and tried to avoid being *pesada,* heavy duty, with my questions. The tabletop thing was easy to explain, she told me, "Wood is expensive."

It was such a great answer. Carlos never could have given me such a direct and unencumbered answer. He would have danced around about the nascent pulp and paper industry and the government protection of their product. América just summed up the main fact about wood: expense. Milk was another matter.

"That milk is skimmed, *Gringuita*, because they skim the money out of it," Then she went on to explain how milk prices were regulated and cheese prices weren't. In other words, the dairy farmers dutifully forked over the whey to sell at the government price and made all the cheese they could to make a living. The price fixing business occasionally blew up in the government's face. Bread, for example, had a set price. Chileans loved their bread and bought it fresh, often twice a day. At first I'd thought Dolores went out before lunch and again in the afternoon to get bread as an excuse to get out of the apartment, but she set me straight on that. She actually would argue about whether *marraquetas* were better than *hallullas*. They all were just basic white flour and yeast dough cooked in different shapes as far as I could tell, but people sure stuck by their preferences.

Anyway, to get the government to vote in a price hike, bread producers would periodically go on strike and cause pandemonium at every dinner table in Chile. In fact, right before I left Chile, right in the middle of the whole Allende mess, there was a huge bread strike. Rumors flew. Friends and foes alike accused *el presidente*, Salvador Allende himself, of having a secret stash of *pan especial* in a Russian-built freezer hidden in the basement of *la Moneda* palace.

Once we were all through the inauguration, I began to think it would be a good thing for me to get some kind of a job. Charlie wasn't such a baby anymore, and anyway I had Carmencita to take care of him during the day. Silvia had been the one to suggest this. She thought I'd either end up having too many babies or playing canasta if I didn't get a job. Having another baby was in fact one of the things I was thinking about, but I didn't tell her that. Her plan was that I should teach English to her and a few of her buddies at the paper, but I thought that would make me a nervous wreck for sure. Hearing all the political gossip firsthand would be too much. Teaching at the American school *Nido de Aguilas* was the plan I settled on. Janet had taught art at *Nido* her first tour in Chile and told me there were a lot of American women married to *chilenos* who worked there. I could be an English tutor or tell them I could direct a play to get my toe in the door. This was good advice, since I didn't have a teacher's certificate.

When she was giving me the pep talk about *Nido* she added a strange bit about, "...and get to know *business wives*. You'll hear things that way, because you won't hear much from us." Odd, her saying that made me realize that I was a business wife. I sure wasn't an Embassy wife. At the time I didn't even think to ask her what it was that I wouldn't hear from her.

One morning I even ran the idea of working past América. I was at her house to buy some treat or other and was sitting there drinking tea and looking for advice. She thought my teaching school was a very dumb idea.

"You'll make about as much money as that maid of yours," was her summation of the monetary value placed on teaching in Chile. I protested, but in fact didn't really know what teachers were paid.

"You need to sell something, *chica.*"

Coming from her, I misconstrued that she thought I should start selling apple pies or something, but that wasn't her idea at all. She launched into a long-winded story about a girl, a young woman really, from a town in the south who came up to Santiago three, maybe four times a year to sell fur coats. She evidently made a fortune. The story went that her father was a tailor in the little lakeside town of *Frutillar*. For years this tailor made suits for a German man who it turned out was a furrier who himself made wondrous coats. I asked, but América had no idea, where he got the fur or even what kind of fur he used for these coats.

"*¿Qué importa?* What does it matter? They came up with *un plan, un esquema.*"

The plan hatched when the German man swore he would be greatly heartened if the tailor could help him sell the fur coats. He categorically denied monetary gain as his goal. He simply wanted his beautiful coats to be worn, and there was no one in *Frutillar* who was interested in buying them. The tailor pondered the dilemma and it was decided that his daughter, Carmen Gloria, would travel by train to Santiago whenever there was a coat to sell. So great was her beauty that women, or men, would surely ask to buy the coat she wore. Thus, she and her father and the German man would get rich.

"You think I ought to start selling fur coats?" was my question.

"No, no. Not coats, but something. There're lots of ways to get rich if you think about it long enough. You need a plan."

Naturally I was dying to know if this Carmen Gloria girl had gotten rich from the scheme. In fact, I was going to point out to América that the girl probably didn't even stand to make her fair share of the money, given that men always seem to wrangle more than their due. I wanted to say I didn't think this girl was a very good role model for me, but before I had a chance, América admitted that the whole fur selling enterprise did end badly. On her last trip to Santiago, Carmen Gloria was caught in the rain as she waited for the train. She stood alone on the train platform in the pouring rain for a solid hour. The beautiful fur coat got wet through. In Chile, in the south, it's as cold on a train as off. Poor Carmen Gloria sat in the wet fur coat all the way to Santiago. By the time she arrived in the big city, the coat was ruined and she was very sick.

I joked, "maybe she'd have been better off teaching school."

América claimed I'd missed the point of the story. Then she said that the story didn't really apply to me anyway because I had never had to live without.

"You're right, *gringa,*" she finally said and flashed a fake smile at me, turning to pick up the teacups. "You might as well just teach school with your *gringa* friends and see how things turn out" is how she ended our conversation.

Chapter

20

———

Before I was able to go to the school to inquire about jobs, Charlie got sick again. It started late one afternoon out in the side yard near the bench. He had been pushing a wagon and suddenly threw up. Just out of nowhere. He'd seemed fine before that. At first I thought he'd been coughing, but as I got closer to him I saw the vomit on the ground, heard him whimper. His face was warm as I held it up against my own. It must have been a full five minutes I stood there and swayed from side to side in my effort to calm him and make the sickness go away. He mouthed the words, *Charlie's sick* as he spit up again. How sick would he be this time, I wondered and carried him back into the house.

He got very sick. His fever was up to 103 by the time Carlos got home. He couldn't even keep teaspoons full of water down. Carlos called his mother to come over, but I had a fit and made him call her back to cancel. The last thing I needed was Dolores, looking efficient in a navy-blue outfit with her pearls and every hair in place, telling me what I should do. We could manage, I told Carlos, and rubbed his back a bit as he redialed his mother. I wanted Carlos to trust me, trust us, not his mother. By evening

Carlos was sitting on the edge of our bed with Carlitos propped up by a few pillows. He sang him a nursery song about *una vaca lechera*. He dribbled water into Charlie's mouth with an eyedropper. I stood in the doorway looking over at the two of them and thought I was going to cry. Carlos was a good daddy, a good *popi*, even if often I thought he was not good to me.

Eric offered to come over that night, but I told him not to. We'd done it before; we knew how to treat a high fever. When Charlie was maybe six months old his fever had spiked way up, and we'd had to wrap him in wet sheets at four in the morning to get it down. I'd filled the bathtub with cool water to soak the sheet, wrung it out, and then the two of us wrapped it around and around our little baby. Charlie's damp face shone red against the whiteness of the sheet. At first I thought he looked like the baby Jesus wrapped in swaddling clothes. Then it flashed at me that he looked dead and was in his winding sheet. There's an almost malicious intimacy to the night when you're up with a sick child and it easily tricks your mind.

By morning the fever was down, and I insisted Carlos go to work. He would have taken the morning off to take us to the hospital, but with all the worry at the company it would be one less thing if I went alone. I was taking Charlie to the *Hospital San Juan de Dios* because that is where Eric worked in the mornings. That was the deal in those days. All the doctors worked in the public hospitals or taught in the mornings. In the afternoons they saw their private patients. It was the government's way to keep the good doctors involved with public health, but heaven help you if you were middle-class and took sick before lunch.

I had done this going to *San Juan de Dios* a couple of times. The first time we took Carlitos there was to have a special kind of stool exam run. Carlos warned me before we got there that it wouldn't be like the *la clínica Santa María* with its sweet little garden out front and pastel painted walls. The *Santa María* was a private hospital, a *clínica*, and looked about like Saint Luke's in Kansas City except it was closer to the street. *San Juan de Dios* is in an old section of Santiago and looms up three or four stories over the low-rise buildings around it. It must have seemed as majestic as a Gothic church when it was built, but by the time I saw it its pale yellow paint had cracked in the sun. On the grounds, nestled in among the overgrown scrubs, I'd seen a plaster statue of a child who stood alone dressed in a floor length nightshirt. It was a curly headed child with an upturned face and a large, beautiful hand on the right shoulder. Seeing the child's face, the position of the head, I supposed the hand was the specter hand of a long-gone angel or saint.

That late November morning as I drove into the hospital, Charlie sat in the backseat of the car without moving. His fever was down, but I could tell he was really sick. The parking lot was huge, but most of the patients arrived by bus so I was able to park close to the hospital's main entrance. Inside the doors, mothers milled around with their children in the hall. I saw an old man with an oxygen mask over his face being wheeled off. In spite of all the people it was oddly quiet. Charlie had his head between my neck and my shoulder. I ran a finger up and down his back to comfort him. One or two children were crying a bit. Many people talked together, in fact they whispered. I thought to myself, the poorer people were in Chile the less noise they made when they were in public. You would have thought they had been taught to be invisible. At the *policlínico* I always had to wait in line, but not here. Here I was *particular.* I was a private patient.

The woman behind the desk—it was more like a podium really—spotted me as soon as I walked through the door. She had a very careful formality about her. She quickly motioned me over to her in order not to raise her voice, "*Señora, Señora,* with whom would you like to speak? The child is sick? *Pobrecito,* poor little thing."

She had turned away from another woman in mid-sentence to address me. I told her my business, and even though I said I knew where Eric was up on the second floor, she insisted on sending one of the guards upstairs with us. A casual observer would have thought Charlie and I were movie stars the way we were being treated. Going up the stairs we passed a young woman who looked about my age, also carrying a sick child. Her baby had on the hand-knit leggings you saw little children wearing on all but the hottest days. The face was flushed, just like Charlie's had been the night before. Sticky black hair framed the round dark face made copper colored by fever. We were, I considered, as different from them as movie stars.

As anxious as I was to see Eric, I felt awkward, out of place, walking up those stairs. Eric met us in the hall and walked us around past the waiting room to an examination station. He admitted right away that he was perplexed. There clearly was acute infection somewhere and his guess was that it was in the bones of the face again.

"We did all that," I pled. "All that penicillin, all those shots."

My eyes went from Charlie sitting on the bare examination table down towards the floor. Charlie held a deflated red rubber ball he played with at home. I noticed the rust on the edge of each table leg.

"You mean the penicillin didn't work, that's it." Fear was giving way to anger. "The penicillin in Chile is no good, or what?"

Eric bristled at my comment. Then I got a long explanation about drug-resistant bacteria and why Charlie would have to have several blood tests now. All of this information felt like blows. All I could think to say was they'd have to use disposable needles. I desperately tried to sound authoritative. I then asked if I could use the phone to call Carlos. The only phone was down at the end of the hall.

"No phone, Sweet Jesus," is all I could think to say. "Go ahead, if you can find the needles, go ahead."

We were there for hours. A nurse bent over Charlie as she patted the thin little spaghetti strips veins in his right arm. Afterwards, she asked me to have him dissolve a lozenge under his tongue. Fat chance of that, I told her. Didn't she see how young he was? How sick? Charlie drank a little juice from a bottle I'd brought and ate three crackers. Eric sent us to see two other doctors. One of them looked in Charlie's mouth with a flashlight, pushing his tongue to one side and then the other. It must have been very painful because it made the baby cry and cry. He asked me if Charlie had ever been seen by a dentist. I told him of course not. Charlie wasn't quite a year old. Eric sent me home with two prescriptions and an appointment to go to his office the following day.

As I carried Charlie back down the hallway to the stairs, I realized there were no pictures, no signs on any of the walls. No women in striped shirts pushed magazine carts. I wondered how all of the people who came there knew where to go. The woman at the front desk spoke to us as we left. As I turned to thank her, I tried to smile.

Driving all the way home was out of the question. I couldn't go to Dolores's with Charlie this sick. She'd talk about praying and lighting candles. There would be the picture of Rebecca staring out at me, and I would start to think about all that blood. Putting Charlie down for a nap at his grandfather's was a much better idea. Tomás ate lunch at home most days, so I knew someone would be there to let me in.

When we got there it was nearly two and Tomás was finishing lunch with a friend. The two men were surprised, and at first rather bumbling, at having the young daughter-in-law barge in with her sick child. Tomás tried to take Carlitos from me. As he reached his hand out he must have brushed Charlie's face. It was a completely innocent gesture, but the slight touch was enough to make poor baby Charlie wince and then scream with pain.

"It's his face, the infection in his left cheek bone has come back." was all I could muster to say. Tomás sort of clicked his tongue and shook his head, but he didn't say anything.

If they'd been any women there I could have talked to them about Charlie throwing up, about how dismal and cavernous the hospital was. Standing there in the hallway holding Charlie, knowing I had distracted these two friends from their lunch, made me ill at ease. I wasn't used to spending any time alone with Tomás and began to think I'd made a mistake in coming. All I wanted really was to put Charlie down for a nap, eat, and go home. After his initial flurry at seeing me arrive unexpectedly, Tomás offered me a rather blank smile and turned to go back to the table and his coffee and dessert. I should join them, he called over his shoulder as he walked away. He was sure there was leftover chicken.

Tomás and his friend, a business friend I guessed since I didn't remember ever meeting him before, were quite spread out at the dining room table. It looked as though they'd been there for hours. The table had a messiness about it. Crumbs were around and Tomás must have spilled a bit of his wine because there was a watery red stain on the tablecloth. He always did that, trying to wash away a wine stain right at the table. He used salt and mineral water. It never worked very well, but that never stopped him from the big flourish of shaking salt all over.

As I came in to sit down, I noticed both men had pushed their wrinkled napkins up under their dessert plates and were settling back with fresh cups of coffee. Tomás flashed me a smile as he pushed the breadbasket in my direction, but I didn't expect to be included in the conversation. I didn't care. I didn't have anything to add to their conversation. It wasn't just that I was young and foreign and not very well informed that made Tomás discount my presence, it was that he considered me *doméstica*. I pertained to that realm of family matters, children, getting wine spots out of tablecloths.

He and his friend were talking about Allende's cabinet appointments, how the *radicales* got the ministry of defense, that the *comunistas* bagged public works and labor. He said things like, "They couldn't give defense to the *comunistas* even if they wanted to. Ha! They're not out to scare the laying hens after all," and then with a wave of his fork at his friend, "I'll tell you this much, though, Chonchol, this Jacques Chonchol, he's the one that'll make us all shit in our pants."

With that last remark, he turned and gave me a sheepish shrug of the shoulders, as though he were a boy trying to avoid getting his mouth washed out with soap. He just presumed I wasn't interested in what he was saying, merely vigilant for *palabrotas,* dirty words. There was such ease to this conjecture, such assurance. He didn't mean to be insulting anymore than when he slowed his speech, wrapping his tongue around each word before he shot it my way. It was always as though I were a hard-of-hearing child he must pay attention to. The thought crossed my mind that Carlos treated me this way a good deal of the time.

"What's the worry with Chonchol? Is he to be Minster of Mines?" Then I added like a fool, "He's French?"

I knew it was a dumb question before it even left my mouth. If I had been Silvia, Silvia with that *Well…at-the-paper…* introduction to all her flamboyant rhetoric, he would have simply answered my question without letting me know he thought I was uninformed.

"It's a French name, but no, he's not French."

Then his friend gave Tomás a startled glare, leaned my way and added, "Julie, he's the one in charge of *la reforma agraria.*" I swear to God this man made it sound like an eighteen-syllable phrase. "*Laaaaaa ReeeFooorrrmmaa Aaagrraarria.*"

Whoever he was, he obviously had picked up on Tomás's lack of respect for twenty-three-year-olds from Kansas City. I knew quite a bit about this, I thought to myself, and proud that I'd remembered Silvia's phrase, figured I'd use it on them, "Well, it's true. Chile needs agrarian reform." And then zinging in, said as coolly as I could muster, "After all, *there are people here with so much property you can see it from the moon.*"

Instead of telling me how smart I was, they just looked at each other and smirked. I presumed I'd misspoken, gotten the grammar wrong. Suddenly I wished Charlie would start to cry and give me an excuse to desert the table, but he didn't. He was deep in his feverish sleep. He was leaving his poor mother, stranded and ready to dangle, with these two unsympathetic, well-fed businessmen. To avoid any more silence, I finally asked, "What is this Jacques guy saying he'll do?"

"He wants to see the oligarchy lose its hold on the farmland," Tomás informed me. Then I guess to let me know he'd heard what I'd said before, added, "If he has his way, what you might see from the moon is the smoke from burning *casas de fundo.*"

Fundos is what they called the huge farms. This was the first time I'd heard someone like Tomás make a specific reference to possible violence. Dolores ranted and raved all the time about the blood that was going to flow in the streets once Allende took office, but I didn't take her too seriously. But this, this made me nervous. Chonchol was a civilized man, Tomás said, but the peasants…his voice trailed off. Chonchol was giving the peasants a plan. He used the word *plan* maybe three times and it made me think about the girl with the fur coats. The peasants would hear about getting their share of land, land they'd worked for generations. If it didn't happen, if the plan didn't work, then in the twinkling of an eye, those same peasants would walk right in and try to take the land themselves.

"It's a provocative appointment, making him minister. The *inquilinos,* the sharecroppers, they'll be thrilled to have a plan. Even if they know they're bound to lose, they'll be thrilled by the hope of it." Tomás was really talking to himself as he said this, but I heard it and it frightened me. A scene or other from *Gone with the Wind* sparked up in my brain. Except instead of seeing Sherman's army I saw slaves overrunning antebellum mansions, setting them on fire. Would that happen in Chile? We were a long way from the *fundos*, but we weren't so far from all those *callampas*. Every day I drove by *callampas*, miles of *callampas*. What if those people decided what they wanted and got a *plan*? Then I realized that had been the point of América's story about the girl selling the fur coats.

The men abruptly got up from the table and excused themselves. They had to return to work. "I've not been expropriated yet." Tomás joked, and then as he straightened his tie added, "I think Allende'll write a special dispensation for Freemasons into the law. Ha, ha."

The two of them gave me a perfunctory kiss on the cheek and left without saying a word about Charlie. I had to wake baby Charlie up from his nap. Bending to change his diaper, I felt how warm he was, noticed how sour his little body smelled. His left cheek was swollen from his jawbone all the way up to his eye socket like it had been in September. I giggled at him and said he looked like a prizefighter that had lost his big fight.

His eyes fixed on mine, but he didn't smile back at me. He just lay in the bed and let me tend to him. He did drink a little water, which was good. I found I was silently counting how many hours until the appointment with Eric the following afternoon, wondering if Charlie would eat anything in all those hours.

Driving home seemed to take a long time. Our car didn't have a radio, and even if it had, all the stations were in Spanish so they wouldn't have been much good for me. I hit all the red lights. Once we passed the *Stadio Italiano,* I saw the first of the *callampas* stretch out to our left. The swirls of oceanic grays and mud browns, the dreariness of it was unrelenting since no flowers or gaily-painted cars interrupted the image. There were lots of low, ugly shacks all huddled up together.

I said out loud, loud enough for Charlie to hear, "Do ya think those people are all huddled up too? Are they all gettin' together to plot trouble?"

I bet that was how it was, too. The people wouldn't contradict the houses they lived in. Then I began to wonder how you figured out how many people actually did live in a field of *callampa* houses.

"What'a they do, sweet pea? Do they count up the shacks and multiply by 6 or by 8?" I made myself laugh, "How many *rotos* can live in a closet?"

I made a quick turn around and saw Charlie's profile set against the seat of the car. He was awake, awake and lying very still there in the back of the car. Listless, that's what he was, listless and grim with a thin arrow of late afternoon sun crossing his face. He didn't wiggle away from it or even squint his eyes.

Rotos was a word everyone used, I had even heard América use it when she joked with friends who were finagling over her price for a cake or an *empanada*. *No sea roto,* she'd say. I thought it meant cheap. Don't be cheap. But then I'd heard it used as a pejorative to shoo an unwanted window washer away from a car, or to insult a friend whom you've caught cheating at tennis. If you were a *roto,* you were literally broken. *Roto* is the past participle of *romper,* to break.

"Charlie, are they mad? Are they mad, those *rotos*? Are they mad rich people broke them?"

I kept right on talking out loud. It was my way to rehearse my feelings. Maybe baby Charlie would hear my voice and perk up enough to fidget, fidget enough to have to tell him to settle down. I dug around in the bottom of my purse for the wrapper with crackers, but then couldn't manage a way to hand them off to him.

"Wha'da you think, Charlie? Does Silvia know how to count *rotos*? I bet she does. If you ask me, com'on ask me, she's worried too, just like *abuelito.*" My voice dropped long enough for Charlie to answer, long enough for anyone to answer and of course no one did.

"O yeah, I know she doesn't have a *fundo* with peasants marching all around, but she has a mighty fine house, oh yes she does, little baby. She has a house she doesn't share with anyone, at least not that I know about. Maybe that's it, maybe she does share it huh?"

More silence. A stray thought about imminent danger. Would Charlie be as sick as before? Would a *practicante* have to come?

"You think she shares it with a couple of *rotos* that she takes to all the movies? She should come right out here and say she'd tak'em all to the movies, all of'em that voted for Allende."

Our car passed through San Enrique.

"That'd be fair, right? All her *get on the boat* talk, all that *Carlos es un chileno* crap. I don't see her over there taking anybody to the movies. Do you, do you Charlie? Charlie?"

Carmencita was standing by the gate with the watering hose when we drove up. She wore a flimsy, yellow house dress over her other clothes. Blue shirtsleeves crept out from under the shorter yellow ones. She was a cheery sight as she pushed the gate open for me to maneuver straight onto the driveway that led to our fine house with its tile roof and living room hung out over the river.

Chapter

21

That evening Charlie sat in my lap, his back up against my chest, his legs dangling over my thighs, as I gave Carlos the blow-by-blow account of the day's events. A jumble formed from the details of the broken angel hand, the hospital corridors, his father and the new minister with the French name who said the peasants could take over any land, *any* houses they wanted. Maybe I didn't actually say the last bit about the peasants storming *fundo* houses, but that is what I was worried about. In my mind the rat-a-tat-tat of the *camioneta* wheels and the shots that killed Schneider bumped into the scream of América's husband. I bounced Charlie some more and felt lonely as I sat there. Why wasn't Carlos telling me not to be silly, assuring me that peasants burning houses could never happen? I wanted him to say that everything would be fine and people were right to trust Allende and that change would be good for the country, good for us. He did not say any of those things, and I was too chicken-hearted to ask him about them.

That's what I think now. Such a dummy I was. I want to kick that self and say, *get tough*, talk back, make him answer your questions. But the *me* sitting back there at twenty-three only knew how to keep quiet and bury her fears like bricks in soft mud. We ended up talking about whether or not I should let Charlie play on the floor. His mother was right, Carlos told me. I shouldn't let the baby play on the floor. Was that his way to mitigate my fear? I didn't know and simply decided that since Dolores had been mentioned, it was easier to think about her and not imagine disasters.

Dolores, to her credit, never came right out and said I was being a bad mother. In her book, that would have been impolite. As far as I could tell, she never told anyone what she really thought. Instead she used a lot of *indirectas* she'd disown as soon as they left her mouth. To a buxom friend I once heard her say, "Marisa has that same skirt and it looks divine on her. Oh, on you too…it is simply perfect on you too. It's just Marisa's …." You always got her message clear as a bell. Every time she came over she'd come up with *indirectas* concerning how drafty the floor was, or how dirty the patio chairs had gotten. She said this even if Charlie were in his bed sleeping with his two feet off the floor altogether.

Then she'd indicate as how Carmencita should tend to Carlitos if I were too busy to do it. By *tend to* him, she meant carry him around morning, noon and night. That was her idea of raising babies. You carried them around, powdered them up so they'd smell good, and you fed them the same *carbonada* every single day of the week. *Carbonada* was a kind of beef stew with lots of vegetables and potatoes chopped up the size of corn kernels. It was okay, but I swear to God, she thought Charlie should eat it every day. I asked her once, didn't Carlos eat chicken and mashed potatoes when he was little. Jell-O? She'd just stare at me and say, rather coolly, *He ate that later.*

In any event, Carlos was letting his colors show. I knew that when it came right down to it, he trusted his mother's views on child rearing more than he trusted mine and it hurt my feelings. Not that he didn't allow me *to try my way*, as he put it. I could read *Dr. Spock*, but whenever baby Charlie threw up or ran a fever, Carlos always suggested calling his mother even though I had spilled the beans to him about the whole Abelardo story and how creepy it was.

"It's the main reason I don't want her here now," I told him that evening. "Everything we do, she's off and telling it to that fortuneteller guy." And then for no reason, or no reason that I understood at the time, I added, "I think she talks to Rebecca's picture about us too."

"Oh my," was all he replied at first, then he added bit about Abelardo being his mother's form of entertainment, but I knew that was a lie.

"You think your mother's so great, but she's the one who's got that crazy man predicting Charlie will end up like Rebecca's baby. Some entertainment that is."

From the look that crossed his face I could tell he didn't understand why I was edgy, why my voice was tight and measured. He was, I suppose now, doing what he had always watched his father do, and was treating me *doméstica*. I should worry my pretty little head with *cosas domésticas* and be glad when his mother helped me out.

"I'm not criticizing you, Julie," were his words, but I heard a condescension lace through his voice.

And with that he moved towards me to smooth my hair as though I were a winsome child who just needed calming down. He had the smile on his face that meant *you're pretty, you're beautiful, let's dance.* I knew that all it would take was the slightest move. If I'd moved even an inch, his leg would have been up against mine and our little shouting match would have ended right then.

"You don't get it." I shook my head as I stood up, pulling Charlie around so I could carry him outside. "Charlie's sick because the penicillin didn't work, not because the floors are drafty or your mother's kook friend says so."

For the first time, as I remember it anyway, I was actually talking back to Carlos, but I was doing it with my back to him and was out the door before I went on. "That's the whole problem with Chile. You people don't know how to make things work." The words *you people* rung in the air as I swung a hand free to slam the door. I went out onto the patio.

"You give shots and they don't work. Now you have communism and that won't work either." Then, with my voice straining in order for Carlos to still hear me, I added, "And maybe I'm not as cute as you think I am."

Charlie, who had been nearly asleep when I started in with Carlos, was awake by now and beginning to cry. I held him with his good cheek against my chest and swayed back and forth in the fading sunlight. As I looked to the side, I saw that we made one shadow against the garden wall, one slowly swaying shadow.

Eric didn't believe the problem was the penicillin, but I did. I hadn't even told Carlos about the next day's appointment. There I was, hugging on to my sick little boy with his swollen face in the November springtime. We just rocked back and forth and caused the undulations of our shadow. I remembered the feel of my grandmother rocking me when I was little girl and my mind went to a story she once told me.

Grandmother had grown up in Kansas City and was full of stories about the pioneer days and the people who had set out from Independence, Missouri on their way west. "It was, it was the last," she'd say, "Independence was the last stop in the civilized world. Once you left there anything, anything at all could happen."

She knew stories about Indians and men who killed each other over land rights, over cattle. She told me about a pioneer woman in Kansas who left her wagon train to go and find a tree. The pioneers were out on a trail that ran through the tall Kansas grasses of the prairie. There had been no trees since they'd left Independence. The men and the other women searched for the runaway woman for days. Grandmother said they finally found her where the flat prairie dipped down to a river. She stood alone with her arms wrapped around a tree, crying. Later they made her mayor of the new town because she was the one who had found the river. I always loved that story when I was a little girl. The woman who ran away sounded brave, strong. I never did ask what would have happened to her if she hadn't found the tree. In my mind the pioneer woman was forever there in her long skirt blown by the prairie wind and with the tips of her fingers touching as her whole body pushed up against the tree. I heard that story so many times when I was growing up I knew it by heart.

I'd ask Grandmother why she hadn't been a pioneer, why she hadn't gone out to Kansas, and she'd laugh and say, *oh no,* giving me a squeeze, "I like lemon meringue pies and to have my hair done at my shop on the Plaza every Friday noon."

It was a telltale answer because the whole family knew she could have been a sort of pioneer. She married at nineteen to a fair-haired banker who worked with men in the cattle business. In 1910 her young husband was offered a job in Argentina and he said yes to the offer. He rushed home that very night to show his young wife the ship tickets and tell her to quick learn Spanish. The story goes that my Grandmother took one long look at those tickets, told the maid to bring in set-ups for whiskey, and then sat right down on her young husband's lap. She evidently wiggled her fanny and whispered, *Jeremiah, you don't really want to go to Argentina, only pioneers go down there. We don't want to be pioneers, do we?*

As much as I adored my grandmother, I always felt torn between her and the woman with her tree. That night so long ago, with Charlie so sick, I thought maybe I should have sat on Carlos's lap when he'd first talked about coming down to Chile. I could have wiggled my fanny and then maybe none of this would have ever happened. Maybe, just maybe, Allende wouldn't be president and baby Charlie wouldn't be hot with fever.

Turning to go back in the house, I heard the river and scanned the trees on display there by the riverbank. They were all tall, thin eucalyptus trees. I figured most of them weren't much bigger around than Charlie. Not one of them was as big as the tree the runaway pioneer woman found. They did not seem big enough to hold on to. As I rocked from one foot to the other, I realized baby Charlie was asleep again. Gazing down at his little boy face I saw that he winced in that sleep every time his head moved even the slightest bit.

The next morning I heard the car start up the driveway while I was still dressing. It wasn't Tuesday, and I'd not told Carlos I needed the car to go to the doctor. I ran out of the house in my petticoat, shouting. Carlos didn't hear me until I was pounding on the back of the car for him to stop. Charlie's fussing hadn't kept him up during the night, so he'd forgotten the baby was sick, I imagine. He listened to me. I can't say that he didn't listen to me. It's just that he didn't do what I wanted him to do. He didn't offer to give me the car. Instead he said there were important meetings about the possible expropriation of the mines and he had to keep his focus. He pursed his lips together to blow me a kiss as he drove off.

I just stood there in my white petticoat and was startled by his indifference. It was kind of like watching my father walk out of a room after I'd been spanked or yelled at. I'd watch the creases the back of his jacket made, see the line of his shoe heels. Funny, the left shoe heel always was run down on the inside edge although I don't remember that he walked with an odd gait. He'd disappear into a world I didn't know much about. I'd tried to draw a thin line around my aloneness, my vague distrust of his allegiance and pray for them to remain cordoned off. That's just what I did as I watched Carlos drive off.

The bus ride wasn't too bad. I'd taken my blue raincoat, even though it was a warm day. Charlie seemed better by the time we left the house and we got the seat right behind the driver. I made a cushion for him by carefully folding my coat into a square. Settled on it, his eyes barely reached the bottom edge of the window, but it did mean he could look out.

Eric sat across his desk from the two of us—me with baby Charlie perched on my lap—and spoke every line with a stilted strain to his voice. He didn't want me to worry, which made me know to worry. Then he went on that the blood test did indicate a high level of infection. He was changing the antibiotic and, and this was the zinger, "I want you to take Carlitos down to the dentist on the third floor."

Dentista, I wasn't sure I'd understood him.

"One of the doctors yesterday felt the infection could be caused by an abscessed tooth."

"A tooth? That's crazy. That's plain crazy."

I felt disoriented more than scared, but instinctively knew I was being overpowered and had to try and defend myself.

"He only has about four teeth, little tiny teeth. You can hardly see the one in the back. "

We backed and forthed. It was clear Eric wanted the back left tooth pulled.

"There's no root, Julie. It's only a baby tooth, only one."

He said it as though that one tooth was less important because it was new, didn't have a root.

My eyes strayed around the room. Books lined up on a shelf. A plant with its small, dry leaves sat close to the window. Too close, I thought, that's why the leaves are burned.

Then he said it, "Julie, you can call Carlos if you like," motioning to his left a bit, "Here, use my phone."

"What? What?" It wasn't that I didn't understand him. Oddly enough, I understood him perfectly. "Call Carlos? And do what? Get his *permission* or? He didn't even let me take the car this morning!"

Apparently not listening to me, Eric asked again if I wanted to call Carlos- maybe have him meet me at the dentist.

"He took the car!" I said it in English this time. "He took the *fucking* car and went to the office to try and find out when Allende is going to take over the *fucking* mines and," my voice rising to a tremble, "I'm not going to call him!"

I think it was the first time in my life I said *fuck*. I am positive it was the first time I said it twice, and to a doctor at that. Eric, of course, had no idea why I was worked up. He knew nothing about the arrogance of Tomás and his friend predicting turmoil, nothing about Dolores going around always dressed in just one color and making ambiguous references to future illness. He knew nothing about Carlos and how I was afraid to say *fuck* to him.

Eric just sat there for a minute. My euphoria at having been assertive quickly turned to awkwardness. Would Eric slap me? My father would have slapped me if I had dared to say *fuck*. Would Eric walk out of the room and say he wasn't our doctor anymore? Instead he just restated his conviction that the tooth might be the cause of the infection. I didn't have any way to argue with him. Baby Charlie, evidently feeling better, opted to walk down the corridor from Eric's office to the stairs.

There was a large window in the corridor wall looking out on the *Parque Forestal*. You could see the top of the statue to the German immigrants. It depicted stalwart men and women, bigger than life and looking like Greek gods and goddesses with their eyes staring off into the distance. For a split second it made me think of the pioneer woman of Kansas and her huge tree, except she, in my mind's picture, looked different from these German pioneers because she was alone and these pioneers were all together.

I bent way over to talk to Charlie about the dentist. He strained at my hand. I wanted him to understand why the dentist had to pull his little tooth. Ridiculous, now that I think of it, ridiculous that I thought baby Charlie could understand a word I was saying.

It was perfectly clear that the dentist in his starched white coat didn't want any advice from me. I was to please sit down across the room, or I should please leave. Mothers were the ones who made their children anxious, not what he was about to do. He knew that a shot of Novocain would be as painful as the tooth extraction, so why bother? He knew, or thought he knew, that it was best for his nurse to hold Charlie's hands rather than to have me do it. He also probably knew how much instinctive fear toddlers have of dentists. He wasn't about to be deterred from his task by the shrill gurgle of a scream Charlie let out as soon as the nurse pried his shut mouth open.

The man's back was to me, but I could clearly see the instrument he held in his right hand. The delicate thinness of the metal caught the light. Charlie flayed his feet in the air as the dentist's wrist made one, clean, sharp rotation. I realized I was standing with both my hands at my mouth to silence my own scream still silent in my throat. Blood. I thought I was going to see blood, just like in the story about Rebecca and her baby being circumcised.

There was no need for me to have pushed the dentist because he'd stepped back from Charlie just as the tooth yielded to that one insistent pull. In the second it took to close the distance between us, Charlie's howl quieted to a whimper. His arms were outstretched and wildly waving like an enraged dancer. There was no blood anywhere.

"*Señora, por favor.*" That was all the dentist finally said to me. His nurse turned and left the room.

I must have jostled him, is what I thought. I didn't mean to, but I must have actually shoved the dentist as I tried to get to baby Charlie. I could feel myself begin to flush at the embarrassment of having behaved badly here in this strange office with this unknown person pulling my little boy's tooth.

I wouldn't apologize to him though. I wouldn't say, "*Lo siento. Lo siento* that I touched you when I was supposed to be sitting down. *Lo siento* that I screamed when you hurt my baby Charlie."

What did he know anyway? I moved around the room gathering up my things, my coat. He didn't really know if pulling the tooth was going to work and make Charlie get well, or not. He didn't know about the Rebecca story and the saint dolls that got prayed to and Abelardo. Leaving that dentist office I felt proud of myself that I had let some anger sneak out from under the cord where I'd usually tried to hide it.

CHAPTER

22

___

As we came up on Christmas 1970, my life pretty much centered on Allende and baby Charlie. Every day the papers had new stories about what Allende was doing, or going to do. Carlos, even Tomás, said it was a race to see how fast he could expropriate the mines. Rumors flew around about the government already working on a constitutional amendment to do just that. There even were articles about trouble the *Banco Edwards* got into. It was clear there were to be no sacred cows. From what I figured out there was a big brouhaha about a loan that *Banco Edwards* had guaranteed to an automobile company. The story went that the bank hadn't gotten all the government approvals. This was a joke, because there were always many stamps and seals required for everything, who could get them all? It was plain to see, though, that if Allende felt he could go after the Edwards and their bank, he'd go after anybody.

Since September *el Mercurio* had been running ads in English for mining engineers interested in working in the U.S. or Europe. Everywhere we went people referred to a doctor friend or a businessman planning his getaway. Silvia's admonishments to *subir al bote* to the contrary, it looked like a lot of the talent would bail out in the scramble to make Chile socialist. What I worried about right then though was what Allende was letting into the country. Charlie was on a U.S. made antibiotic for nearly five weeks before Eric felt the infection in his face was clearly gone. After he nationalized the mines, would Allende block U.S. drug imports? Say they were a form of *imperialismo yanki,* or that they didn't have the right government approvals? Would Allende do something to hurt my baby Charlie?

Looking back on it now, I recognized the *Unidad Popular* policies weren't directed right at me, right at Julie Escala and her little family, but that's how it seemed at the time. Whenever I read a newspaper headline or overheard a conversation about expropriations or land reform, it felt like a door sliding the wrong way and hitting me. The night of Tomás's birthday when I ate the whole artichoke had been my one chance. If I had only been more bold, I would chastise myself, if I had spoken even a little more Spanish I could have spoken to Allende that night even if he had been about ready to run for president of Chile. I could have run a hand over my pretty hair and told Salvador Allende our whole lives depended on the copper mine, depended on the right medicine. I wondered, did Allende remember me? Did he remember that Tomás Escala had a *gringa* daughter-in-law who now had a little boy who got sick a lot?

Between the time Charlie got better and Christmas two things happened. I got offered a part time teaching job at *Nido de Aguilas* starting in March, and I got duped by Carmencita. The first event happened over the phone and was very straightforward. In spite of América's warnings about low pay, I thought teaching would be fun. Also, I figured I'd make enough money to buy a thing or two. The job was to start in March, just after the summer vacation. I was to teach two classes a day as well as substitute when needed. What happened with Carmencita was far more complicated and tied to my generally rising level of anxiety.

Christmas never really seemed like Christmas in Chile because it comes right at the beginning of the summer. Still in all, I longed for the holiday as a way to take my mind off my troubles. We could have another party maybe, or go to the beach for a day or two was my plan. As it worked out, Silvia called one morning to offer us free use of a little beach house in *Con-Con* that she and Pepe had rented for two weeks. They couldn't get off until after Christmas, making it ours for four days. *Gringa, you are the perfect one to keep any house-hungry peasants away,* was the joke she made. She said this rather tongue-in-cheek and then added we could even burn a couple of lights all night so folks will know people are there.

When I told Carlos about the offer I made the quip, "Oh yeah, it's always more fun to *redistribuir* someone else's income, or house, as the case may be, rather than your own."

He flashed me a big smile and said I was beginning to catch on to how things were running. Typical, he almost laughed, even the committed left-wingers wanted to keep their beach houses to themselves. I'd made the first remark, but I didn't think it was very funny because I really did weigh the possibility of people trying to take our things. That old man on the white-faced mule had climbed over our fence to steal fruit, after all.

People, a whole throng of people, I thought, could decide to occupy our house if it were left empty.

Naturally I knew better than to voice this fear around Carlos because he would say I was getting paranoid. But if we were going to house-sit Silvia's beach rental, it made perfect sense to me to tell Carmencita she'd have to stay at our house while we were away. She could housesit for three days and then I was going to give her three days off for Christmas. This plan sounded generous enough, given that most Chileans considered themselves saints if they gave the help Christmas day off. Truth be told, Dolores only let her maid leave on Christmas after breakfast was served. "After all," she'd qualify the apparent harshness of this treatment, "there are no children in the household. How much is there to do? Really?"

By this she meant that if there were children, the maid would surely work straight through until midnight. Every other year, she reminded me whenever the subject came up, she gave the maid Christmas Eve off. *La noche buena* was the real holiday after all. Given this kind of a norm for Christmas work for maids, I felt very pleased with myself when I told Carmencita our plan about the beach and about her three days off.

She'd have three days off with pay, is how I started my little oration that Wednesday night just after dinner. I swung open the kitchen door and just started talking to her. She turned from the sink, but didn't really look at me. She just stood with her eyes fixed on the floor about three feet in front of her and gently shook her head. At first she didn't say a thing. I was puzzled and repeated everything I'd just told her, but still no answer. Looking around, I spotted the calendar I kept hanging on the door and started to point to the square of December with the 19 in it, when I heard a sigh and saw that Carmencita had started to cry. *"Señora, Señora* I am so sorry, so very sorry, but I must go home for three weeks."

That was how she began. It was clear she was telling me she was going, not asking my permission. Carmencita was young and a good deal shorter than I. Those things, together with her crying, made it easy for me to slip into a maternal stance, arm around her shoulder, chin touching her head. I noticed a smudge on her forehead, just up at the hairline. It could have been a streak of jam left there as she'd pushed back her hair. She seemed young, I thought, young and she worked so hard.

Her shoulders relaxed, and before I'd had time to ask her what the matter was, she blurted out, "It's my father, *Senora,* my father has been arrested."

I say I got duped by Carmencita. Actually, to this very day I don't believe she hoodwinked me, but the rest of the family does. Before Carmencita had gone any further in her story, I already imagined her father living in privation, feverishly resorting to petty robbery and definitely in need of his comforting daughter. I have to admit, the particulars of the story she told me that night were extraordinary and quite wide of what I'd expected to hear.

"You know, *Senora, we are mapuches,"* is how she began.

Well, I knew no such thing. It never had occurred to me for one split second that Carmencita was a *mapuche* indian. The *mapuches* lived in the southern part of Chile, mostly on reservations as far as I could tell. That said, frankly it was hard to know because I felt Chileans never liked to own up to the fact that there were indians in Chile at all. They would tell you all about how noble *Caupolican*—an indian chief at the time of the Conquest—was and how the Spaniards never defeated him, but when it came to live indians; they were mute. There was a funny line you'd hear in Chile, *no llueve y no hay indios.* It literally meant: it doesn't rain and there are no indians. The joke being that while it didn't rain in the central valley in the summer at all, it sure could rain come wintertime. Anyway, that *just pretend they aren't there* approach pretty much defined the discourse on rain and indians, at least among our friends. I did of course know that the straight black hair—hair as straight as nails, people called it—and the dark round eyes of so many children were echoes of an indian ancestor. My own thinking on the topic never went much further than that. Before Carmencita said another word, my mind wandered around between rain and Indians.

"For hundreds of years we have been abused, our land stolen, our pride in tatters," is what Carmencita blurted out.

The tenor of her voice did rise a bit as she went on with her story. There was a stiltedness to her speech that made what she said sound like a recitation. At the time I didn't think much of this incongruity, I merely stared at her dark hair as she stood there in the kitchen. I just listened to her. Her people had suffered for hundreds of years, she insisted, they had their land stolen and were forced onto reservations. *Now, now they would rise up,* she began. Her head tracked slightly from left to right as though she were actually seeing before her eyes the very scene she was describing. She never looked at me, she just told me her story about what her father did and how he got in trouble.

On a very dark night or maybe a night lit by the moon, Carmencita didn't really know, her father had *risen up* against oppression. He had snuck out of his *casucha* at eleven o'clock, taken a heavy, rusted shovel and an awl from the shed and gone with a man named Carlos Melipeu to dig up fence posts. They worked with other men. They spent the whole night digging. They dug up the fence posts and they dug new fence postholes. Moving a fence is back breaking work. By dawn nearly a kilometer of the barrier fence that separated the privately owned *Fundo Rinconada* from the *mapuche reservación Catrileo* had been moved. Carlos Melipeu had the original land deed papers to prove what they had done was legal, Carmencita insisted. *Nadie ayuda a un mapuche.* When the *carabineros* came the next morning, they wouldn't even look at the deed. *My father had proof, Señora,* was her point.

Carlos walked into the kitchen as she said this last bit.

"The *Rinconada* farm had stolen that land from us. It was our land, ours to take back."

Before she could get any further with her story, Carlos interjected, "What on earth are you talking about, Carmencita?"

Carmencita did not look at Carlos, in fact she looked away.

"Your father? What do you mean, *your father?*"

"He was with Carlos Melipeu, my father was with Carlos Melipeu and now he has been arrested. That's why I have to go home for three weeks."

Carlos, instead of laughing, which would have been bad enough, then did this thing I absolutely hated. He had a creepy way of being able to roll his tongue, drawing the sides together to make it look like a sausage, and keep it all inside his mouth. The effort drew the checks in and pushed the lips forward to give his whole face a fish look. It's his way of saying, *something fishy, to me*. He turned on his heel to better face me, made the fish face, and left the room.

For the life of me I didn't get what his point was. What was fishy? This was a *tragedy*. Carmencita's father had been arrested. No telling what was happening to him. Carmencita could go home for three weeks, what else could I possibly say. I told her I'd even pay her salary in advance so she'd have money to help out at home. Christmas with her father arrested, in jail I supposed, would be dismal, frightening. She wasn't to worry about us. We'd be fine. Yes, yes, I could manage perfectly well. I assured her of all of this as I stood there not more than three feet from the kitchen sink.

Walking back through the kitchen door I could see Carlos spread out on the sofa in the living room looking like his handsome self. Newspapers covered his lap and as he glanced over at me with a wide grin crossed his face.

"*Gringuita*, little *Julita*, you swallowed that whole story? You got sucked in by every single word of it."

"What's not to believe? That poor girl, my God, of course I believe her."

"Julie, it's been in every paper in Chile that story about the fence runners down in Cautín. You think her father was actually one of those men?"

He put down his paper and I could tell he was warming up to poke fun at me. "Fat chance." Then he added, "Anyway, it all happened last August. Now they've settled it all up,"

He sounded as though he was about to start laughing. "Why would it be such a family crisis now? Except that it's Christmas, *of course.*"

My mouth must have been hanging open. It had never occurred to me that Carmencita could have delayed telling me about her father, was telling me now just to get home for Christmas.

"You think he was arrested back in August? All this time, he's been in jail?

First Carlos sort of groaned, and then he made the damn fish face again. "Did she say, *'Crime is a protest against the abnormality of the social order'?'*" Then he came right out and did laugh, "Julie, she made it all up. She's not from Cautín. Since when is Carmencita from Cautín?"

Carlos knew as well as I did that neither one of us had a clue about where Carmencita was from. We'd never asked her. Carlos had told me that. When we hired her, he advised me *we're not running the Peace Corps here.* She's just going to be the maid, don't get all involved with her personal life. That kind of thing always backfires on you, he said. I figured he was right, and never did nose around looking for personal information about Carmencita.

"Well, maybe she is from Cautín. What do you know?"

"Julie, don't you see…."

I sensed I'd triggered his passively superior stance. He motioned me to sit down next to him and then continued. "That whole story has been written up a thousand times because it's a very famous case. The *mapuches* that ran the fences did have the land deed papers. They had the original deeds from the 19th century. You know, from when the reservation was set up for Christ's sake."

I was going to get a lecture.

"She wants to go home for Christmas, see? She wants a paid vacation so she made it all up to tug at your little heartstrings. It worked."

With that, I marched right back into the kitchen. As I pushed the door, I felt my face flush with, I didn't know, anger or embarrassment. Carmencita had her back to me because she was at the sink washing the dishes. I knew that either she was lying or Carlos was wrong. I determined to find out there and then. After all, three weeks was a pretty long time to be gone, especially over Christmas. At first I pretended like I was looking for things in one of the cupboards, but really I was trying to think up a way to quiz her, to find out if her father really was in jail. Find out if he really had run fences in Cautín.

"Bueno," I began, trying to appear casual after our previous conversation marked by tears and gasping, "your father was just put in jail, just now?"

"What? Oh no, no *Señora*, I never said he was in jail. *He's been arrested."*

"Oh."

She'd answered my question without really turning to face me, so I couldn't look into her eyes. Dolores had once told me that was the way to tell whether or not a maid was being truthful. "Look them right in the eye, if they've stolen something you'll see it reflected there," she'd said. "There will be a small reflection right in the center of the pupil of the eye." Naturally I'd thought that this system of determining righteousness was ridiculous, but Carlos told me it sure had worked with him when he was a little kid "Believe me," he told me once, "she saw those two *chocolates* I swiped from *tía Asela's* dresser drawer. They were right there in my eyeball, right there for her to see."

At that moment, as crazy as it sounds, I was trying to get Carmencita to turn around so I could steal a look into her eyes, into the dark, black pupils of her indian eyes. By then I had decided she could be an indian. The *mapuches* were short, and Carmencita was short. They had dark hair and dark eyes, high cheekbones. Did the indian women in Cautín wear braids like the women in México, I wondered?

"When exactly was he arrested then?" I was trying not to be confrontational, but Carlos had made his point. I didn't want to be a sucker, after all. Carmencita didn't answer my question; she just kept on washing the dishes. I asked her again about when her father had been arrested and that time she looked up.

"He has been arrested many, many times. *Señora* you must believe me. Fernando Schultz is a thief, all of them are," she was crying again, "all of them at *La Rinconada* only steal. They only steal from us, from the *mapuche!*"

And with that, she banged the skillet down against the kitchen counter. For the life of me, I simply didn't know what to do. She clearly was, or at least seemed, very upset and I didn't want to keep a daughter away from her father if he had really been arrested.

Then, without my having said another word, Carmencita started to speak, "On a very dark night, or perhaps it was a moonlit night, I do not know, my father left his *casucha* and went with Carlos Melipeu...." She repeated word for word the same story I'd just heard only fifteen minutes before, only this time she looked me right in the eye. She stared at me as though it were a reprimand for my having doubted her in the first place.

"Oh my goodness," was all I could think of to say. I left the room thinking, "My God, Allende's revolution is going on right in my own kitchen."

Back in the living room, I told Carlos about Carmencita repeating her entire story.

He rolled his tongue up for one more fish face and said, "See. She had the whole story memorized. She probably read a story about 'Land or Death: The Revolutionary Peasant Movement strikes again.' and you, my dear, are the perfect target for her tricks."

That next Sunday when we went for lunch at Tomás's apartment Carlos joked with his parents about how gullible I was to even consider believing Carmencita and her fence runner story. It was good-natured, all this teasing, but I figured this was my chance to show the family that I wasn't just *doméstica* in what I knew.

"Laugh all you want," I called to Carlos across the table, "you don't know any more than I do about whether or not she's telling the truth."

The words twisted around a bit making my statement sound more like a dalliance than a talk about land reform and the desperate measures of poor people. That's how I usually dealt with Carlos; I flirted with him, showed him how cute I was. About most things it seemed he always knew more than I did. Chile was his country, after all. He always read the papers, and he was older. Surprisingly, my father-in-law said he was inclined to believe Carmencita's story.

He leaned into the table and held my eyes with his. "Back up, back up, Julita, tell me that part of the story again. When did all of this happen?"

Every question he asked me I beamed, I warmed with pride. He asked me if I know the exact dates, had Carmencita given any other names. I felt like he was taking me seriously; I remember as clear as day sitting there at the dining room table, hands wrapped around my napkin as they lay in my lap, and thinking Tomás was on my side. But then my hands started to tighten around the cloth napkin as I gradually realized he really wasn't siding with me as much as he was preparing to make a philosophical comment.

He said something heavy-duty like, "*Illiterate people write no history, so they create myth.*"

The fence runners were already mythic was his idea. They were the embodiment of every poor person's fantasy of taking from the rich to right the scales of justice. It gave me a chill. Looking down at my lap I saw the napkin tied in a tight knot. My image of our house, our *parcela* being snatched away was never too far from my mind. The newspaper headline would read, *Maid and family intervene property of Julie and Carlos Escala*. It could happen, I thought, things like that really could happen.

As part of the conversation, Dolores piped up that she thought Allende was being manipulated. A friend had told her Allende was going to appoint a *mapuche* as head of the Bureau of Indian Affairs. It never could have been his idea, Dolores was sure of that.

She sounded like she was defending him, defending this sworn enemy I never heard her say a pleasant thing about.

"He's been my dinner guest several times," then she qualified, "no, many times. Such a polite man, *tan bien educado*, even if he's *comunista*. He'd never dream up appointing *un mapuche* to government office. Who could want such a thing?"

I didn't exactly agree with her, but I knew what she meant. The people who lived in Prairie Village, Kansas, sure didn't want any indians getting appointed to anything.

Then Tomás added that Jacques Chonchol was talking about moving the Ministry of Agriculture to the south to better supervise and control the accelerated agrarian reform. With that remark Carlos glanced over at his mother, sure she would be fired up and she was.

"*Accelerated reform,*" Dolores spit out the words. "It's *robo*, that's all it is. *Dios mío*, 250 farms have been stolen, plain and simple. First the government lets the indians steal the land, then they are going after the mines. Just watch."

Tomás gave a broad, tolerant smile and a wink, "Dolores, you don't think anybody stole the mines? Nobody stole the farmland first?"

If Dolores and Tomás were going to have a fight about politics, I wanted to be in the other room. Realizing the impossibility of that, I unknotted my napkin and set to eating all my vegetables and looking around the room. I wondered how many other families in Chile were fighting over politics that Sunday, every Sunday.

My parents never fought over politics. They always both just pulled the Republican lever and that was that. I don't think they even cared much who was running as long as he was a Republican. They must have had other Democrat friends, but I only remember one lanky, awkward looking man who used to argue with my father. Dad would end any discussion they ever had with the phrase, "Awww, you just say that *cause your uncle was union.*" The man himself wasn't in a union; he sold insurance, but unions, unions anywhere in your family, that's what made you a Democrat. Though nobody ever said as much, I was raised to think that politics were sort of a genetic thing. You just did what your family did. The acrimony between my in-laws seemed foreign to me, but they were separated after all. I always thought that was probably why they were separated. Frankly, I think all that talk about mythic history Tomás had just come out with would have driven me crazy if I had been his wife.

Maybe, I thought to myself, you had to actually be friends with Allende to understand what he's trying to do. Maybe it was all part of the Freemason thing. My mind wandered, and the next thing I realized was that Dolores was asking me about Christmas.

With us planning to go to the beach and Carmencita going home for Christmas and *whatever all else,* as she put it, Dolores suggested that either she or Asela and their maid ought to come out and stay at the house. It was never a good idea to leave a house alone, she said. I knew there was nothing I could do to stop her and Asela from coming over and spending their days ironing all of Carlos's and Charlie's clothes. They both thought it a great neglect that I didn't have the underwear and the socks ironed, and they never missed a chance to get the job done. Oh well, I'd be at the beach and Carmencita would be wherever she would be, what did I care?

CHAPTER

23

We spent a full four days in Con-Con and it was glorious. Con-Con is a little town north up the coast a bit from Viña del Mar. There's one road that hovers along the water's edge and you drive from one town to another. I never could tell which town I was in, but Carlos could. He saw them as all as different. One was where cousins lived, one was where he went to his first wild party. To me they all looked about the same with their fill of summer cottages and seafood restaurants perched on huge boulders that look out over the Pacific. I grew up in a land-locked space, so the ocean always amazed me with its unfailing movement.

The house we'd gotten from Silvia and Pepe seemed like a child's magnificent fantasy dollhouse. It was a one-story white cottage with a bright red door that was huge, going up to within two feet of the roofline. On either side there were narrow windows with wooden shutters that could be drawn shut and bolted. Inside, except for the kitchen and bathroom, there was one space divided by an arrangement of painted screens. There were three, maybe four of these screens and you obviously used them to partition off sleeping areas.

Since there were only the three of us and the room was small in any event, I decided to prop the screens up against the wall and consider the little house like an efficiency apartment. Once we'd moved the screens, Carlos was the one to remark that he thought they were meant to be seen together, that they formed one picture. Frankly I hadn't noticed because I'd been intent on getting them out of the way. He first scrutinized them up close, and then, kind of squinting his eyes, looked at the group of them from across the room. The one to the far right he put in the center.

All in all he rearranged them a couple of times and then said, "See, see that. It's a map of the coast, only going along horizontally. You've got, let's see, *Algarrobo, San Ant*onio over there, *Santo Domingo, Viña*," he called Charlie over, "see here, Carlitos, here's *Con-Con*. Here we are."

The map went all the way up to *Zapallar*. The more you looked at it, the more you discovered its magic. I couldn't tell if it was oil paint -or what- on the wood panels, but the colors were shimmery and vibrant the way a butterfly's wings can be. The painting, done in a sort of cartoon style, had a vigor, a bounce about it. All the names of towns were written in swirly black calligraphy. There even were street names spelled out. With the screens stretched out, the panels lined up together must have covered twenty feet of wall space, nearly the width of the house. There was so much to look at. It almost made you think you could hear the pictures too. You saw little pirate ships tossed by waves and knew that the pirate captains would be shouting, *ship ahoy* or threats to the crew. Furious monster fish were breaking the water's surface. Off the coast from Algarrobo were fishing boats and nets being thrown out over the water by tiny little men no bigger than apple seeds.

I had been to a good many of the towns. The winter before Charlie was born Carlos and I went to Valparaiso for two days. We shopped in the big open-air market and raced up and down the precarious steps of cliff-hanging neighborhoods. South of Valparaiso I found *Isla Negra* on the map and said, "We've never been there. Look how dinky it is. Janet's gone, remember? They went to Neruda's house."

Carlos was with Charlie down at the Zapallar end of the panels. I couldn't tell if he'd heard me or not.

"Neruda's house, have you ever seen it? It's not here. With all this other stuff, you'd think they'd have painted in Neruda's house."

"They'd have had to paint his house in Valparaiso too," was the answer I got, "he has a house there and another one in Santiago. Not bad *para un poeta comunista*."

"You're kidding, three houses?"

"Ask Janet. I heard he has three sets of sterling silver flatware too. He's got stuff from all over, even a first edition *don Quijote*."

"God, they could have painted all those forks, all those tiny, tiny knives, floating here, here by Isla Negra."

We both laughed.

Since we'd arrived at the house by late morning, we decided to leave all our stuff in the bags and get down to the beach before Charlie would need lunch or a nap. Once he had his sunglasses on his head and a towel over his shoulder, Carlos turned around to look at the screens again.

"These are phenomenal, bizarre, but phenomenal. I wonder who painted them."

I told him I'd ask Silvia. She and Pepe must know, it was their summerhouse after all.

Charlie loved the beach. He loved the sand. We had bought him a little red plastic bucket and he had a wooden kitchen spoon. He was in heaven. I just didn't want any sand to get in his mouth. He'd been so well since the tooth thing, but I was always on the lookout. The three of us ate raisins and drank soda. Carlos always laughed at raisins as a snack, but I knew they were perfect. I learned it in Kansas City, I'd tell him. *They aren't sticky, they don't make crumbs. They are good for you. What's bad?* Well, what was bad was that they weren't a treat. Every time I'd produced raisins as a snack, Carlos would drop his voice to a funny kind of a stage whisper and tell Charlie that every *chilenito* knew that a snack should be a treat like a cookie or ice cream.

"*Hijo*," he'd say, "Who do you vote for? Kansas City and raisins or Chile and treats?" His cinnamon eyes would lock on to those of his son.

Charlie loved to be part of a game and would laugh and wiggle. That whole late morning, early afternoon, the three of us giggled about our private jokes and played in the sand. It was such a happy time, the three of us with our bodies pressed into the warm sand and just thinking about the length of a leg or the sharp cold of the water. Carlos used a bucket of that cold seawater to make wet balls out of the sand and rubbed them up against my back so I wouldn't get burned as I lay in the sun. Feeling the scratches of sand on my back, I thought about writing my parents a long letter and in this letter everything I would tell them would be the truth. I'd write all about the cute, funny little house we were in and the sun. There'd be a long list with the names of the beach towns. And this was December; in December in Kansas City all a blue sky could do was reflect the cold.

It was after two before we went for lunch in a kind of dive of a place. At first I thought we were walking up the wrong street, but then I saw the sign and realized it was someone's living room and front porch that had been turned into a restaurant. The day's menu was written out on a piece of cardboard and stuck in the window: chicken or sea bass, rice or mashed potatoes, tomato salad and stewed apples. It was just what your average Chilean would eat at home. Chilean restaurant food always seemed unadventurous to me.

As we walked in, Carlos saw someone he knew already at one of the three or four tables. The guy motioned us over and the three of us sat and drank beer while baby Charlie fell asleep on my lap. It was great. We talked about the weather, the coldness of the seawater, girls they both had chased in earlier years. Once we were ready to leave, Carlos gave the guy a big hug and said, oh yes, he'd write, and take care, *and don't forget us all here on the bottom of the world.* I was confused.

"What was that all about? What did I miss?"

"Oh, they're leaving. He and Maricruz leave the day after New Year's for Canada."

Carlos didn't look at me. He carried Charlie and eyed the ground ahead as we walked back to the water. He went on that his friend had gotten into a Canadian university to study economics and his wife was a dentist, so they were all set. The wife was home right now trying to sell the car to finance the trip. Carlos thought they both were cowards.

"Nothing has happened to them, not one single thing, and there they go running off like scared jackrabbits." He shifted Charlie from one arm to another. "Not even willing to give it a chance. They won't even give the change a chance."

Carlos was about to say something else, but I moved up closer to him as a way to cut him off because I wasn't sure I wanted to give the change a chance either. In late 1970 I felt as though Salvador Allende himself were knocking at everybody's front door, saying, *Let me in, let me in, or I'll blow your house down.*

Charlie woke up just as we got back to the beach. I put a big hat on his head to keep the sun off his face and fed him a cheese sandwich and a bunch of grapes. What I remember the most about the rest of that trip is the time we spent looking at the panels on the screens in the little beach house. We must have spent hours every evening talking about the towns, how they were all different one from another. They didn't seem so different to me, but they were to Carlos. He told me stories about when he'd gone to which one with his father, or with his mother. He and his father used to drive down the coast from Viña to Algarrobo to buy fish because it was fresher there. You could go right out on the dock and argue with the fishermen over the price then have them scale and gut the fish just the way you wanted. He said his father used to buy fish this way and then take the fish wrapped in a newspaper to a good restaurant in Viña and tell the waiter how he wanted it prepared.

"Just charge me full price," he'd say, *just make sure this fish, this very fish, is on my plate* I won't eat some day-old dead fish." As a boy, Carlos told me, his father seemed larger than life to him.

"Imagine a man doing such a thing? The waiters hated him, but who cares? He'd get his very own fish, that's for sure."

I had been to Zapallar, the town at the far side of the map. A lot of Embassy people rented up there in the summer, and April and her husband invited us once for a Sunday lunch and long afternoon at the beach. It was a party late in the summer before Charlie was born, and I had waged a campaign to get the invitation.

Zapallar is one of those communities that really doesn't have a town with stores and sidewalks. The one inn seems to always be booked, so the only way to go there is to be an owner, a renter, or a guest. That's how the residents want it, no untidy tourists or shrill children to interrupt their convalescence from Santiago and the pressures of city life. Zapallar's beautiful houses and cottages built on the hills that surround a horseshoe-shaped bay have impossible gardens that plummet right down to the water. At the inner edge of the horseshoe there is a lovely beach with the only restaurant, at least the only restaurant I ever saw. When you are on that beach you feel like you have insinuated yourself into a friend's very exclusive country club. Looking at the panels and reminiscing about Zapallar gripped me with a longing for that time.

"Funny, it being less than two years ago."

My eyes were fixed on the curlicue painted black letters on the edge of the last panel propped up against the wall. The *Z* floated right in the center of the horseshoe bay.

"You know, we weren't even parents then."

"We were almost parents," Carlos walked up behind me to look over my shoulder. He put his arms around my waist. "Don't you remember throwing up in the car on the ride home? You're the only woman I know who got all her morning sickness at night."

"Yeah, but that's not the same. We didn't have all this responsibility then." I paused. "Charlie." The pronouncing of the name seemed to draw a veil across the ordinariness of that recollected day at the beach. "You know, we weren't worried about Charlie getting sick, or, or anything."

The word *anything* of course to me meant *everything.* Now I was worried about everything. I succumbed to my list of laments about Allende, expropriations, Rebecca's baby. Even Carmencita got perversely twisted up in this *everything.* Carlos was part of *the everything* too. I kept remembering being in the back of the *camioneta,* the look on Carlos's face when he'd talked to María de los Angeles Pérez. He'd been sneaking around up there at the mine with her. What was that about? What had he heard from her? Who did he tell?

"Oh come on," he said. And then to cajole me out of my funk, added, "Chile was no fun before Allende. Really, we were boring. Now," and he spun around, arms held high, "now we're the talk of the world. *The first freely elected Marxist president.* It's great!"

"You won't think it's great when you lose your job," was my retort.

As soon as the words left my mouth I knew I shouldn't have said them. Carlos's job was part of that world where he wrote *reports* and went to *meetings*. It was, now that I think about it, not much different that when my father went to the *office*. All the details were as hidden from me as if they had been clamped shut in a steel box.

"Or what if Charlie gets sick and we can't get the right medicine?" My voice strained. "What then?"

Carlos smiled and reminded me we were on vacation. Then he scratched up and down Charlie's back to get him to giggle and announced he had a game for the three of us to play. It was kind of a pin-the-tail-on-the-donkey game except we played it with the picture map of the Chilean coast. Whoever was blindfolded would walk up and move a finger over the surface of the map until a town's name was touched. The other two would shriek and call out the name and decide where the people from that town were to go *to accelerate reform*. I was the first to be *it* and caused the removal of people from San Antonio to Santo Domingo.

"Good, good," Carlos laughed, "all the poor dock workers get summer homes on the golf course."

Baby Charlie didn't get the game and just waved his hand all over the map when it was his turn.

"Oh yes," bellowed Carlos in a radio man kind of a voice, "little Carlitos has suggested a program that has even eluded brilliant government officials. Every man, woman and child in the area around Viña is to switch houses with their neighbor. This will, *damas y caballeros, accelerar reforma.*"

I thought I would pee in my pants I laughed so hard. Charlie laughed out loud with our hilarity and, for a time, I didn't realize what I'd later consider the inappropriateness of playing such a game.

After Charlie was in bed and we'd closed the shutters against the night, I looked again at all the names of those little towns frozen up against the sea. The shrieks of our game reverberated in the room. The disquieting thought of people forced to move, people inadvertently shuffled from one place to another, snapped into my brain. All of us had houses up on an embankment, I thought, just like the people in Valparaiso. One person points a finger and the houses could slip right down the hillside. Any gesture, any maneuver at all, could trigger that. By this point, by Christmas 1970, I had stopped even talking to Carlos about this kind of fear. If I did, he accused me of being as bad as his mother. He'd call me his *pajarita* and say Allende was only in for six years, explain how the senatorial elections were coming up. Balance of power, Chile a balance of power.

These reassurances didn't calm me much. The image of Carmencita as a subversive *mapuche* drifted around on the edges of my reasonableness and, of course, there was always the Abelardo thing. Abelardo and Rebecca's dead baby came to mind every time Charlie coughed or I heard Dolores's voice on the phone or across the dining room table. It's not to say that I thought about all this stuff all the time, I didn't. It is just that together these things seemed to form a slack noose bobbing just above my head.

All in all though, the four days in Con-Con truly were wonderful. We all got suntanned. We ate a lot. We slept a lot. It's just what you are supposed to do at the beach. Driving home we left the cliffs over the sea and the flat of farmland. We went up the one side of the coastal mountains and out the windshield of our blue car could see in the distance the backdrop of the high Andes. In central Chile those mountains define the entire horizon with their grandeur. We wiggled along mountain roads for nearly two hours. Our car didn't have much pick-up, but we weren't in much of a hurry. There's something sort of dreamy about the mountains and those roads if you don't hit traffic. You drive along and could swear you're headed straight into clear sky before the road turns and saves you by hugging back to the mountain stone.

Carlos knew not to drive too fast. He knew I'd cover my eyes and start to sing "Indians are high minded/ bless my soul, they're double jointed/ they climb hills and don't mind it/ all day long" if he drove too fast. It was a song remembered from childhood, remembered from when my father drove too fast in the Rocky Mountains. It was the song my mother would have us sing when she couldn't get my father to slow down. On that drive home I didn't start to sing, not even one time. We talked about Christmas and what we'd do New Year's. Carlos made some jokes about the holidays without a maid,

"Silvia and Pepe ought to approve, don't you think? So egalitarian and all."

Him saying that just made me think about washing all the diapers myself. Our wringer washer was going to be traded up for a newer model, but in unspecified future.

"Our kitchen is in 1922, you know that. Carmencita is no luxury, not as far as I'm concerned."

I was of course secretly terrified she wouldn't come back. In my mind I constructed odd fantasies about what Carmencita might be doing. What if she stayed in the south and started working with MIR? As far as I knew at that very minute she was living in a *fundo* house that she and her father and a whole gang of *mapuches* had taken over. She might be planning her Christmas dinner, deciding which set of the former *patron's* china to use. She could be swishing around the dining room, getting out all of the pretty things that were now hers. Looking out at the mountain scenes as they shifted by made daydreaming easy. I realized I'd never asked América what she thought about Carmencita and the story. América would be the one to know, after all. Living near the plaza, she probably saw Carmencita all the time at the bakery or walking around San Enrique. América would have talked to her I bet. She would know if Carmencita were part of a sinister plan. Holding América and Carmencita in the same thought made me wonder if Carmencita were connected to the girl who sold the fur coats. That could have been why she wanted to go home. Maybe her father knew the man who made the fur coats and she was going to get a chance to sell them.

"A penny for your thoughts." Carlos put a hand on my knee.

"Oh, oh I don't know. Just think 1971, God, 1971 is coming right up."

And we drove the rest of the way home.

CHAPTER

24

América thought it was all hilarious.

"You gave your maid a three week-paid vacation? *Gringuita,* don't you know even the unions don't do that."

She laughed, held her side and laughed more. I hadn't gone down to América's house to have her snicker at me too. In an effort to not seem too much the fool I did try and defend myself by saying something lame about the money really being a Christmas bonus, not a paid vacation. I had my whole list of questions about Carmencita all rehearsed, but at the end of the day it seemed América didn't know any more about Carmencita than I did.

"Of course," and she underscored this because she thought I ought to know it, "we all are from the *south,* all of us who aren't from *barrio alto. I'm from the south, just not lately.*"

By this, I took it that she meant she hadn't been born there. Or maybe she'd been born there and moved up to Santiago as a girl. I remembered that was it. Her confirmation party, the party she never got to have because she got pregnant instead, that had been in the south. As anxious as I was, América was completely uninterested in my preoccupation about the whereabouts of my maid.

"Julita, Julita *cálmete*. She comes back, or she doesn't come back. You think she's the only *criada en todo Chile*?

More laughter.

That was easy for América to say. I was anxious. Naturally I wanted Carmencita back to work, but I was concerned about her too. What if something terrible had happened to her? Sure enough, though, two weeks after Christmas, Carmencita arrived on a Tuesday morning before breakfast. I saw her out the window as I was putting coffee on the stove. If it hadn't been for the suitcase, you would have thought she'd just come back from a usual day off. I was dying to ask her about her father, but thought better of it since I still didn't know if I believed her story or not. She fussed over Charlie a bit and then started sorting clothes for the laundry. For days I kept my eye on her, looking to see if she trailed some sort of revolutionary aura. If she had spent Christmas with left-wing radicals, she kept it as her secret. The only thing she ever told me about that Christmas was that she had learned how to knit and was going to make Charlie a scarf for the fall.

Once the holidays were over, that summer everything went back to politics. Dolores—and she called several times to tell me this—decided 1971 was going to be a tragic year because she was witness to a very bad omen.

Right after New Year's she contracted to have her apartment kitchen painted a lemon yellow with a boarder of blue flowers on the edge where the wall meets the ceiling. The two painters did admirable work, finishing in just two days, which was nothing short of a miracle. Over the phone her voice dropped. She nearly whispered the bad omen was that the three canaries that lived in an elaborate brass cage in front of the window that looked out on the *Plaza Brazil* had all died. Off the top of my head I thought the birds had died from the paint fumes. I thought the oil-based lovely yellow paint she was talking about probably had lead in it. Dolores insisted *no*, the painters had promised to move the birds into the dining room. They always painted with the windows open.

"These are very professional men Julita, very professional. The best families use them, *the best*. No," she said, "the birds died as an omen, a warning."

It was impossible to argue with her when she got her mind stuck on an idea like that. I didn't even mention the paint again, I just mumbled into my end of the phone and said *sí* I'd have Carlos call her as soon as he got home.

"You know, your mother thinks her birds died because Allende's president. She says it's a harbinger of, I don't know, the silencing of anything that sings, I suppose." I thought Carlos would sneer at this news, make his usual comment about his mother being unyielding in her suspicion of the left. Remark about how petty she could be. He didn't though. He rather seemed saddened by the news, and then he told me his mother got those birds years before, right after she and Tomás separated. Of all things, she had gotten them at a grocery store not a block from the *la Moneda* palace.

"It was years ago. There aren't any grocers near *la Moneda* now, not now. Now it's the hotel and offices."

The storeowner where Dolores got the birds was the new owner at the time, having recently purchased the shop with its contents from the estate of the man who had run it since before World War II. The first day this new owner went to open his enterprise, he'd found three canary birds in a small cage wedged up on a shelf next to sacks of sugar. They were completely silent, and at first he hadn't realized they were real. The shop had been closed for nearly a month and nobody could figure out how the three birds had stayed alive all that time. After he'd cleaned the loose feathers out from around the bags of sugar, he put the caged birds up by the cash register with a sign reading *se regalan*, to give away. Dolores must have been the first customer in the shop, or at least the first customer who wanted the birds. Carlos claimed they started to sing just as soon as his mother put their cage near the window looking out at the *Plaza Brazil.*

"They gave her hope, I think. It was very hard for her to separate from my father, Julie, and live in that apartment with Asela, very hard."

Once I'd heard the story, I felt terrible that I'd been making fun of Dolores, but how was I supposed to have known how important those birds were? I only knew snippets of what had happened in Chile before I got there.

Dolores wasn't the only person who thought 1971 was going to be a bad year. Municipal elections were coming up in April. They were to be the first test of the popularity of Allende's programs. Our friends were pretty divided in their predictions, but for sure the government was dancing as fast as it could to make lots of people happy. Big articles in the papers announced the *Unidad Popular* would build a hundred thousand houses for low-income people. Among our friends on the right rumors spread that the printing presses would run at night to accommodate all the deficit spending. A cloth factory I'd never heard of, *Bellavista Tomé*, was nationalized. Big deal, I thought. I couldn't for the life of me see why Allende, knowing the whole world was watching his every move, would fool with a firm that made *ponchos* and suit yardage. Carlos said it was the *test case*. It was the test case meant to set everything else in motion. Before the government could launch an extensive program to nationalize the textile mills, the phone Company, the copper mines, they wanted to be sure they had a legal mechanism in place for doing it. Whenever Carlos would launch into this kind of an explanation my mind would wander into dark places.

When he'd paused in all this talk about the test case, I blurted out, "Maybe I'm gonna cut my hair. What do you think? *Bangs*, maybe bangs?

Carlos was clearly dazed by my non sequitur, but with all the revolutionary everything in Chile my long hair done up on top of my head was beginning to seem passé to me. It sounds frivolous I suppose to think that there is much of a connection between revolution and fashion, but of course there is. In 1970, now 1971, a lot of women in Chile dressed about like Dolores. Not that they all wore just one color, but that super put-together look with the string of pearls was very popular. Even young women my age in their miniskirts resembled the matrons, so pressed and starched were we. Once at a dinner party a young wife went on about how she had her maid press her skirt and brush her shoes every day after lunch. I guess she wanted us all to think she was clever to manage to look neat as a pin, but I stood there listening to her and thought, "Oh my God, that's worse than Dolores, that's worse than anything I've ever heard." As it was, with all the fixation on peasants and the downtrodden—that's what you saw in the papers after all, not neat-as-a-pin miniature matrons from *barrio alto*—I decided it was time to loosen up, and that meant getting rid of some of the long hair Carlos loved. On one level it was a gesture of my willingness to accept at least part of the *change* Carlos talked so much about, but, of course, on another it was a signal of my independence.

In a funny way, what had first gotten me thinking about the hair thing wasn't my growing desire to demarcate myself a bit from the world of sick babies and slightly imperious husbands, as it was Allende politics. That Chilean fall of 1971 a French journalist named Regis Debray came to Chile to interview Allende. I had never heard of him, but evidently he was very well known and, and this was the grabber, he had just gotten out of prison in Bolivia. In the late 60's he'd actually *been* in prison with *Che Guevara.*

Well, with Regis Debray in Chile you couldn't help but think about Fidel Castro and Che Guevara, since their pictures were all over. Everywhere you looked, there was Fidel in his beard and fatigues or Che Guevara looking cool with all his long hair. No maids were ironing their clothes after lunch, that's for sure. I might have been thinking about hairdos, but Regis Debray wasn't. He had come to Chile to interview Allende, or as he put it, *to have a series of conversations.* From the bits and pieces I heard, these *conversations* were more like arguments with Debray pounding the point that socialism couldn't be established in Chile, or anywhere else for that matter, except through violence. This kind of talk was tailor-made to make people like me panic, I suppose, but since I didn't read the papers I wasn't really worried about Allende and *constitutional legality*, I was worried about my hair. I thought the whole kind of *look* Che Guevara inspired by running around with a gun and his hippie hair might make Carlos take me more seriously.

Another reason to cut my hair was the job. Even though classes didn't start until March, February was the month to get the teachers in gear. In February I started going to *Nido* for in-service teacher training and wanted to look good, make a good impression. To me the school radiated a sense of enchantment. To me it was an American place. American, as in from the States, and this had taken on great significance for me.

When I'd arrived in Chile, arrived in 1968 at twenty-one with my Chilean husband whom I hardly knew and carrying my grandmother's flat silver, I hadn't thought of myself as a pioneer. Hadn't considered that I was like those German immigrants depicted in the statue there in the *Parque Forestal*, those men and women with their chests thrust out, boldly gazing forward at lord knows what. By 1971, however, that was just exactly how I felt. By 1971 when I thought about pioneers, I saw that behind the gallant gazes they were tired and wondering why they'd left their homes in the first place.

Purposely I never had joined the American Women's Club or gone to the English speaking church. I imagined those things were for the transients, for the diplomats, not for people like me. I had come to Chile to stay. As things worked out, though, Allende—and Allende everything else that was about to happen—baffled my innocent sense that one could hook into a new country and make it your own just because you wanted to. By the first day I strode up the hill to *Nido* from the bus stop, I was ready to get my feet on a little piece of territory that was officially American, even if it was only the American school.

Carlos kissed me and wished me luck that morning. Poor baby Charlie cried and cried. He never liked me leaving him and must have sensed the excitement as I scrambled around the hall looking for a scarf, the keys. After all the warm months of summer, I'd even gotten out my blue raincoat again. With the morning chill it was time, I thought, time to start taking a coat around with me again. It probably had been seeing me in the blue raincoat that made Charlie cry. Intuitively, I guess, he knew he was being left out, and he didn't like it one bit. From the door to the car I could hear him wail, and I resisted turning around to avoid possibly seeing his little crying face in the doorway. With my hair cut short, my denim skirt and my blue raincoat I was on my way to *Nido de Aguilas*.

Nido wasn't a totally *gringo* place. Nearly half the students were Chilean and so was a lot of the staff. This produced an often kooky dichotomy as far as school policies were concerned. U.S. parents wanted a seamless transition for little Johnny once the family moved back to the States, and the Chilean *papás* wanted their kiddies well prepared to get into *la Universidad Católica*. From the get-go I knew to stay out of the fray.

Since I'd come up with the idea of working there, I'd clutched at Janet's notion that *Nido* was a place where I might *hear things*. Janet had been exactly right. My second day attending a workshop all about how education is pitched to white, middle-class, obedient females—and that as teachers we needed to change all of that—I met my source for hearing things. Her name was Barbara Berrellez. Since she pronounced the two "L's in Berrellez with an *L* sound, not a *Y* sound the way you do in Spanish, I just presumed her husband was from the States. The minute I met her in the breezeway that ran in front of the lower school classrooms, I knew she was divine. Tall, thin, erect, she had a huge head full of bright red curls held just back from her face with a skinny little headband. Her voice grabbed your attention with its arresting clarity. She looked at you with that voice. It wasn't until we were all settled in our seats in the cafeteria that I realized Barbara was the instructor, the leader of the workshop. She'd studied education at the University of California at Berkeley and had been in Chile since 1960. She lived in *el Arrayán*, she said, and you could identify her house because it was the only one with a sidewalk running in front of it. She said *any* of us could visit her *any* time for more information on her teaching techniques.

"I'm easy to find. I have the only house in Chile that looks like it's straight out of California."

I couldn't believe I'd never met her before, seeing how we lived in the same neighborhood, and I was sure I'd never seen her house with its sidewalk. Within a week I took her up on her offer to go pay a house call. I didn't bother to call her before I dropped by because in Chile in those days lots of people didn't have telephones. If a friend said you could just drop by, you did.

Driving up to her house, I was startled. She lived just across the ravine from us, up on the other side of *el Arrayán,* and to my amazement the house did look straight out of California.

Not that I'd ever been to California, I hadn't, but the house looked how I envisioned California. There was the sidewalk she'd mentioned, but more amazingly there was no fence. It was just a big, beautiful stucco house with sash windows, a TV antenna and no fence. In Chile, as a rule, the fancier the house the bigger the fence. It was only *callampa* houses or government-issue projects that had no fences at all. Even the most modest homes would have rows of bushes or a jerry-rigged wicker contraption to block the view from the street. Here was this imposing looking structure sitting right square in the middle of its green grass and nothing to block the view. The house loomed as bold as Barbara herself.

Her maid let me in. Barbara didn't get up as I walked into the living room. She just patted the sofa seat beside her as an indication for me to sit down.

"*New teacher*, you're a new teacher. Great! Sit down, you sit right down and tell me all about yourself."

It was like being interviewed. The maid brought us coffee and chocolate chip cookies that I swear were made with Nestlé chocolate chips straight out of their bright yellow bag. I started off talking all about teaching and how nervous I was to actually start teaching a class. What if the students wouldn't listen to me? Barbara nodded, then got up and reached over to a bookshelf. "You're going to read these," she said. She thrust two books at me, both with long titles about elementary education. "Actually, just bother reading the parts I've underlined in magic marker. The rest is *garbage*, not real garbage, sweetie, just verbose redundancy you don't need." With that pronouncement, she sat back down. "Well, now that we have your little job out of the way, tell me about you. Babies? Husband? Lovers?"

Her voice permeated the entire room. It materialized from the sofa I sat on as much as from her. I felt like such a kid sitting there giving her the fifteen-minute version of my life story. She thought it was a hoot, my being from Kansas City.

"Wow wee baby, you are a long way from home. A far piece from all those stern faced mid-western Protestants. I bet you write them long, *nice-nice* letters all the time"

She said this with what she must have thought of as her cowboy voice. I didn't think it was very funny. Then she sidled up closer to me where we sat, stretched an arm across the back of the sofa and opened the door of every fear I'd ever had about Chile.

"Here you are with you *marido chileno,* a cute little *chilenito,* and you're scared shitless because the *commies* have taken over the government. Right? I'm right, right?" She didn't give me a chance to answer, didn't expect me to. "Oh yeah, Allende has ruined our party here, that's for sure."

She was on her feet now and I thought she seemed kind of like Silvia and half thought she was going to switch into Spanish. "It could have been worse, though, you can tell your *chileno* husband that. We're damn lucky it was Allende and not a Fidel. I'll tell you, all the fat cats oughta count their lucky stars it's Allende."

She didn't know that my *chileno* husband wasn't such a fat cat and that he liked Allende just fine. Barbara went on and on about all of us expatriates acting like it was our country and not theirs. *Blood in the streets*, that is what she kept saying. Blood in the streets, and did I know who wanted blood in the streets? The Americans, that's who. All that go-go on Wall Street and the businessmen had their pockets lined with money. Those guys were telling the CIA *the business of America is business and don't you forget it.* They didn't appreciate Allende messing things up for them at all. The owners of *Chiltelco*, the Chilean Telephone Company, waved money right at the White House, that's what she said.

"Julie," she told me, "there are dozens of Americans right here, right now, trying to destabilize this government."

When I asked her how she knew all this, she just smirked and said she had sat on the edge of a bed at the *Hotel Carrera* and listened. The bed was in a room where the curtains were drawn shut in the middle of the day. She went into a lot of details I didn't exactly follow about bonds and the copper companies, and then rattled on about the U.S. government having to protect the businessmen. She hinted that these men, the men she'd heard talking in the darkened room, would stop at nothing. I guessed she'd been there at the hotel perched on the bed listening to expatriates plotting all things sinister. Maybe, I thought, it had been her husband. For all I knew she could have been CIA and one of the expatriate plotters herself. I didn't even really know this woman. I'd only gone to her house because she lived in our neighborhood and I'd met her at school. I'd just gone to her house to have a little social life, not hear this kind of stuff.

Funny, I didn't think of myself as an expatriate exactly, even though I certainly wasn't living in the States. As quickly as Barbara had launched into this tirade about corrupt businessmen and how we could be hearing From *the Halls of Montezuma* sung in front of *la Moneda* palace, she spun the conversation back to personal matters. I couldn't believe my ears. Bold as brass she just started asking me about my sex life with Carlos. Was he as good as *latino* lovers are supposed to be? That kind of thing. And was he bossy in bed?

"These *latino* men really do just think they're in *control total*. In the boardroom, in the bedroom, it's all the same to them. They learn it from their fathers, all that *la mujer es para servir* crap" She'd never even met Carlos, never laid eyes on him and she was saying all of this. "Don't you let him be the *centro de mesa* all the time, sweet thing."

By the time I left her house I was sorry I'd ever gone. It was my business if I thought Carlos tried to be the *centro de mesa* too much of the time, and I didn't appreciate some stranger opining about it. If I'd had any guts, I would have told her, *Well, it takes* one *to know one,* but I didn't. Furthermore, I hated being called *sweet thing.*

As far as all her talk about destabilizing the Allende government and secret bank accounts, I figured she was showing off, exaggerating. I might have been tempted to believe Carmencita's story about her father, but I wasn't about ready to swallow this spy movie talk from a woman I hardly knew. She was a teacher, a seminar giver. I decided she was a kook.

That night I brought up the whole story the minute Carlos walked in the door. In a funny way I figured this was a chance for me to shine, to be the *centro de mesa* myself, and I didn't want to miss it.

"Don't you think she's a weirdo? My God, Carlos, it doesn't square with anything we're hearing. She makes it all sound like the Japanese marching into Singapore."

Once I'd said that, I realized it didn't make much sense except that maybe the *gringos* were like the English and the Japanese were the communists being led by Allende.

"Why would *Chiltelco* even care about Allende? They ought to get people some telephones, that's what they ought to do," I said.

Surprisingly, Carlos said he thought maybe Barbara did know something after all. Rumor had it IT&T threw money around in an attempt to block Allende's election and then his inauguration. He'd heard an ex-CIA guy who was on the IT&T board of directors had probably been dumb enough to think that throwing an election in Chile was like fixing a traffic ticket in Mexico. Once I heard him say that, I thought to myself, that's how it is down here in Chile. U.S. businessmen are playing cops and robbers to keep Allende away from their money pile. And meanwhile people like my own husband are playing footsie with the unions.

Once I'd been at *Nido* for a handful of meetings, I realized Barbara didn't just talk to me about conspiracies all the time. She talked to anyone who would listen. She could have made a movie about the Schneider murder she knew so much about it. And she wasn't the only one. A blond woman who taught fourth grade told me and another new teacher that she'd heard Gillette was *doing things* to *get Allende*, whatever that meant. She didn't specify what, except to say that they weren't going to roll over and empty out their pockets to a bunch of thirty-year-olds who were growing beards in order to look like Fidel. She leaned across the cafeteria lunch table to tell me this. With her head practically in my soup and sliced carrots, I felt my stomach quite literally twist around itself.

The school was up on a hill above the town of *lo Barnechea,* a country town like *San Enrique* only larger. Since most days I came to school by bus, walked up from the bus stop in the morning and down to it in the afternoon, I was well aware of just how high up on a hill the school sat. From that hill you could look down and out across the valley towards Santiago. In the spring and summer the weather was clear enough to see bits of the city off in the distance, but as winter came smoke from heating furnaces combined with factory fumes and car exhaust to blanket the city. To me it looked like the smoke from distant fires. Seeing it made me worry about fires nearer to home, about disruptions, although I knew the smog I was seeing had nothing to do with that kind of thing.

The smoke and smog made me remember the time the Missouri River had flooded in Kansas City. Smog can be like water in a way; it drifts up and then can submerge a city. When I was a kid the Missouri River flooded the stockyards and all of the low-lying sections of Kansas City. Cattle had been shipped up from Texas by train and were being held in pens before being slaughtered when the waters came. We all went to see it. My parents and sister and I stood on a bluff some distance from the flooded flatland. We stared down and out over to where cattle stood on boxcars. What's going to happen to those cattle, I wanted to know. My father said, "They're going to have to shoot them."

He'd spoken to my mother, not to me, or my sister. *Shoot them? Why?* At the time I hadn't understood. I just carried away the image of the helpless cattle poised above the dirty floodwaters; their feet invisible under the water as they stood on the boxcars. Once I'd remembered about those cattle, I couldn't stop thinking about them. In the early afternoons, with maybe a book or two to carry, I'd walk down to the bus stop, see the smog, and think about those cattle. It made me feel lonely and sorry for myself.

Just about the time classes started that March I started going to *Nido* five days a week to teach my one class. It was around then that the heat turned up about the expropriation of the copper mines. The talk was about how it would be done and how much, if anything, would be paid to Anaconda, Kennecott and the others. The companies had made *excess profits* in Chile, that's what Allende said. The deal was that the *yankis* could make money in Chile, make a profit on their investments, just not a huge profit. *Excess* was the sin. Excess is what made the U.S. companies into villains.

Carlos had copies of reports showing Kennecott's *el Teniente* mine had made an *excess* profit of 410 million dollars. That was a lot of money in those days and I knew, because he actually told me he was going to do it, Carlos gave the reports to Pepe, who in turn passed them off to journalists and government officials. I figured the reports must have come from María de los Angeles Pérez.

Did she push them across the front seat of the *camioneta* while I banged on the rear window all those months before? I didn't know. There was a lot I didn't know about Carlos, about what he did when he was away from our house with its living room hung out over the river.

In 1971 not everybody in *lo Barnechea* thought the new government was so bad. I first heard from América that there was new government housing scheduled to be built right alongside the road that ran from the main street of *lo Barnechea* up to *Nido*. She had a friend on the waiting list for this new housing. She was a woman with a flock of children who lived in one of the *casuchas* you saw down by the river. América's told me the ground breaking on the government houses was to be any day.

"You *gringos* are gonna get to look right into her windows." Peels of laughter. "Imagine that. Gloria Sánchez in a fine brick house right smack on the road going up to *la escuela yanki.*"

America found this side-splittingly funny. She told all of her neighbors that her *gringuita* friend, her *gringuita* customer, worked at the *gringuito* school and how Gloria Sánchez with all of her kids was going to move onto the school playground. *Ha, Ha, Ha.* There was nothing the school could do about it, having a government project built practically in its front yard, but it did make people talk. One teacher even told me that several families were going to take their children out of *Nido* because of the project, but I never knew if that happened.

If my new friends at *Nido* were distraught about the government building project, but it made Silvia and Pepe's faces light up when I told them about it. They had come by to pick us up one night to go to the movies. Just as the four of us were getting into the car, kind of out of the blue I mentioned about the houses going up by school and what a big to-do it all was. I was pulling my skirt up under me to better slide into the car when I blurted this out. It was a transparent effort to make myself sound important. I was reporting my bit of info to them, our most left-wing friends. This was my chance to seem cool, my chance to counter my reputation as a *nervous Nelly*—and a not very well informed one at that. There hadn't been many times during my years in Chile when I had actually been the one to start a conversation like this. There was an excitement to it.

As I settled into the front seat of the car, I was already thinking about how I could wedge the Barbara story about secret meetings into the evening chatter. Carlos hadn't paid me much attention when I'd brought it up with him, but I figured Pepe and Silvia would. Before I got as far as Barbara and her theories, Carlos tried to hush me up on the *Nido* story. He evidently didn't think my tale of American diplomats having to drive their children by government housing was terribly interesting. Pepe, on the other hand, was engrossed. He wanted to know all about it. Had the school tried to stop the development? Did people see it as positive? See it as a kind of a counter to all the scare stories about land takeovers and expropriations?

"This is the promise, Julita," Pepe began, "This is how the government will build community."

That was the kind of platitude he loved using, *build community*. He sounded like a priest. Before the conversation could get much further, Carlos jumped in to cut us off, or rather to cut me off, and launch into some boring stuff about the April elections. The memory of the poor cows with their hidden feet standing on the boxcars spiraled around me again.

Is that what was going to happen to us? My hands, now in the pockets of my coat, reached down to finger the seams the pockets made against the coat. There was nothing there to find, but I kept fingering the inside of my coat pockets until we were inside of the movie theater and I took the blue raincoat off. That night at the movies was like a lot of nights we spent. Nothing really terrible was wrong. It was just that I didn't know quite what was going on in Chile or with Carlos. I crossed and re-crossed my legs there in the movie theater and thought about Charlie as the Argentinean film flickered on the screen.

CHAPTER

25

That fall of 1971 baby Charlie seemed blissfully well. He babbled along, sometimes in English, sometimes in Spanish. His top and bottom sharp baby teeth were all lined up in his mouth. Carmencita actually knitted him the scarf she'd promised. Charlie, grinning like the cat that swallowed the canary, carried it with him everywhere. It was a long *bufanda* with seven, maybe eight bright colors worked together in alternating thin and thick bands. One end had fringe on it. Charlie wrapped it around toys and managed to poke the fringe through the knit stitches to thus secure his package so he could drag it across the room. He looked sweet, this blond headed boy with his tummy sticking out over his diaper, dragging a toy truck, or a doll wrapped in a scarf.

Every time she saw him do it, Carmencita would wail, *"No, no, eso no se hace niño.* Not like that, you must wear the scarf. I made it for you to wear it." And she'd unhook his treasures and swaddle the scarf up around his neck. Charlie loved it. It became a game.

By this time Charlie was used to my going off every morning to school, so for a time we were all in a seemingly safe enough routine. The one thing that was becoming more noticeable was the scarcities. People talked a good deal about scarcities. There'd be no butter for three days or the lack of a certain cut of meat, but I never fixated on it the way other people did. To me the meat was terrible and I liked bean dishes for dinner. You could always get beans. Food just wasn't a status symbol for me. Eating *filete* instead of *porotos* didn't give me a lift the way it did Dolores.

As *blasé* as I was trying to be about the whole thing, one particular scarcity did catch me off guard. One afternoon I politely asked Carmencita to get out the cookie sheet, I wanted to make Mexican wedding cakes. She stood right where she was in the kitchen and said, *no.* At first I thought it was *no* she didn't want to get the cookie sheet, then I realized it was *no* I couldn't make the cookies. We had no powdered sugar. Well, I told her, I'll go buy some. *"No hay, Señora."* She went on that powdered sugar had disappeared from the Chilean horizon. Then she added, "And we shouldn't waste eggs making cookies."

Ever since Christmas, for some reason I never figured out, Carmencita had become rather maternal in her dealings with me. She'd hand me a handkerchief if she heard me sneeze, tell me not to drink the tap water. It was sweet, I thought. Maybe her family troubles had grown her up, all that seeing her father in jail, or whatever it was that she saw.

What she counseled that afternoon, since making cookies seemed to be out of the question, was that I make *marrons glacés.* Glazed chestnuts? How on earth did this maybe *mapuche* girl from southern Chile even know about glazed chestnuts? Chestnuts were in season, she told me. They were for sale on almost every street corner in downtown. Once I was excited at the thought of making such a delicacy, Carmencita confessed that she didn't know how to actually make *marrons glacés*, just where to get the chestnuts. It became a project, an ambition, to learn how to make this confection I had actually never eaten in my life. I asked Dolores, Janet, even Silvia. I asked every person I could think of at school. I even joked to Silvia that this would be my way to resist the government's price control policies. The distribution of chestnuts was beyond government control apparently.

Not surprisingly, at the end of the day, it was América who knew how to turn pedestrian chestnuts into *marrons glacés*. "*Azucar, agua, castañas* and a whole lot of time." That was her recipe.

"Dolores tells me that you wrap them in little pieces of silver paper. How amazing." I added.

América said I could wrap them in anything I liked, but she wouldn't show me how to make them. "*Chica, estas cosas se compran.* You buy these things, you don't make them. Nobody makes them anymore."

"But you know how? You'll show me?" I had become obsessed with the subject.

"Too much time, *gringa,* even for you, even for a friend."

I begged and begged and she finally agreed to teach me how to make *marrons glacés,* but was going to charge me by the hour. She'd do it at her house. I was to bring the chestnuts, and I might as well come with a couple of friends. Anyway, she added, and with this I could see she was preparing me for the stiff price she was going to charge, it was the kind of thing where the more hands you had, the faster the work went.

Two days later, carrying a large paper sack of chestnuts, Janet, Dolores and I pulled up in front of América's house. I don't think Dolores had ever been in a little wooden house before, but she was there, neat as a pin, all dressed in navy blue, and ready to take notes. I think she planned to regale her friends with *marrons glacés* once she'd learned how to make them. Janet of course loved stuff like this and had been everywhere imaginable. América had tea going in the kitchen and set us in a row of chairs like schoolgirls. Plates were stacked up on the open shelves by the stove. There was a lone paper flower bloom in a china cup on the ledge over the sink.

I could tell América wasn't going to waste any time on pleasantries. Opening the paper sack, she started right in that first we had to boil and peel the chestnuts. She then turned to me and asked if I could please pour everyone tea. The larger kettle bubbled boiling water and the smaller one held the inky tea. It was incredible, all of this efficiency. You would have thought she gave cooking classes every day of the week. I had thought maybe she'd be nervous, having women she didn't know in her house, but there was none of that. Boiling the chestnuts took about fifteen minutes. We drank tea, Janet asked América about her *empanada* business.

"People still eat *empanadas*, it's the parties… No one is having parties, except *despedidads*."

Despedidas are farewell parties and had become very common what with all the professionals trying to leave the country.

"*El señor Presidente* is ruining my business." Saying this made América laugh.

Dolores got up and sort of nosed around, looking first around the kitchen and then through the doorway into the other room. She asked about *empanadas* too. How did América manage with the meat scarcity?

Then she inquired about the children. "And where are your children today?" Her voice was sharp, superior sounding.

God, I thought, what kind of a question is that? It's none of her God damned business where América's children are.

América stirred the chestnuts as they boiled in the large pot. The wooden spoon must have been eighteen inches long. She stirred from her shoulder, not her wrist. After completing three slow circles, she looked straight at Dolores.

"My children? Where are they? They are not here, *Señora,*" was all América answered.

With her steady eye and that answer, she exhausted Dolores's pretense. América began to ladle the hot chestnuts out onto a worn, cracked platter she held with her other hand. She was very much in charge of everything that afternoon. Before the steam had even stopped rising from the hot chestnuts, she began running her hands over them, using thumb and forefinger to pick out the smaller ones.

"Once you see what's required, you'll agree. *You were not to be glacéed,*" she spoke to her handful of leftovers, "*Pobrecitos,* too small, but not to worry. I'll puree you later and you will make it into a very nice desert indeed."

We all chuckled and waited to see what was to be next. After she had rubbed the hot chestnuts to release their skin, she pulled out a large piece of some odd kind of paper and cut it into squares. We all were put to work tying chestnuts one by one into the cloths and then securing each bundle with what América called a dipping string. The thick simple syrup—one part water to two parts sugar, boiled until it thickened—was in a wide, shallow earthenware bowl that must have been used to serve hundreds of stews and salads over the years.

"Hold the string and dip the chestnut in and out, in and out. *Very slowly*. No rushing. If you rush, the syrup will not adhere and you will have no *glacé*."

The last bit about not rushing wasn't an admonishment, it was a statement of fact. She must have witnessed people fail at this. It took over an hour, and that was with all four of us dipping up and down with both hands. When two chestnuts got close together, they stuck.

It reminded me of pulling taffy with my grandmother when I was a girl. She'd make the taffy and anybody there at her house could butter their fingers, scoop up hot taffy and stand by the door to pull and pull. You stand by the door to be in the cold. The taffy hardens as it cools. The pulling puts air in it, turns the sugary mixture from transparent to opaque. While we made the *marrons glacés*, for that hour or two, the three of us were like América's children or grandchildren. We watched everything she did. We imitated her. We drank her tea and giggled. Once the chestnuts were lined up, glistening on the platter, América told us all to try one.

"I'd rather paint them than eat them," Janet said as she stretched out her hand, "they're wondrous. Imagine. They seem covered in frost. All that boiling, all that heat and they look covered in frost."

And they did, too. There must have been forty-five of them arranged on the painted platter, each one covering a piece of a flower, a snippet of a leaf or a twig. Staring down at the plate, I hesitated, but only momentarily, not knowing if I should reach for a large chestnut or one smaller. If it had been a chocolate, I would have put the entire thing in my mouth at once. As it was, I bit off one side of the nut I'd chosen and pushed its sweet smoothness up against the roof of my mouth with my tongue. The chestnut was still vaguely warm from all of the trips in and out of the hot syrup. The grittiness of the sugar crystals rubbed on the top of my tongue. I looked up, caught Dolores's eye and smiled. Here we were, four women, three of us with *marron glacé* in our mouths. After Janet said her bit about wanting to paint the plate, América was the next one to speak.

"*Bueno, damas*, they are not cheap, those *castañas.*"

Just like that she said it. She wasn't going to wait one more minute to let us know just how much this cooking class of hers had cost us.

"Five hours of my time," and she gave a little wave of her hand across the plate of *marrons glacés*. That's what she figured it had been, five hours. She told us about how she set up the kitchen, got the chairs, the two hours with us, the cleanup. She summed up her calculation by saying, "I could have made a Sunday's worth of *empanadas* to sell in five hours."

We all fumbled around in our purses, still not knowing how much she expected from us. At the end of the day we each paid $8 in *escudos Chilenos* for the class in how to make *marrons glacés.* Did América really make $24 on a Sunday in 1971 by selling her *empanadas* door to door? I doubted it, but we were all happy enough to pay up.

CHAPTER

26

———

It started with the ice thing, at least that is how I remember it. Carlos always kidded me that I'd bring up a glass of water with ice and leave it on the bedside table overnight. I rarely drank it. I just liked knowing it was there. It reminded me of hot summer nights when I was a girl I suppose. Like other little things, it became one of our ongoing jokes. He'd bug me about it, and I'd counter with an invention about the necessity of ice by the bed.

"But why all the ice, it's not summer now," was how Carlos began that Sunday night in April.

I paused a second before I let my nightgown slip down around me. I ran my tongue along the bottom edge of my front teeth. "It's a sex thing. One of these nights I'll do the ice thing and you'll love it."

I actually reached into the glass to finger an ice cube and was ready to slip it down the back of his tee shirt as he put his arms around me. His lips were on my neck. I felt the pressure of his legs up against mine. One of my arms turned against his shoulder, my other reached up behind his back. Cold wetness ran between my fingers and down towards my wrist. Feeling the sting of the ice on the back of his neck, Carlos growled a cackle into the hair behind my ear and turned his fingers inward to tickle me.

"Ice? Ice?"

I wiggled like a small child against his tickles. I tossed my head.

"You think I want ice? He growled the way he imitated grizzly bears for Charlie.

Such a long moment it was. I fell laughing back towards the bed, Carlos grabbed my toes to lift them up. "I think you need just a little ice."

We both shrieked with glee. We whispered things to each other. It must have been a long time before either one of us heard Charlie crying. Not a cry really, more of a whimpering sound that seemed to stop momentarily almost as soon as you heard it. I was accustomed to interrupting things to go and tend to Charlie, go and see what was making him cry, but I didn't that night. I waited until afterwards.

Carlos was deep in sleep when I carried baby Charlie into our room and got back into bed with him. It made me feel abandoned. The house was still, dark. But what could I do? I sat up, my back on the headboard and started checking Charlie out by the light of the bedside lamp. I couldn't figure out what exactly was the matter with him. He didn't have a fever. He was way too old to be fussing to be fed. I looked down at Charlie in his yellow pajama suit lying right alongside my bent legs. He seemed listless and still the way he lay there. Every few minutes he'd turn his head from side to side and whimper. I ran a finger up and down his left cheek. I pressed it as hard as I dared.

"Oh God," I pleaded, "don't let it be that infection again." His face didn't feel swollen against my touch. Charlie didn't turn his head away from the touch the way he would have months before when the bones in his cheek were infected. I picked a piece of ice out of the glass and barely touched it to his forehead at the hairline.

"What's the matter, little baby? What's the matter with you?"

My question went on and on in a singsong. I rubbed the ice back and forth a bit. Charlie looked at me with his round, sad eyes and then looked away. There was no point to waking Carlos up, I decided. Just a bad night, Charlie was having a bad night. As I bent to pick him up, I slipped my hand under his back. He gave out one sharp cry. Carlos, asleep on his side with his back to the light and us, gave a shudder but didn't wake up.

Once I had Charlie back in his own bed, he slept through the rest of that night. It was another two days before I called the doctor. I usually didn't rush to call the doctor. I'd been through enough medical emergencies not to be undone by a bit of vomiting, a low-grade fever. Eric was a friend. I knew I could call to talk to him if anything seemed funny with Charlie and that is what I did.

Over the phone I told the nurse I just wanted a consultation, "He's not really sick," was how I began, "just funny. *No está en sí,*"

He'd have to call me back. Her voice had an edge to it. She'd have rather given me an appointment no doubt. I turned from the phone and stared over at Charlie. You feel so intimate, so connected to a sick child. Charlie was in his highchair with a little pillow behind his back to hold him straight, and Carmencita was failing at even getting him to eat applesauce.

"*Te hace bien, niñito, una cucharada, para mi, para mi una cucharada Carlitos.*"

She murmured on and on, but Charlie won't eat even one spoonful of applesauce. She'd gently force the baby spoon to his lips and then he'd squeeze them closed leaving applesauce to run from his lip to his chin. If you don't eat you can't get strong, that was Carmencita's worry. It was my worry too. He seemed listless, utterly lacking in energy. There was no sound ready to bulge up from his throat, no directed movement. All he did was sit there and refuse to eat a thing.

At a year and a half he didn't use a baby bottle much anymore, but that was all I could think of to do. Get out a baby bottle and fix him rice water with sugar and cinnamon. I sat near a window in the living room and held him like a nursing baby. The soft sun outside the window contradicted my feeling that Charlie and I were *dos pajaritos,* in a storm. He drank three, maybe four ounces of rice water before I heard the phone ring with Eric returning my call.

"Hard to tell, Julia. A little fever, no appetite, fussy, it could be anything. Bring him in. Do you want to bring him in?"

I'd wait until tomorrow, I finally decided. Just hearing Eric's voice calmed me down. I promised him we'd make sure Charlie got plenty of fluids. We'd call if he got worse.

By that night, by the time Carlos got home, Charlie's eyes were red. I washed his hands a couple of times because he was rubbing his eyes so much, and I made a lame joke about him having rabbit eyes. Carlos wasn't alarmed at all, at least not initially. By ten that evening Charlie's fever was up to 102. He had a dry, hacking cough and I was sorry I hadn't taken him to Eric's that afternoon.

"Shit, damn, shit. I should've just taken him, not called, just gone there." I yelled at myself, jabbing my right elbow into my side. "What was I thinking about? What on earth was I thinking about?

Carlos wasn't mad at me. How could he be mad? It's nobody's fault when a baby gets worse instead of better. Maybe he wasn't even all that sick, that's what Carlos told me, but I wasn't convinced and called my boss at *Nido* to say I had a very sick child and couldn't go to school the next day.

Charlie barely cried that whole night he was sick. Carlos was just getting up by the time I was ready to leave at seven the next morning to drive to San Juan de Dios to meet Eric. He thought I was overreacting, running off that early in the morning, but did say to call him once we got home.

In town, on *calle Huérfanos,* I kept looking up to see the hospital. I wanted to see it looming up the way it did, casting its shadow on the surrounding buildings. It wouldn't seem strange or threatening to me now, not the way it had the first time I'd gone there. Charlie was wrapped in a blanket and around that was swaddled with my blue raincoat. For all the world I must have looked like a woman carrying a giant newborn baby once I got there, because that is how I carried him. His head, nearly hidden by the blue of the coat, was in the crick of my left arm, the folds of the coat trailed down past his feet. He lay in my arms and did not make *one sound*. For a split second on my left I saw the statue of the child standing among the bushes, the child with the specter hand on its shoulder.

"I think once there was an angel behind that child." I murmured to my baby. "That angel will pray for you baby Charlie." My head was bent down next to where I knew his little boy ear was under the coat, under the blanket. "There's an angel there with his hand to protect all the children." I repeated what I'd said, not knowing if it was true.

Eric was fairly used to his private patients bringing their children to the hospital in case of emergencies. He knew the mothers were frantic and tried to counter that with his own resolute calm. Charlie looked thin and pale stretched out naked on the examination table. He turned his heard towards me as Eric went to work. Like a good doctor, Eric's fingers ran up and down every limb. He looked into the eyes, in the mouth, behind the ears. Sitting Charlie up to better thump his chest and listen to his heart, I caught an expression of distress cross his face.

"I can't be sure yet, but it looks like measles." He motioned me closer. "See there, there right behind the ears, that rash. The rash, the fever, the dry cough, it adds up to measles unless that redness is caused by something else. Could it be soap? You know, you forgot to get the soap off back there."

"Measles?" I was relieved. Just the measles, I thought, not a bone infection, not a parasite, not a weird illness.

Eric was running his hands over Charlie's chest again. "He'll get more rash here, then all over." As an afterthought he added, "His eyes look dull, don't they?"

"But measles isn't too bad. Just a childhood disease, right?" I countered. Then I reached out my arms to start dressing Charlie.

Eric was very straightforward right from the beginning and during the whole thing, everything that happened to us back then. I am still grateful to him for that. It is things he didn't do that I regret.

He said I was right, ordinarily measles isn't too bad, but this wasn't an ordinary case of the measles. First off, Charlie was very young to have measles, and secondly, he had been vaccinated against it.

I remembered that vaccination. It was the one he got the day I met América at the *policlínico*. I met América and Miguelito while I was standing in line and she had become my *testigo ocular* in Chile, my cherished friend.

Two live viruses, Eric said that's why the vaccine hadn't worked. In Chile they had started giving measles, a live virus vaccine, together with smallpox, another live virus vaccine, and evidently the end product wasn't completely effective. The fear from the past two days coiled together with anger as soon as I heard this explanation. To me it sounded as though he were making a logical excuse for why my baby was sick again.

"Didn't work? The vaccine didn't work? In Chile they give vaccines that don't work!" I glared fury and could hear my own shouting. Charlie began to cry. Eric was sorry, very sorry. The vaccine was from the States, bought from the States because Chile didn't manufacture these vaccines.

Later I found out that often drugs manufactured and then disapproved for use in the U.S. got shipped off shore. But right then I blamed the whole thing on Chile, or, more specifically, I suppose, I blamed it on *being in Chile*. At Saint Luke's in Kansas City this wouldn't have happened, was all I could think.

"He may get very sick, Julia. You need to be prepared." Eric said in a practiced, steady tone meant to calm me down.

He didn't want Charlie in the hospital even if he got worse. Contagious illnesses were better treated at home was how he felt. Anything we needed we could have at home. The mere mention of this jarred loose my memories of *practicantes* and injections of penicillin. Before Charlie was dressed Eric gave me a long list of instructions, told me what to look out for.

First, he explained, the fever would stay high. Then it might be a day or two more before the rash would spread. Most important, we were to keep Charlie in a darkened room. Sunlight, bright sunlight could hurt his eyes, so I was to keep the shutters closed against the day. He would stop by every afternoon and I wasn't to worry, is how he ended his list of instructions

"Fat chance of that," was the only thing I could think to say as I prepared to leave his office.

Walking back to the car I didn't see the standing child with the angel hand. I looked all around, stared at different groups of bushes, but didn't see it anywhere. It must be in there somewhere. It can't have disappeared, I reasoned to myself, but I couldn't find it again.

Dolores lived only five or six blocks from the hospital. If she hadn't been that close I probably never would have gone there that morning. Once I carried Charlie up the flights of stairs to her apartment, I felt a wave of fatigue settle over me. Telling her about the measles made it not seem so bad somehow.

It wasn't until Asela slunk into the room that I sensed my fear retool itself. She poked at sleeping Charlie lying on the bed and murmured on about *pobrecito,* then she turned to Dolores and, still under her breath, said, "I'll call and ask him. He'll know. He'll know about this time too."

Watching her leave the room I saw her slightly sideways gait. No one had ever told me, but I supposed there was a problem with one hip. She was headed right for the phone to call Abelardo, I was sure of it.

I called over to her, "Don't get on the phone yet please, I need to call Carlos, let him know we're all right. Just fine. Charlie is just fine, just the measles, I'll tell him that."

Those are the words I said even though I knew they were a lie. I rushed up behind her in order to beat her to the telephone. I wanted to say something insulting about her *brujo* friend, a stab about her getting in my business with a fortuneteller. I didn't. I just made my call to Carlos, heard he was out of the office, and went back to check on Charlie. He was sound asleep. As I slipped the nipple of a bottle filled with water between his lips, he suckled it as peacefully as a little baby. Gazing down at him I thought how frail he looked, how hollow-eyed. And he was so quiet. For days all I had heard from him were cries and whimpers. How could Carlos not be at the office to take my call? I kept asking myself. Why wasn't he here with me and with baby Charlie?

It was late morning as I drove home. I heard only muted traffic noises, saw only shadowy shapes along the road. "If

Charlie gets worse," my whispered fear echoed around the little car, "what am I going to do?" *Dear God, what am I going to do?*

In another day Charlie did get worse. By then he had been sick for about four days and was covered with the measles rash. Even the inside of his mouth was smeared with minute white spots surrounded by angry red blotches that I swabbed with wet cotton balls three times a day. Other than small amounts of applesauce, he didn't eat a thing. Eric came to the house and said he'd decided Charlie should be put on an intravenous drip of glucose solution and an antibiotic. He told me this as I sat straight up in a hardback chair in my living room with Charlie balanced on my left knee. As Eric spoke he had a pleasant smile on his face, as though he told young mothers this sort of thing all the time.

"His left ear is developing an abscess, which we need to head off. Anyway, you don't want him dehydrated, Julia, so I'm ordering an IV setup for *suero* and antibiotics"

He said it just like that. You would have thought he was talking about ordering a chicken at the butcher from his tone of voice. After all these years it's hard to remember, but I think it must have been the word *intravenous* that vibrated in the air for such a long moment that it was able to change everything. I knew I wasn't going to get mad and say *fuck* like I had months before, or start to run around the room in a fury. I could feel the hard seat I was on push through my flesh and up to my sit bones. The back of my ribs seemed to go through my blouse and hit the wood of that chair.

"I'm going to call my parents, my parents in Kansas City," is what I finally said to Eric, as I got up to see him to the door.

Carlos was home by late that same afternoon when a fat nurse arrived to set up the IV equipment and to stick the needle in Charlie's little-boy arm.   She silently glided around the darkened room going about the business at hand. Out in the hall I told Carlos I was going to call my parents and have them talk to doctors at St.Luke's about the measles.

"It was a bad vaccine. Eric even said so," I said, straining to sound authoritative.

Carlos tilted his head up and closed his eyes as he let out a long sigh. He took his glasses off, put them back on and stared straight at me.

"Julie, listen. You are not calling your parents." His eyes went from me to the darkened room where Charlie lay. "What on earth do they know about sick babies?" His voice trailed off as though someone had knocked the wind out of him.

"Not them," I blurted, "I have a plan, don't you see? St. Luke's, the doctors at St Luke's or the doctors at the University of Kansas Med. School," I desperately wanted to convince him that my idea made sense. "They'll know what to do."

"Eric knows what to do," he said in measured cold words, his eyes on Charlie's room. Looking back at me again, he added, "Call your folks if you want, but no talk to them about Carlitos being sick. I mean it."

Then he bent to kiss my forehead as though I were a sweet child and turned to walk into the living room and read the paper. I just stood there and then moved closer to the doorway of the darkened room that was just off the front hall of our little house by the river. It was a room not bigger than a minute, that's what my grandmother would have said, but it made sense to have Charlie there because that way everybody could see him, hear him, all the time. I looked in at the nurse. I felt as though I had fallen into a deep well where my vision was completely blocked by her fat, white arm and hand. As my eyes adjusted to the light, I could see she held the IV needle connected to its supply tube and thumped at the veins in Charlie's forearm with two fingers. This is just like when they pulled his tooth, was the first thing I thought. Then Rebecca's baby floated between me and the back of the fat nurse. I heard only one quick suck of air and the briefest cry.

"*Eso no más, eso no más, niñito.*"

Her name was Gila. She was very fat, wore a starched white uniform, and that is all she was doing to him, only that one stick with the needle.

Charlie stayed on the IV for four days and the fat nurse stayed at our house. He got better and she left. He got worse again and she came back. The day she came back, Gila set up a card table in front of Charlie's crib with all of her supplies on it. Scissors, tapes, IV tubing were lined up by size: the larger things to the left, the smaller to the right. It went on for nearly four weeks. Charlie had the measles, or complications from the measles, for all those weeks that April into May of 1971. During those weeks I called my parents on the long-distance telephone three different times. I always called in the mornings after Carlos had left for work, and each time I cried for what seemed like hours afterwards because Charlie was so sick, because Carlos would get the telephone bill and blow up, because the penicillin in Chile didn't work.

The first telephone call I lied. I said Charlie had the measles and was pretty sick, but my mother knew not to believe me.

After hearing my version of events, she started in, "You must be in a pickle, honey," after that she went on, "You haven't called me all the way from Santiago, Chile just to chat about your sick toddler." Then in her soft mommy voice she asked, "*Are you pregnant*, Julie? Is that it, honey?"

Two days later I told her everything. I was terrified and didn't know what to do. And Carlos wasn't worried at all and wouldn't even listen to me and I was *terrified. Terrified.* The words I hadn't spoken to her in over three years came out in a jumble. My mother at first didn't say a thing. For all the world I felt like I was talking to my grandmother, sitting on her lap when I was six years old after my sister pushed me down the stairs. So many words went down the telephone cord as I stood alone in my kitchen in *el Arrayán*. I could feel my grandmother's arms around my shoulders and her chin on the top of my head.

Mother admitted she didn't know a thing about the measles vaccine, but promised me she would call every pediatrician in Kansas City until she found out what the protocol was for what Charlie was going through. She wrote me letters after that phone call where she told me they all were praying for Charlie and for me.

After those first two calls, I remember Carlos still went to work most days. I quit my job at *Nido*. We decided to pay Carmencita extra so she would only take Sunday afternoons off. Inside the house we were a little family wrapped in the cocoon of sickness and struggle. The third time I called my parents was three weeks later. I started to cry as soon as I heard my mother's voice. I cried and cried until I realized she'd started telling me the story about *the doggie that crossed the river*. It was a story my grandmother made up when I was a little girl. A story I don't remember my mother every telling us when we were children. Her words were slow and steady on the long-distance phone and they forced me to stop my sobbing to listen to them.

"To get to the other side, first he put his toe in the cool water and it made him feel afraid. He didn't stop, though. He put his other little spotted foot in and then, pretty soon, he had all four feet right there in the cold water."

I knew the whole story by heart. I had heard it a thousand times. A thousand times when I had been crying or sick.

"I just called to tell you," I finally began, fighting back more tears, "Carlos won't let us come. He won't let me bring Charlie up there to see Dr. Kasabaum." I finished, drained, worn out, "He won't let me do anything."

As I said those words, in my mind's eye I saw my father's face float in front of Carlos's face, hover there, fade, and then reappear. My teeth closed in on the softness of my cheek as I saw that stern face with its set jaw, transparent against Carlos's cinnamon eyes and dark hair.

Dr. Kasabaum was at the University of Kansas Medical School. He was the doctor my mother had found out about, the specialist in drug resistant infections who thought maybe Charlie had a systemic infection. The plan had been for me to take Charlie to the University of Kansas hospital and have him stay there for three weeks while tests were run, different antibiotics tried.

"No, no, *I swear to God,* I begged him," my throat hurt and I could hardly speak. "I absolutely begged, Mother. He just says *no.* He says Eric is a fine doctor and no son of his is being dragged out of Chile to chase around looking for better doctors."

I had talked to Carlos for days about this, tried to cajole him. I had in fact been flabbergasted when he'd said he didn't want Charlie to go to the States. Weeks had gone by then. Eric came every day. Nurse Gila now lived at our house, and still Charlie wasn't better. Both of his ears were infected, his jaw was swollen again, and he only drank rice water. It made so much sense, my plan.

"Medicine is better in the States, don't you know that? Everybody in the world knows that." Carlos didn't even look at me. I think now that maybe he couldn't look at me. "We can all go. We can sell the car to pay for it. I can borrow money from my parents."

Carlos never explained himself really. I thought it must have to do with Allende being in power and the mines about to be nationalized. All I knew was Charlie wasn't going to States, no matter what. That was all Carlos would say.

"Even if your own child might die?"

It wasn't a question. I stared at the cord of veins in Carlos' neck, saw the way his right forearm tapered towards his wrist, and repeated my words. I wasn't trying to be winsome anymore. There was no smile, no toss of the head. As plainly as I could I was just telling him not to let our child hollow out and disappear.

"A big medical school like KU sees this kind of thing all the time. They have the best labs. Don't you see that? The best antibiotics."

But Carlos didn't *see that*, didn't want to hear about it, or at least that is what I thought. For a long time I stood stock still in front of him and pulled on my hair, and then I screamed. It was all such a jumble. All those faces rubbed together in my memory and all I could think was that no one ever listened to me.

Twice I called Eric to his office and once I even called him at home. I pleaded with him to convince Carlos to let me take Charlie to KU. Eric was nice, but he wouldn't help me. His voice was smooth. He said things like,

"I think Carlitos will turn the corner any day now, Julia, don't you worry. His left ear seemed better yesterday."

Wouldn't KU be better, I asked him, and he wouldn't answer the question. *These things happen* is how he'd answer.

Eric was such a pleasant man, but thinking about all of this now, I see it as a significant betrayal, what he did. He could have said *yes. Yes*, I'll talk to Carlos. *Yes*, I'll be bold like those pioneers I see from my office windows. He could have done those things, but he didn't.

Dolores helped us and, for the most part, Tomás stayed away. Dolores came over every couple of days with a basket of treats. Once it was shrimp in a spicy lemon sauce-where she got the shrimp I never knew. Asela was a different story. I never did hear what exactly Abelardo had told her, what predictions he made about Charlie, but whenever she came over her tone was hushed, her demeanor somber, she frightened me. She'd lean over Charlie's crib and whisper things at him and then say to me that Carlos had never been this sick, *never*.

"*Pasando tan mal. El niño está tan mal.*"

During the whole time Charlie was sick Asela never picked him up, or tried to get him to look at a toy. One rainy, gray afternoon she stood over his crib and said to no one in particular, "He's going to get thinner."

"Get thinner," I repeated from behind her back as I walked into the room. "What do you know? You don't do anything to help."

Passing her on the left I swung my whole body in front of hers, as a way to get her to leave the room. I got past the nurse's table and bent down to pick Charlie up. The IV was in his left arm making it tricky to gather him up without having the needle pinch him. I held baby Charlie, his hot little face up against my own, and looked down at the long, thin tube running from us to the stand, tethering us both to the drip bottle. His head felt very round and light. After some minutes of swaying back and forth, back and forth, I pulled him away from me a bit and looked into his little-boy face. My gaze ran all over: his hair, his cheeks, his throat. It was his eyes that were different. I realized I couldn't see Carlos's eyes anymore in baby Charlie. The cinnamon was gone.

"What are you doing, baby Charlie?" I murmured, my lips against the flesh of his neck. "What are doing, being this way?"

A melancholy routine developed during those days with baby Charlie sick. Seeing the mountains no longer was sufficient comfort against the apparent triumph of loss. We had a long series of gloomy, rainy days. The circle of my life was

completely proscribed by Charlie's ups and downs. I blamed
Chile for Charlie's being sick. Chile, and Abelardo, and the
picture of Rebecca with her long hair and no destiny were what
I thought about. Those three things were suspended together in
my mind that May.

Of all the visits we had from friends, the only one I really
remember clearly is the time Janet came by. She came over to
tell me about Che Guevara. Actually, she stopped by with a
stack of magazines and a jar of peanut butter, but what she
wanted to talk about was an artsy *chileno* friend of hers who was
reading a Che Guevara diary from January 1952. It was the
diary he wrote when he was twenty-three and set out on a
motorcycle to see *Latino America*. Che Guevara just up and left
Buenos Aires and then *Córdoba*. Left his beautiful girlfriend
Chichina and set off to wander and see what he could see. That's
how Janet told the story. She was fascinated with Che Guevara
and couldn't wait to get her hands on this book. She made it
sound as though her friend were reading the actual diary; had
his hands on the worn, penciled pages. It wasn't until later I
realized the diary must have been published because *Che* had
ended up being so important.

"Twenty-three. You're twenty-three, right?" I was twenty-
four by then "By '59 he was in Cuba with Fidel." She was
breathless. "God, they were babies. We're babies, ya'know. I'm
older than you, but we're still babies to go off and do things like
that. Like, change Latin America."

You would have thought Janet had memorized the book
about Che Guevara the way she recited the details. According
to the diary, he'd stayed with a German family in *San Martín de*

los Andes in February of '52 and gone fishing there. After zooming through Chile, he hit Lima and sojourned with lepers. In letters to his father he claimed the most powerful medicine against leprosy was a firm handshake. I could tell Janet had a crush on this guy.

"What vision," she said powerfully, "What hope from such a young man. *A firm handshake*, get it?"

I got it.

"I dunno, Janet," is how I began. "I bet if he had any kids he probably would just up and dump them in Cuba or Argentina or wherever his poor wife was and then dump her too." The whole story had made me mad. "Running all over on his motorcycle like a fool, checking out the slums. He wasn't making rice water for any sick babies, I can tell you that." I added. "*Revolución* my ass."

Janet didn't have any babies. She wasn't forlornly standing with her feet in cold water like the cattle from the Missouri River flood. At the Embassy she could still buy her peanut butter and cigarettes. She could afford to dream about Che Guervara with his *ojos penetrantes* looking like a movie star in his black beret with the red star.

"Look it, Janet," my voice edgy, "all this *seeds of revolution* crap isn't a picnic."

I could hear myself start to cry as my voice quivered. "My baby's very sick. Carmencita's father is in jail for christsake. Don't you see what a mess all this is?"

My mentioning Carmencita made Janet give out a little burst of laughter. By then no one believed the fence runner story but me. Janet gave me a tight hug before she left and told me not to give up, not to get discouraged. Once she'd left, I realized she had never once asked about Charlie.

CHAPTER

27

Eric kept telling me he thought Carlitos was getting a little better, and maybe he did. But then he'd get worse. Carlos did have Eric call in a consultant doctor from the University of Chile Medical School. The tall, angular, older man, whose name I don't remember, came twice. I don't know what he said or did. Charlie was very thin by this point and never out of bed unless Dolores or I stood there and held him in his tangle of tubes and wires. Carlos stopped going to work most days. Around the house we were like shadows that couldn't speak to each other. He would try to kiss me and I would turn, walk away from him, knowing his eyes were trailing after me. We both would sit in the darkened room and hope for Charlie to make a sound. In the dark we listened for the bang of his toys against the floor, the slamming of his feet in a tantrum.

Say *nite-nite*, Charlie, I'd say over and over to myself like a prayer. Say *Mamá*, say *Popi*. It was always night in that room, and after one long night I heard the silence begin to change. At first it deepened, and then slowly, very, very slowly it began to hollow out. Carlos heard it too. He grabbed a hand to his mouth and then rushed to step beside me at the crib.

"*Ay Dios,*" is all he said. The words hung in the silence a long time. Once they were gone he added, "the nurse, where's the nurse?"

He flashed out of the room, and I reached into the crib to pick up my dying baby. Over and over I whispered as I wept, *"Don't let anyone come into this room."* I must have repeated that phrase for five, maybe ten minutes. "Don't let anyone come into this room."

Carlos heard me, and he did keep Gila out in the hall. He kept Carmencita out of the room too. I slumped on the floor next to the crib with Charlie stretched out against me. I felt his check against my face. I felt his stomach, his thin legs, the feet below my waist, and I heard his silence. I ran my fingers into his ears, around his sharp little shoulders. Every place my hands could go, they went. I wanted to slip them over every fold, into every void.

The first thing I heard was the distant ring of the telephone. They are all in the kitchen, I thought to myself. They're in the kitchen and called Eric, and that's him calling back. I stood up, still holding Charlie against me and started to walk the three or four steps towards the light at the doorway. My left forearm supported Charlie against me. My left hand held the back of his neck and cradled his head. It's the way you hold a newborn. It keeps the head from flopping around.

As I crossed in front of the crib, one foot tripped on something and I stumbled. I freed my right hand to reach out and down to brace myself if I fell. Doing this, my hand brushed near, too near, the table nurse Gila had set up with all of her instruments, her gauze and tapes. The open palm of my right hand passed smoothly over a blade as sharp as a scalpel. Rather than retract my hand, jerk it back from the pain I felt, I let it continue to run over the entire length of the metal edge. One long scream pierced the supremacy of the silence in that little room.

In the brightness of the hall, I flung my right hand up palm out to shield my eyes. Blood went everywhere and ran down one side of my face. Droplets of bright red spread across the front of Carlos's blue shirt and turned dark in an instant. He tried to stop me, tried to hug the two of us, but I wouldn't let him. I saw Dolores and Carmencita. Then I saw Asela. She was back near the door to the kitchen and standing crooked because of her bad hip. Dolores pushed hair out of my face and tried to run a damp cloth over my cheek. It was then that I could see Asela was coming up behind her.

I turned with Charlie to spin away from them both and heard Asela say, "Now she'll run out into the yard."

Dolores didn't say a thing. Maybe she didn't hear her sister, but I did. I heard what she said as clear as a bell. Words screamed in my head, *Asela has it wrong. Rebecca ran into the yard when her baby was dying. My baby is already dead.* Nurse Gila grabbed repeatedly at my hand. I must stop, she told me, I must stop walking around and let her tend to the cut or else I would have a permanent scar, she said. Finally, looking down at my hand, I saw the blood running across my wrist.

"*I want a scar.*" As I said it, my crying slowed down, almost stopped. "I want a scar as long as Chile."

Then turning with Charlie, I made my way towards the front door. I moved very slowly. I was very careful not to run.

Carlos followed me out the door. He cried. I had never seen him cry before. He wanted to have more babies. We were so young, he begged me to listen to him. He put his hands on my shoulders, his lips were pursed with the pain of a kiss I wouldn't let him give me. These are things that happen in life, he said over and over. There was nothing we could have done about it. I looked right past him at the trees as I spoke.

"These things happen? They happen? What? What, *you think Charlie had no destiny?* Is that it?" Then I shifted my eyes to look right at him, right at his face. I could see the tears beginning to dry on his cheeks. I felt hard and cold and without love. "Is that why you wouldn't let me take him to KU, because he had no destiny?"

Everyone I ever knew in Chile came to our house the day Charlie died. Eric stood right beside me most of that day. His arms supported me when I called my parents to tell them what had happened. He kept saying,

"Julia, it breaks my heart to see you face such sorrow."

CHAPTER

28

Sadness held me like an invisible membrane. It held us all. Once Charlie died, Carlos knew I would go back to Kansas City. What I said was that I needed to visit my parents and think about what to do. In fact, I didn't know what I would do. I didn't have a clue. América came to see me nearly every day. She held me and let me cry. She never told me to be brave, never talked about how life was long and I'd get over this. One afternoon as we sat drinking tea in the kitchen she told me she had a buyer for her *techo, mi techo de tejas.* Within three days men were going to remove the tiles one by one from the roof of her little house and haul them away.

"A buyer for your tile roof?" I couldn't believe my ears.

She loved the roof of her little frame house. Everyone in San Enrique loved it. They were old tiles, *tejas coloniales,* or so people said. They were a worn, dusty earthen color and held enough loose dirt where one tile came together with another that occasionally you could see a sprig of grass grow up from a crack. Her daughter told me that once a buttercup had bloomed up on the roof.

"How can you sell a roof?" was the simple question I asked her. I had never heard of such a thing before. "Who buys a used roof?"

Apparently a lot of people, she told me. Old tiles were prized. They could trick the eye into seeing new stucco walls as old *adobe*. Someone planning just an ordinary new house would drive around for hours, days if need be, looking for a roof to buy. A roof to enhance, to falsify in a way, the newness of their project.

"What could I do, *Gringuita*? It was a lot of money the man offered me."

You'd think she'd sound woebegone telling me this, but she didn't. "He even paid for the zinc panels."

That's what people did when they sold their *tejas*. They replaced them with sheets of corrugated zinc. A metal roof keeps the rain out of course, but it makes a house, any house, seem cheap, thrown together. That's how América's house would look after her tile roof was gone. Not having the tile roof would make the house seem lower somehow, its walls dirtier. She'd only gotten about $95 for the roof which to me seemed pitifully little. She was happy enough with the price though. She didn't seem to blame her misfortune on anybody in particular as far as I could see. She certainly didn't see it as connected with Allende, but I did. By then I saw everything bad that happened as being caused by Allende. América just brushed the bangs off her forehead and laughed at me.

"*¿Qué?* You think Allende sent that man to buy my roof? Sent him to torment me?" She shook her head, "*Julita*, this is not a problem. My roof is not a government problem."

"I didn't mean that. It's, don't you see? It's that everything has gotten bad," my voice trailed off. "The roof was beautiful and now it's gone."

She reached her hand across the table and let it rest on the open palm of my hand for a long time. "None of these things are government problems, *chica,* not even the silence in your house." The weight of her hand pressed hard against mine. "There are no *demonios,* Julita, just the things that happen."

CHAPTER

29

On June 8th, five days before I was leaving Chile, a man named Edmundo Pérez Zujovic was assassinated. It had been eight months since the Schneider murder. That first political murder still burned mirage-like in the Chilean imagination. Dolores kept saying in October, "How can it be true? *Tan tropical, tan brutal.* René Schneider murdered *por política.*" And now everything about this second killing seemed a strange exaggeration, a caricature almost, of the first. Pérez Zujovic had been Frei's interior minister from '68 to '69 and was hated by the left because of his treatment of land grabbers in *Pampa Irigoin.* In any event, this poor man had seven children and was ambushed while driving down a nice, safe residential street. A *terrorista* from VOP (*Vanguardia Obrera del Pueblo)* opened fire with a submachine gun and hit him twelve times.

"It's like a Western movie," I said to the television set more than to Carlos as I moved around the room gathering up odds and ends. He bent to move one of the bags I had packed.

"You have quarry rocks in here or what?" Carlos said, trying to sound friendly.

I had my grandmother's silverware in with my clothes. Every piece of it was polished. People emigrating from Chile by then weren't allowed to take valuables out of the country.

"Pretty clever, huh?" I said and managed a smile. I hope customs doesn't look in there."

The other treasure I was sneaking out of Chile, wrapped up in my clothes, was the set of double Old-Fashioned glasses that Salvador Allende had given to Tomás nearly three years before. Dolores gave them to me as a strange kind of going away present.

"They are lovely glasses, even if they came from a *comunista*. Be careful with them Julita, *son finos*. They should last you forever."

Carlos smoothed both his hands over my hair and kissed my head over and over. Even feeling the weight of his hands, I don't think I realized I was taking those glasses so he would follow me

"*Te quiero, pajarita,*" he said. "We all love you. We can have a good life, Julie."

He bent his head to kiss me on the lips. I kissed him back and realized it was the first time I'd kissed him since Charlie died. *Rat-a-tat-tat.* The television announcer talked on about the Zujovic murder as our bodies moved and then swayed together.

"Come back, *pajarita,* come back," he whispered in my ear.

Every corner of my heart felt empty, but still it skipped as the clothes came off and we slid the suitcase to the edge of the rug.

When I was finally on the plane, I pressed my face to the curved airplane window to look out at Carlos standing all by himself on the tarmac. The blue raincoat was ready as both a pillow and a blanket for the long night flight. It had been over a week since I'd seen América. She knew I was leaving Chile, but I hadn't really given her a proper goodbye. Fixed there in my airplane seat I realized I didn't know her mailing address, didn't even know if her house had a number on it.

CHAPTER

30

It all is like ribbons now, ribbons furling out in the wind from that time so long ago. So many memories splice together and form odd angles: a bride running down a sidewalk, Schneider being shot at, *rat-a-tat-tat*. In dreams I still walk through the room in *el Arrayán* that hangs out over the river, I still hear the man ask me, "*Señora,* where are you from? Hollywood?" His laugh still puffs out into the cool air. Men waving three fingers in the air, shouting *ganamos, Unidad Popular, ganamos* march around in my memories. The little canaries are there too. Those little birds that died when Dolores had her kitchen painted yellow really were a *mal augurio.* At the time Dolores said the birds died because Allende was president and Chile would unwind. Later I decided they died because they knew Charlie's death would mean they could no longer sing.

And the mines. Of course, Carlos worked for a mine and that made them important to us, but in Chile the mines are like the mountains, they affect everybody. I remember so much worry back then about who would own the mines. *Chile para los chileos.* Kenocott is a *bloodsucking, yankee, imperialistic....*

Somehow nationalizing the mines was supposed to make everything fair, everything even up in Chile, but of course it didn't. For generations barefoot boys named José, Sebastian, even Carlitos left towns in the *Atacam*a desert, towns like *Calama* or *San Pedro*, turned their backs on childhood and marched towards *Cuquicamata* and its mine. If there was no work at *Chuqui*, they could wander down the spine of the Cordillera and work at places like *Rio Blanco*.

When I first met her, Silvia once showed me a photograph of *San Pedro de Atacama*. It was, still is I suppose, a picturesque little town with a few streets of low, whitewashed adobe houses. The colonial church sits across a square from a house that town locals claim was built by Pedro de Valdivia. In the picture— Silvia had gotten it for a newspaper story—two cats are rambling across the tattered roof of Valdivia's house as though it were a walkway. The larger of the cats, the one nearer to the viewer, looks straight out at you as if to say, *so, he was here too*. The great man, the *conquistador*, had tarried in such a small place and perhaps, it occurs to me now, that's why the men that took to the mines from a dinky little town like *San Pedro* felt they had a claim on a better life.

In 1971 the nationalization of the mines was high excitement in Chile. Carlos wrote me letters and sent along newspaper clippings with long sentences underlined in yellow marker so I'd be sure and *ponerme al día* with all the news. Life would get better for people, for *the people,* he said. Then he'd write me snippets about his mother and a new dress-or-other she'd had made, or mention that Carmencita seemed to finally have a boyfriend. He never wrote about Charlie, about missing him, about jerking awake in the night, sure that he had heard his baby cry. Most of the letters came written on onion skin paper that would crackle as I handled it. Each transparent sheet bled through to its other side. I used to run my fingertips over the backs of Carlos's letters like a person trying to read Braille. There must be hidden messages in the backward ink lines, I thought. He must be telling me about finding Charlie's long scarf, the one Carmencita knit for him. *It still smells of our little boy.* That's what I thought he was trying to write down, but didn't write down. Or maybe he just couldn't do it. Maybe, I'd think to myself, his stomach sinks hollow and low every time he sees a child's toy. He was a good Popi, I'd say under my breath like a prayer, he just can't write the words.

Instead he wrote about politics and the mines and how other children were going to have better lives. Carlos never could have dreamed back then that those mines, grabbed away from greedy Americans, would end up financing the Chilean military once Pinochett was in power. Even with Pinochett long gone, they do it to this very day. That, I guess, is what the backward ink in Allende's grand plan said. *The government takes the mines, but soon the mines support the soldiers.*

For months, once I was back in Kansas City, my life revolved around getting letters from Carlos and fighting with my parents. Charlie was invisible to them. They never knew him, never stroked his hair or held up his head.

"You need to see a plastic surgeon, Julie." That's what my father talked about. "That's one hell of a scar, why you can't even hold your index finger out straight."

He was right. Somehow, as I sliced open my hand on the sharp metal of nurse Gila's instrument, I must have cut a nerve or some fragile tendon whose job it was to run up to control my finger. Once the pain of the actual cut began to subside and the scab had softened a bit, I saw my finger keep a curve every time I tried to jut it out. I didn't want plastic surgery. "This way I can't point my finger at anybody," I would say, one time even yelled, to my father. Whom could I blame for such loss? What I had, still have, is a long thin scar that runs from the crease between the index and middle fingers on my right hand all the way down my palm nearly to where the hand bends at the wrist.

For years the scar, though not wide, was raised and as hard as a nail. Its dark, shiny red color made me think it was filled with blood. I still often run the thumb of my left hand up and down this ridge and think it feels like the *cordillera* because it has what looks and feels like valleys and ascendant tips. I can look down at my hand and swear by my sorrow that as a young woman I should have stood a better chance against what life had in store for me. When I first was back in Kansas City I felt as though I might as well have been Rebecca after all. I was only twenty-four and thought the scar on my right hand, the scar as long as Chile, wrote that I had no destiny. It took years for the scar to fade, for the intrusive tissue across my palm to quite down, to recede.

A daughter can't replace a son, but a new child is a new story after all. The body changes. Memories retreat. And now my Julie is off to Palo Alto with this young fool Jonathan who wants to call himself Miles. I sit in this car and mutter out loud something about heaven keeping her safe. I am seeing houses, and then my Julie's grade school building slips past the limousine windows. First my Julie's grade school buildings reflect in the glass, just next to the driver, and quickly they are on the other side of the window so gaily marked with lipstick. *Border Star School* sits right up close to the street with its sturdy red brick and rows of bike racks. My head shifts a bit to look at the building straight on. "They've never really changed a thing about that school," I say out loud, "all those little girls dreaming of growing up and becoming brides."

As my right hand comes up to brush the top of a rhododendron blossom, a firefly appears out from the stillness of the fuchsia petals and blinks, giving off one slow flicker. How odd. Before she wore lipstick, before she even went to school, Julie used to catch lighting bugs on summer nights and force them into glass jars with her little-girl hands. I showed her how to poke holes in the metal screw tops of those jars, *so the bugs can breathe*. I'd tell her. "Bugs can live a long time in a jar if they have food and air." Memories are like that I think, looking down at the firefly crawling up my finger, if we keep our memories sealed tight and allow them to breathe they too can stay alive. The bug moves down into the crevasse between my finger and the upper palm of my hand, the place where the scar begins. It flickers again as a sharp thud on the car window makes me look up.

I see Carlos through the mark of lipstick Julie left on the car windowpane not thirty minutes ago. It is a grownup-girl kiss, her way of telling me, her mother, not to worry about her. She is telling me to let her go, saying she will have her own adventure. And there is Carlos waving his arms over his head for the car to stop right at the edge of the church driveway. As both my hands hurriedly smear the lipstick I try to rub off the windowpane, the little bug falls back into the flower blossoms. The scar on my right palm looks dull, faded compared to the cheeriness of *raspberry glacé* streaks and all the rhododendrons

"You really are going to do all of this yourself? Arrange all of those flowers?" Carlos ducks his head into the backseat of the car and smiles. "I brought you some raisins *parjarita*, we can't have you faint from hunger at the wedding."

So close to his face I see how cinnamon his eyes remain. In the space between us I don't see anyone now: not my father, or baby Charlie, or even us when we were young.